STARMUS

50 YEARS OF MAN IN SPACE

This book is dedicated to two great pioneers of the space age:
Neil Armstrong (1930-2012) and Yuri Gagarin (1934-1968).

EDITORS IN CHIEF GARIK ISRAELIAN & BRIAN MAY
EXECUTIVE EDITOR DAVID EICHER

Published in 2014 by STARMUS
© Starmus 2014

Produced for Starmus by Canopus Publishing Limited.
Director: Robin Rees
Executive Editor: David Eicher
Art Director: James Symonds
Photographer: Max Alexander
Publicist: Nicole Ettinger
Cover Design: Brian May @DrBrianMay
Proofreader: Sarah Tremlett

For sales in the U.S. and Canada, please contact Shelter Harbor Press. info@shelterharborpress.com
ISBN 978-1-62795-026-8
Cataloging-in-Publication Data has been applied for and may be obtained from the Library of Congress.
For sales in the UK please contact Carlton Books. sales@ carltonbooks.co.uk
ISBN 978-1-78097-559-7
A catalogue record for this book is available from the British Library.

www.Starmus.com
@Starmus @RobinRees
Book printed and bound in Exeter, UK by Short Run Press.
First printing 2014. Reprinted with corrections 2014.

Acknowledgements
Our gratitude to the following, without whom Starmus could not have happened:
Inaki Soroa, Alejandro Calvo, Tom Hicks, Ashot Bagdasaryan, Emma Kandevosian, Veronika Borovik Chilchevskaya, Manel Iglesias, Miger Lorenzo, Sara Bricusse, Juan Ruiz Alzola, Glenn Smith, Mercedes Garrido, Francisco Sanchez, Pedro Alvarez, Juan Carlos Perez, Luis Martinez, Terry Mahoney, Aleksandra Shetrakova.

Additional photography: Don Camp, Alex Cherney, Alejandro Calvo, Satik Seyranyan.

Photographs on pages 4,5: Yuri Gagarin, Neil Armstrong. Credit: NASA.

CONTENTS

STARMUS: 50 YEARS OF MAN IN SPACE

FOREWORD

By Stephen Hawking

Stephen Hawking (b.1942) is the Director of Research at the Center for Theoretical Cosmology at the University of Cambridge in England and was for many years the Lucasian Professor of Mathematics at the same university, the chair held by Isaac Newton. One of the world's leading thinkers on cosmology and the history and evolution of the universe, Hawking is the bestselling author of A Brief History of Time, A Briefer History of Time, The Universe in a Nutshell, *and* Black Holes and Baby Universes.

When he was diagnosed with motor neuron disease in 1963, Hawking was given two years to live. Despite this, he went on to an incredible career pushing the boundaries of thought and is considered to be one of the most brilliant theoretical physicists since Albert Einstein.

Starmus is an important and very unique interdisciplinary festival of people working in different fields — astronomers, astronauts, cosmologists, physicists, philosophers, musicians, artists, biologists etc., who share an interest in the universe, how it began and is now and how we may explore and use its many facets. Starmus was created and directed by an astrophysicist, Garik Israelian.

Speaking as a cosmologist and physicist, there have been two exciting developments since the first Starmus Festival in 2011. The first is the discovery at the Large Hadron Collider of the Higgs boson with a mass of about 125 gigaelectron volts (GeV). This completes the Standard Model of particle physics, which describes nearly all physics. The Higgs potential has the worrysome feature that it might become metastable at energies above 10^{11} Gev. This could mean that the universe could undergo catastrophic vacuum decay, with a bubble of the true vacuum expanding at the speed of light. This could happen at any time and we wouldn't see it coming. Fortunately, the estimated lifetime to decay is longer than the age of the universe.

If the Higgs potential is metastable, it places important constraints on the evolution of the universe and uses the fact that the universe contains more baryons than anti-baryons. Whether or not the Higgs potential becomes metastable depends critically on the values of the Higgs and top quark masses and the assumption that no new physics beyond the Standard Model enters at energies up to 10^{11} Gev. All these are uncertain and need further experiments.

These can't be just particle physics experiments. A particle accelerator that reaches 10^{11} Gev would be larger than Earth and is unlikely to be funded in the present economic climate. However, there is another possibility. The very early universe probably contained particles of much higher energies. We can't observe it in electromagnetic radiation because the universe is opaque until about 350,000 years after the beginning, but gravitational waves can propagate freely to us from the earliest times and so could give us a unique view of the creation of the universe.

It is generally believed that the very early universe underwent a period of exponential expansion called inflation. Nearly 40 years ago, Gary Gibbons and I showed that an exponentially expanding universe would have an effective temperature equal to the expansion rate, H, divided by 2π. This is the analog of the black hole temperature I had discovered two years earlier, except that this temperature was associated with the cosmological horizon, rather than the black hole horizon.

Thermal fluctuations arising from this temperature would create two kinds of perturbations of the early universe: scalar perturbations, which correspond to density variations, and tensor perturbations, which correspond to gravitational waves. The scalar perturbations cause temperature variations in the microwave background on the surface of last scattering. These were first observed by the COBE satellite in 1993, and later in more detail by the WMAP and Planck satellites. The observations agree with the predictions and provide experimental verification of the theory of inflation.

The tensor perturbations are more difficult to detect because they are weaker, and because they don't directly affect the temperature of the microwave background, but only its polarization. In March 2014 the BICEP2 team announced that they had detected tensor perturbations with an amplitude of 20 percent of the scalar perturbations. This is much higher than anyone expected. However, they later admitted that their signal might be caused by dust which also polarizes the microwave background. A number of other attempts to observe tensor perturbations are underway. Hopefully, some will report before the second Starmus Festival in September 2014.

I have a bet with Neil Turok, Director of the Perimeter Institute, that the tensor perturbations are at least 5 percent of the scalar perturbations. If I win, I get a bottle of Canadian champagne and $200 Canadian!

STEPHEN HAWKING. CREDIT: PHILIP MYNOTT.

PREFACE

By Brian May and Garik Israelian

BRIAN MAY AND GARIK ISRAELIAN AT STARMUS.

In June, 2011, a distinguished group of astronauts, cosmonauts and scientists (including two Nobel laureates) gathered on the island of Tenerife to participate in the first *Starmus Festival*. Their aim was to take stock of what has been achieved during the first half century of the Space Age and to discuss key issues concerning our future activities in space.

It was then fifty years since Yuri Gagarin's epic first flight into Space – Man's first ever voyage beyond the Earth's atmosphere. In that fifty years, Astronomy and Space Science have been transformed. Twelve men walked on the Moon, but the *International Space Station* now provides our species with a permanent home in space. Our mobile phones are the product of space-borne telecommunications systems, robotic probes have explored all the planets in the Solar System, and orbiting space-borne telescopes have reached into the remotest depths of the cosmos. We have listened to the faint microwave echoes of the Big Bang, moving current thought away from any ideas that the Universe might be in a steady state. New worlds – some of them Earthlike – are being discovered almost daily, and the infant science of exobiology has recently evolved from early speculative beginnings to a penetrating search for possible homes of alien life.

At the other extreme of the scientific spectrum, biologists have at last succeeded in mapping the human genome, and are making progress in the quest to understand the origin of life itself. For the first time, astronomers and biologists can now find a viable basis on which to work together to take the hitherto Earthbound science of biology towards new frontiers.

The stellar cast of speakers at the festival included Apollo astronauts Neil Armstrong, Buzz Aldrin, Jim Lovell, Bill Anders and Charlie Duke; Russian cosmonauts Alexei Leonov (the first man to walk in space) and Victor Gorbatko; biologists Richard Dawkins and Nobel laureate Jack Szostak; astrophysicists Kip Thorne, Michel Mayor, Jill Tarter, Nobel Prize winning cosmologist George Smoot, Robert Williams (President of the International Astronomical Union), Sami Solanki, chief *Nature* editor Leslie Sage and astronaut/astrophysicist Claude Nicollier.

The speakers were asked to pitch their talks to be understood by a non-specialist but intelligent and inquiring audience, and the verdict of those lucky enough to experience the event, was that all of the lectures succeeded admirably in their brief.

Now, ahead of the second Starmus festival, held in September 2014, it is time to make the astonishingly insightful material we had from our speakers in 2011 into a book which offers a wonderful set of perspectives on our lot and our future, from the hearts of the highest achievers we have ever met. Sadly, in 2012, one of the greatest pioneers of all, Neil Armstrong, passed away, and so we have extended our dedication to him as well as Yuri Gagarin. We salute you both!

Brian May and Garik Israelian

TOP TO BOTTOM: JIM LOVELL GREETS ALEXEI LEONOV AT STARMUS 2011.

ALEXEI LEONOV AND BUZZ ALDRIN.

NEIL ARMSTRONG AND ALEXEI LEONOV.

LEFT TO RIGHT: NEIL ARMSTRONG AND ALEXEI LEONOV AT STARMUS 2011.

INTRODUCTION

DAVID EICHER, EDITOR-IN-CHIEF OF ASTRONOMY MAGAZINE

In the beginning, Earth was a difficult and dangerous place. Bathed in the cool light of a young Sun and awash in a liquid water environment, early Earth was rocked by flurries of impacts from planetesimals, asteroids, and comets that crowded the inner solar system. Following the so-called Late Heavy Bombardment, however, some 3.8 billion years ago, the situation on our young planet began to settle.

And then one day it happened. Somewhere in the broth of Earth's oceans, atoms did their thing, because that's what atoms do. Drawn by the electrical charges that pull them together in specific combinations, atoms in this hydrogen and oxygen-rich environment, perhaps at first beside deep-sea hydrothermal vents, assembled to form amino acids, proteins, and eventually, RNA. From that point on, complexity and evolution took over. A young planetary world — at first a deeply hostile abode — had, over the span of a billion years since the planet accreted, given birth to life.

Since its appearance at least 3.4 billion years ago, life has transformed Earth, pushing it into new evolutionary directions. But it didn't happen quickly. The first 1.5 billion years of life on Earth featured nothing more than prokaryotes, primitive microbes lacking a cellular nucleus. A buildup of oxygen in Earth's atmosphere eventually led to dramatic changes. In the last half-billion years, Earth's climate and its set of living organisms underwent a colossal overhaul. Eventually, mammals evolved, and humans came onto the scene only in the last 5 million years or so. Our closest ancestors evolved over the past 2 million years and led, starting roughly 100,000 years ago, to *Homo sapiens*. And here we are.

But the magical year in the relationship between humans, our planet, and space beyond came only in 1961. By that illustrious year, human beings had developed the technology to carry us off our planet and into space. When Soviet cosmonaut Yuri Gagarin and his Vostok craft completed an orbit of Earth on April 12, 1961, his achievement marked a stunning milestone in the human quest for science, for technology, for meaning.

Cloaked in the Cold War politics of the day was a sense of competition, of anxiety — and in the West, of panic. But the reality was an extraordinary achievement for all mankind, and one that led — in short order — to many other milestones. In the United States, on May 25, 1961, President John F. Kennedy delivered his famous speech challenging Americans to land on the Moon before the decade of the sixties was done.

Fifty years after Gagarin's historic flight, humans came together to mark the event's anniversary. The brainchild of Armenian-born astronomer Garik Israelian, in conjunction with his friends, English musician-astronomer Brian May and Russian cosmonaut Alexei Leonov, the Starmus Festival took place on the Canary Islands, off the northwestern coast of Africa, June 20–25, 2011. Israelian is an astrophysicist at the Instituto de Astrofísica de Canarias (IAC) in Tenerife, and he uses spectroscopy to study the chemical evolution of the Milky Way, solar-type stars, stars with exoplanets, and massive stars. He has also done research on compact binaries, including x-ray binaries and systems with neutron stars and black holes. May is the well-known guitarist, singer, and songwriter of the rock group Queen, who left his astronomical studies when the band took off, only to return to finish his Ph.D. some 35 years later, studying solar system dust particles in the plane of the ecliptic. He may be one of the most famous Ph.D. astronomers in history. Leonov is of course a legend in space exploration.

This unique conference brought together many of the world's greatest astronaut-explorers, astronomers, cosmologists, planetary scientists, biologists, and musicians for a week of lectures, enjoyment of the observatories, and rock and roll. Never before had time and space brought together such a crowd of explorers. The list of participants at Starmus reads like a who's-who in astronomy and science, and their lectures fill this unique volume.

The event not only featured a stellar array of talks, but also explorations of the observatories on La Palma and Tenerife, including the world's largest optical telescope, the 10.4-meter Gran Telescopio Canarias on La Palma. It also featured astrophotography displays and a contest, space art exhibitions, documentaries, star parties, and a concert featuring Brian May along with Edgar Froese and Tangerine Dream.

This book of material from the talks at the 2011 Starmus conference is a unique resource for those interested in space and astronomy. Never before has such an event taken place. And all of us who are interested in these topics owe a debt of gratitude to Garik Israelian for putting this event together. And also to Brian May, who helped enormously and lent great resources to the completion of the meeting.

The energy and drive of both Garik and Brian are inspiring to me. And with Brian, I can't help but to almost think of him as two people, in a sense. There's the brilliant man I communicate with on a variety of subjects, with regard to science and related topics. And there's the younger man I recall so well, seeing him on stage when I was very young, inspiring me in great ways when he, Freddie, Roger, and John transformed the world of rock and roll. How amazing it is to now know him and appreciate all sides of this complex and kind man.

As everyone finds out as they age, great events of the past are a lot closer to us in time and space than we might assume. For many years, Dayton, Ohio, was my family's ancestral home. My father John, now age 93 and a long-retired organic chemist, grew up in a house on Ruskin Road in that southwestern Ohio city. Two houses away from the Eicher house stood the house of one Ivonette Wright Miller. Every once in a while, in the 1930s, a big black car with oversized bumpers and acetylene lights would pull up on the street and Ivonette's uncle, Orville Wright, would step out, go inside, and visit his niece. By that time, Wilbur was gone and Orville was old — bald, graying, and with a mustache.

From time to time my father, then a young teen, spoke to the famous neighborhood visitor, and Mrs. Miller, realizing my father loved stamp collecting, allowed him to take some envelopes and stamps sent to Orville Wright from a stash in her attic. And my father is around to talk about it yet today. Here, not a link just to the early age of spaceflight, but even to the invention of powered aircraft flight itself.

Sometimes we fail to appreciate the lightning speed of all this progress. Where will the future of spaceflight take us? The future of our knowledge of the solar system, the Milky Way, the hundred billion galaxies in the cosmos? The rapid evolution of technology that will continue to transform our lives in multitudinous ways? Our knowledge of and sensitivity to ourselves and toward other forms of life on our own immeasurably valuable home planet?

Only time will tell, and the possibilities are exciting, even head-spinning. But one thing is for sure: there will be many more conferences like the 2011 Starmus event, and we will be sharing our collective wonder for generations yet to come.

BRIAN MAY

ALEXEI LEONOV

SECTION 1

OUR MISSION IN SPACE

Fifty years ago, humans first launched into low-Earth orbit, shattering the limitation of living only on the surface of our home planet. But what should a human presence in space mean? What are its limitations, its responsibilities?

The first man to walk on the Moon, Neil Armstrong, delivers a state of the planet report on humanity and our relationship to space, and to Earth.

In an interview with Garik Israelian, Buzz Aldrin reflects upon progress in space during the past 50 years and our future prospects.

The first man to conduct a walk in space, Alexei Leonov, describes the exhilaration of being in orbit about Earth, the dawn of the space exploration era, and the political relationships between countries and space explorers.

And Brian May, world famous musician and astrophysicist, asks whether we should take much better care of our planet and the creatures inhabiting it before we spread our ways throughout the cosmos.

BUZZ ALDRIN

NEIL ARMSTRONG

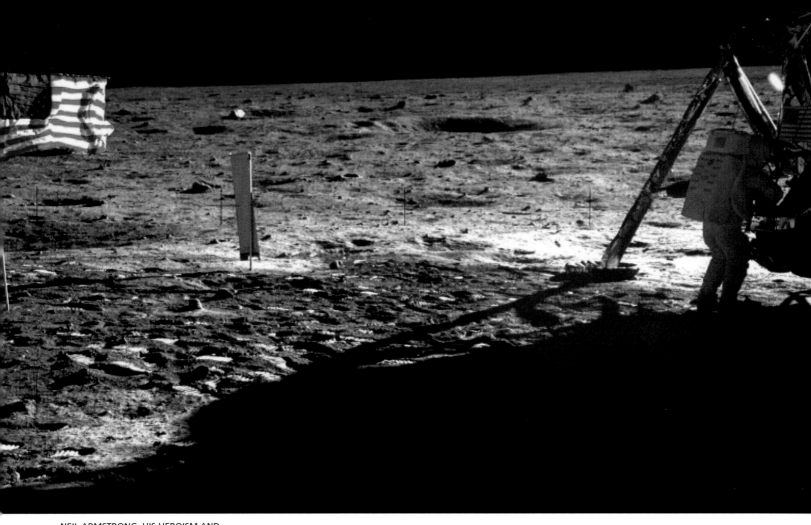

NEIL ARMSTRONG. HIS HEROISM AND
MODESTY SET AN EXAMPLE FOR THE ENTIRE
HUMAN RACE. CREDIT: NASA.

AMONG FRIENDS AT STARMUS 2011. ALEXEI
LEONOV, VICTOR GORBATKO, NEIL ARMSTRONG,
JIM LOVELL.

NEIL ARMSTRONG

Reflections on Starmus and the Future of Earth

Neil Alden Armstrong achieved worldwide fame on that mission in July 1969 when he became the first human being to walk on the surface of the Moon. Armstrong (1930–2012) was born near Wapakoneta, Ohio, and his family moved around the Buckeye State repeatedly during his youth, a time when Armstrong developed a strong interest in flying. He earned a student flight certificate and studied aeronautical engineering at Purdue University. Korean War service as a naval pilot interrupted his college career. Following the war, he returned to school and finished, also earning a Master's degree from the University of Southern California.

In 1955, at Edwards Air Force Base in California, Armstrong became a test pilot. Seven years later he entered the second group of astronaut candidates, launching in March 1966 as command pilot of Gemini 8. In 1967 he participated in training for the Apollo program and a year later was nearly killed when he ejected from a training aircraft.

Selected to command Apollo 11, Armstrong joined colleagues Buzz Aldrin and Michael Collins for the July 1969 mission that would rewrite space exploration, and the rest, as they say, is history.

After Apollo, Armstrong became a professor of aerospace engineering at the University of Cincinnati and then engaged in business activities before his retirement, becoming legendary for his aversion to publicity and his simple, somewhat reclusive life. Sadly, Armstrong died August 25, 2012, age 82, from surgical complications.

NEIL ARMSTRONG AT STARMUS.

Fifty-four years ago a little known, but particularly important, research program was underway. It was called the International Geophysical Year (IGY). Sixty-six countries joined together not to analyze the sky, but to analyze Earth: oceanography, meteorology, solar activity, Earth's magnetism, and cosmic rays. High performance rockets were being developed for military use even before the IGY began. Scientists, particularly Soviet and American, soon recognized that if it were possible to use such a rocket to put a manmade object into orbit about Earth, carrying scientific instruments, such a satellite would have a perspective that would allow accurate measurements, perhaps solving or at least shedding some light on Earth's mysteries.

Both the Soviet Union and the United States announced their intention of developing an artificial satellite. They did not recognize it at the time, but they had started a new competition that would become known as the Space Race. The Space Race was possible because of the emergence of two technologies: the liquid-propellant rocket and the digital electronic computer, which just happened to arrive nearly simultaneously. The engineering progress of the 20th century made it possible not only to put small objects into orbit about Earth but also to place human beings in orbit about Earth.

The performance increased to allow the possibility of accelerating a human to sufficient velocity to escape the gravitational pull of Earth. In all human history, only 24 people have achieved that speed, known as "escape velocity," which is about 10 times the speed of a bullet from a high performance rifle.

That success and the possibilities suggested by these achievements might put us in a position to go to destinations throughout the solar system. Perhaps 21st century technology might provide increases in that spacecraft velocity by a factor of 100 times. Such an enormous speed suggests that we might be able to go to distant

NEIL ARMSTRONG'S FAMOUS OFFICIAL PORTRAIT AHEAD OF THE APOLLO 11 MISSION. CREDIT: NASA.

places in a reasonable amount of time. But simple arithmetic demonstrates that with such speed the flight to our nearest star, Alpha Centauri, would take something like 65 generations. That prompted C. S. Lewis to define the difficulty of interacting with other cosmic societies, should they exist, as God's quarantine regulation. Space is a really big place.

During Starmus, Dr. Brian May, in a thought-provoking essay, properly asked, "Should we go?" He selected 10 of man's least admirable qualities and asked, "Should we really want to spread our human shortcomings throughout our solar system?" It was a rhetorical question and of course we would not. He looked on our home planet, as a beautiful, benevolent, and perfectly placed location, which, of course, is our general perspective.

But I have had the privilege of looking down on Earth from high above the atmosphere, and I have seen shooting stars far below me. I have seen the violence of nighttime thunderstorms like giant mushrooms illuminated by ferocious light-ning. I have seen gigantic hurricanes with enormous winds. Were I the captain of a spaceship approaching Earth from a planet near Vega and had seen these sights, and my instruments warned me of potential earthquakes, tsunamis, and other rages of Mother Nature, I might very well say, "No, this planet is too dangerous — this planet is not for me. Mr. Spock, Warp 5, please!"

Dr. May also reviewed our treatment of other Earth species and, indeed, the record is inconsistent. For there are very few gentle deaths in the wild. Only humans make the effort to defend some of those creatures, protecting and preserving endangered species.

Our preeminent challenge is to improve the human species. Let us hope that our grandchildren at our age can look back and say, "The 20th century was a century of advancement and improvement in human character." That may just qualify us, as humans from Earth, to sally forth and expand the human presence beyond Earth. Not to take with us our worst behavior but rather to be accompanied by our best behavior and be willing and happy to share it.

I am not an astronomer, but I enjoy reading about astronomy and want to share some of what I've read that I find fascinating. A relatively small fraction of Earth's population has studied astronomy, but they know that Earth is warmed by the Sun, and that the tides are related to the Moon's position in the sky. The best planting time for crops and many human superstitions are related to the phases of the Moon. But the positions and motions of celestial bodies beyond the Sun and Moon seem irrelevant to the lives of most earthlings.

So it's not surprising that some people wonder what the importance of astronomy is to humans and to everyday living. I respond with a simple example. The first significant and reasonably accurate measurements of star and planet positions were made by the Dane, Tycho Brahe, before the telescope was invented. Those measurements led his young assistant, Johannes Kepler, to derive three crucial laws of planetary motion. Kepler's laws were used by Isaac Newton to devise Newton's laws of motion, which had such wide applicability that they were largely responsible for the Industrial Revolution and the resultant complete change in the character of life as we know it. Astronomy can and occasionally does have a signifi-cant impact on social activities.

Astronomers believe they are beginning to understand the life cycles of stars: birth, growth, and death. The inevitable consequence of such a life cycle is the eventual death of our Sun, which among stars is now an adult, perhaps not yet middle aged. With its eventual demise (five to 10 billion years hence) follows the end of all life on Earth, life that is to all intents and purposes completely dependent on the energy from the nuclear fire on Sol.

Fortunately, we need not worry about the Sun's death. Long before it becomes terminal, it will have metamorphosed into a bloated red giant, boiling away Earth's oceans, barbecuing and perhaps swallowing the carcass of our planet. But we need not concern ourselves with being engulfed in the red giant either, because eons earlier, another astronomical effect will have become very obvious.

Earth's rotation is slowing. The friction of the ocean tides is said to be a principal cause of the lengthening of our day. Imperceptibly, but definitely, eventually the day will have stretched to weeks, the weeks to months, and finally to a year, when we will have one face of Earth locked toward the Sun, like the Moon's near side is locked toward Earth. The side toward the Sun will sear, the opposite side will freeze, both will be uninhabitable, and everyone will be moving to the edges. But phase lock is hardly an immediate problem either. The passing of a million generations may not make it appreciably closer.

We can conjecture a hundred reasons for migration from Earth: change in our atmosphere, overpopulation, radiation growth, and other scenarios that would result in the extinction of mankind (nuclear holocaust, disease, collision with a comet or an asteroid). The last time such a cataclysmic collision occurred, 66 million years ago, according to a widely accepted hypothesis, much of Earth's life including the dinosaurs was extinguished.

Amateur geologists will remember that Earth's magnetic polarity changes from time to time when the north and south magnetic poles reverse positions. It hasn't happened for about 600,000 years, but there is evidence suggesting that another reversal is possible sometime soon. We don't have the foggiest idea of what the effects of such an event might be.

I'm not prophesying an apocalypse; nor do I believe that we should all be overly concerned about such catastrophes, but it does suggest that there is some importance to the fact that we now know that the home of the human species is not necessarily restricted to Earth. The universe around us is both our challenge and perhaps our destiny. As Heraclitus said, around 500 B.C., "If you do not expect it, you will not find it for the unexpected is hard to find." Nevertheless, the unexpected will occur. Who can foresee what discoveries, inventions, and events will characterize the change ahead?

We know a thousand times more about the universe around us now than we did just a half century ago. We can expect that increase in knowledge to continue, even without breakthroughs. It's possible that in the future, migrations of humans away from Earth will occur, both to other natural planets and to manmade habitats. We will send probes to learn about stars beyond our solar system. We have ample evidence that other stars are accompanied by planetary families.

The longtime human fascination with gold has been replaced with a fascination with life, and the possibility that we are not the only creatures of reason in the universe. But if we are not only to survive but prevail we must continue to improve. We must eventually rise above our differences and become a true family of nations. We take great pride in our heritage and in our principles, and rightly so: they strengthen us, but they also imprison us. Based on our record here on Earth, we are not yet qualified to populate and govern a larger segment of the universe. We may or may not have time enough to grow as a species to control our ultimate destiny.

Yet there is a great reason for hope. And we have no other choice. There is no doubt that our instincts will force us to try. On reflecting on the same subject two millennia ago, Plato, around 400 B.C., said: "We must take the best and irrefutable human doctrines and embark on that as if it were a raft on which to risk the voyage of life," which indeed it is and indeed we must.

Like that of Ulysses, each of our lives is a miniature Odyssey, going to new places, seeing new things, understanding new ideas, and each day penetrating the biggest unknown of all: tomorrow. For each of us it should be, and can be, an exciting voyage. Buen Viaje!

NEIL ARMSTRONG WITH THE X15 ROCKET PLANE HE FLEW BETWEEN 1960 AND 1962 REACHING SPEEDS OF ALMOST 4,000 MILES PER HOUR AT ALTITUDES OF UP TO 207,500 FEET. CREDIT: NASA.

BUZZ ALDRIN – THE ICONIC IMAGE FOR OUR ERA. CREDIT: NASA.

BUZZ ALDRIN

FROM THE MOON TO MARS: AN INTERVIEW WITH BUZZ ALDRIN AT STARMUS BY GARIK ISRAELIAN

Buzz Aldrin is an imposing figure. Even at 81, his hair white and as he wears a broad smile, you can still plainly see this is a tough guy, a fighter pilot, and a hero of world culture. Born Edwin Eugene Aldrin on January 20, 1930, in Glen Ridge, New Jersey, Aldrin picked up the sobriquet "Buzz" when a sister mispronounced "brother" as "buzzer," and the family embraced the shortened name.

Aldrin is an icon, the second man to walk on the Moon, a celebrated hero of the famous Apollo 11 crew, and a worldwide celebrity who has spawned pop culture resonance that extends far and wide, as with Disney's "Buzz Lightyear." His career had deep roots. He graduated third in his class from the U.S. Military Academy and went on to fly 66 combat missions in the Korean War. He served as an aide to the dean of faculty at the U.S. Air Force Academy before earning his Sc.D. in aeronautics at the Massachusetts Institute of Technology.

Never having been a test pilot, Aldrin was nonetheless selected as one of the third group of astronaut candidates in 1963. He became a celebrated Gemini pilot and walked in space during the Gemini 12 mission, the final manned Gemini flight, in 1966. He then of course made his historic flight as a crew member of Apollo 11, walking on the Moon along with Neil Armstrong, in July 1969.

Aldrin retired from NASA in 1972 and has since been active in many areas, chiefly promoting space exploration and most recently supporting a manned mission to Mars. At Starmus, Aldrin provided an engaging interview touching on his experiences and the future of worldwide efforts in space.

BUZZ ALDRIN AT STARMUS.

Question: Welcome to Tenerife and to Starmus, Mr. Aldrin. It's an honor to have you here as one of the heroes of the 20th century. Today we are celebrating the 50th anniversary of the first manned space flight. It's an important day for us and it's an important year for civilization. As the Russian and Soviet rocket pioneer Konstantin Tsiolkovsky suggested, we are "leaving the cradle," and now we've made a first step and are starting to walk. Indeed, now we are running. Given our entrance into space exploration, what do you see as the main achievement in space exploration in its first 50 years?

Buzz Aldrin: Well, I'd just like to put it into perspective. We look at the achievement that America was able to make because of the initial flights of Sputnik and of Yuri Gagarin. It was 66 years from the Wright Brothers' first flight to the first landing on the Moon. And now it's been 50 years since Yuri Gagarin's flight, from President Kennedy's challenge to go to the Moon, both in 1961.

And if we move 66 years from landing on the Moon, that'll put us into 2035. That is my reasonable estimate for permanence on Mars. Things have progressed very rapidly from Sputnik to Laika to photographing the far side of the Moon, all from three pioneers: Konstantin Tsiolkovsky, Hermann Oberth, and Robert Goddard.

I never had a chance to meet Tsiolkovsky. He has a beautiful crater on the backside of the Moon named after him. I did meet Oberth, on his 90th birthday, in Germany. He was the teacher of the apprentice Wernher von Braun. Now the American, Robert Goddard, was my father's physics professor at Clark University, and my father initiated some actions, through Charles Lindbergh, to Harry Guggenheim, enabling Goddard to continue his research.

So there is an interesting interweaving of my family. My mother was born the year of the Wright Brothers' first flight. And of course it's just an accident — a pure accident — that my mother's maiden name was Moon, m-o-o-n. But it was nothing

BUZZ ALDRIN AND GARIK ISRAELIAN AT STARMUS.

ON MY FIRST SPACEFLIGHT AS PILOT OF GEMINI 12, I WAS ABLE TO SET A 5-HOUR WORLD RECORD SPACEWALKING WHILE CIRCLING THE GLOBE EVERY 90 MINUTES AT A SPEED OF 17,000 MILES AN HOUR. WHAT A SIGHT TO BEHOLD THE EARTH BELOW WHILE FLOATING OUTSIDE OUR CAPSULE! CREDIT: NASA.

ONLY 66 YEARS LATER AFTER THE WRIGHT BROTHERS FLIGHT, NEIL AND I STEPPED ON THE MOON, FULFILLING THE DREAMS OF MILLIONS. CREDIT: NASA.

unusual growing up. My grandmother was known, by my sister and two cousins, as Mama Moon. It was normal — perfectly normal! The Wright Brothers' flight created an acceleration of technology, and then came World War I.

After the war, pilots were engaged to fly the government's airmail from one city to another, proving the reliability of both pilot and airplane. And then private airlines began carrying passengers — a very big step! — and I think this provides a lesson as to where we are now, with government missions to low-Earth orbit being replaced by private access. This move will enable governments to continue to do pioneering exploration from Earth orbit to other locations — comets, asteroids, around the Moon — and most importantly the moons of Mars and the surface of Mars.

That's the government's area. Such goals are just too resource consuming for the private sector, as there's no return involved. But there is a return for the private sector going into low-Earth orbit. They can take government astronauts to the space station. They can eventually take private citizens on expensive trips into orbit, eventually at more and more reasonable costs.

So we are in a very exciting time, I believe. We are capitalizing, to use an economic word, on the technological achievements that have been made over the past 50 years. And it does look a little bleak for the depressed economies of the world, but we can hope that will improve over the next 10 years, to enable funding. There needs to be governmental funding. The big projects, flying to Mars or building a big space station, cannot be funded with monies from private industry.

There isn't enough of a return from many of these big projects. Going to the Moon is very uncertain in terms of payoff. What is the business? Perhaps many of us who have looked at that would say it's fuel for space travel, from the water and the ice on the Moon, but it has a long way to go. We need to refuel somebody who wants to pay for the fuel.

Question: The field of astronomy is facing a tough situation right now due to declines in state and federal funding. You often hear that astronomers and directors of observatories say we have to charge the public to come and visit the telescopes and to observe the sky in order to help with funding. And of course that money could help,

WHEN MY TRAINING CONCLUDED, I WAS POSTED TO THE KOREAN WAR AS A JET FIGHTER PILOT. CREDIT: BUZZ ALDRIN.

but it couldn't fund large telescopes in the range of 10 meters or 40 meters. So we do need some serious funding.

Aldrin: Well, I remember that planetaria that show the public the universe would often bring in laser light shows with lots of action and color, and that was certainly attractive to the public. And then they learned about the stars, about the movements of stars and galaxies, and about planets and astronauts. So we really have to do that with the space program, because early on, the Mercury, Gemini, and Apollo missions happened in fairly close succession, one after another. But when we start traveling great distances we will be doing well to have one or two major missions in a year, not six or eight.

Question: You are a hero of our generation, a hero of the generation of the 1960s, 1970s, and 1980s. Many of us grew up with science fiction movies, with 2001: A Space Odyssey, with your name, with Gagarin and with Alexei Leonov. Things changed in the 1990s and 2000s with the new generation of young people. So we now see less interest in space travel and in astronomy, and the newer stars are Hollywood celebrities.

Aldrin: Well, heroes still exist. Maybe not the traditional kind of hero who rescues the damsel from the demon, with a damsel in distress and the hero rides in on horseback and grabs the damsel and off they go. It's a little different with heroes now. Now we have basketball players and baseball players and rather than the violin, it's the guitar.

Question: Some people think we need a second Cold War in order to make progress in the space industry and with space exploration. Do you agree? Do we need a confrontation, this time between China and the United States?

Aldrin: Of course I was a youth, a teenager, during World War II, and it amazes me how rapidly those conflicts took place, from European involvement in 1939 to American involvement in 1941 to the end of the war in Europe in mid 1945 and the

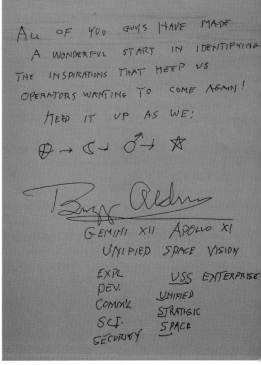

BEST WISHES TO STARMUS FROM BUZZ ALDRIN.

LUNAR MODULE RENDEZVOUSING WITH THE COMMAND MODULE IN LUNAR ORBIT. "IF SPACE WAS GOING TO BE OUR NEXT NEW FRONTIER, THEN I WANTED TO CONTRIBUTE TO GETTING THERE. I ENROLLED AT MIT IN THE ASTRONAUTICS PROGRAM AND IN 1962 EARNED MY DOCTORATE: LINE-OF-SIGHT GUIDANCE FOR MANNED ORBITAL RENDEZVOUS." CREDIT: NASA.

Pacific in late 1945. That was quite compressed, but then out of that grew the Cold War for decades and decades. And just to put it into perspective for me, when Sputnik and the initial space flights happened, I was with my supersonic airplane in Germany, on five-minute alert with nuclear weapons to deliver to Poland, Czechoslovakia, and some parts of the Soviet Union.

Fifty years ago I moved from that military environment to advanced graduate education. While Yuri Gagarin was in flight I was already working on my doctoral dissertation on bringing spacecraft together in orbit. One of the wisest decisions I could ever have made was to move from flying airplanes intercepting each other in combat to satellites intercepting each other in orbit. There's a great similarity. Aided tremendously now, of course, with computers.

Question: What do you remember about the Gagarin flight? How was your reaction to the TV and newspaper coverage to the fact that Gagarin was in flight? Can you recall your mood?

Aldrin: I knew that we had a program of American astronauts that had started in 1959 and I had read in a magazine about the selection of the seven Mercury astronauts, that all were test pilots. My career was not as a test pilot and I felt I wasn't eligible for that. As it turned out, I applied to be in the second group of astronauts, in 1962, even though I wasn't qualified, because I wanted NASA to know what I was studying at MIT. And so, fortunately, the requirements were changed in 1963 and I was selected as one of the third group of 14 astronauts.

Question: But you heard about Gagarin's flight from a newspaper? Do you remember? Did you associate his flight with the Cold War?

Aldrin: Well, it's coincidence. April 12, the date of Gagarin's flight in 1961, is my father's birthday, which I was happy about, and I was at MIT. The flight was not a big shock; it was anticipated. Why did America select seven Mercury astronauts? Because, of course, we expected that from the nation that had put up Sputnik, that was doing things with dogs in space, that had photographed the far side of the Moon.

Of course the Soviet Union had a considerable lead over the United States and perhaps they would be able to orbit Earth in April just before Alan Shepard's suborbital flight. And then John Glenn finally orbited Earth in February 1962, almost 10 months after Gagarin.

So there was a distinct lead. But events also took place rapidly back then — much more so than today. The pace of activities today is just so much more stretched out. And because of that, the impatient public wants to see things happen right away.

We saw the rapid acceleration of new and different things back then. We lunged ahead to the Moon and then, with the space shuttles, we started using very expensive spacecraft that could be used again and again. And then the space station took much longer and was much more expensive than anticipated. So things have slowed down because of that. Manufacturers anticipated that the shuttle would fly 40 or 50 times a year. At most, it flew 9 times a year, and typically 5 or 6.

Question: Had you heard about the Soviet lunar program?

Aldrin: Of course. And Leonov would have been the commander, with Gagarin and Vladimir Komarov in the crew. It never happened probably because the engineer Sergei Korolev died, Gagarin died, and Komarov died. So all the people who were going to make it happen died in just one year. And that was a big shock to the Soviets.

Question: In 1966?

Aldrin: In 1966 and 1967. Those two years were critical and very negative. So that's what really killed the prowess of the Soviet Union. Ah, but Leonov was still there.

Question: Yes, Leonov is still here. He's pretty much like you, with a lot of energy. Do you think the next big flight, to Mars, will happen in the next 20 or 30 years? What timescale would you put on that big flight?

Aldrin: Well, a little more than two years ago I began assembling a list of what I think we need, primarily from a spacecraft perspective. We need spacecraft that can go great distances, which requires propulsion. The crew is on board in radiation and with cramped quarters for exercising, during a one or two year duration. We need the equipment, the life support, to be far away from Earth with very little reliable support — oxygen, water, nutrition, food, and protection from radiation.

There's much to be learned as we begin to venture. But the spacecraft we will need will have to use the space station for testing, building a prototype, and then commence flying. And I think we need two spacecraft, a small one and a big one, that doesn't launch from the ground, just to move outward.

Question: Do we have to assemble a base on Mars before we actually go there?

Aldrin: Oh, yes, and I think it's logical to do the same thing on the Moon. We should have international involvement to establish a base somewhere on the Moon and also have outposts to assemble what NASA is calling an "international lunar research park." That should no doubt be assembled, but we should assemble one here on Earth first on the island of Hawaii. That gives us a place to practice.

And then we can do it on the Moon. And then again we can practice in Hawaii before constructing such a place on Mars. The controllers for such a coordinated mission will be in Houston, Texas, at NASA's Mission Control, and also in Moscow and in China and in other places that will be part of the venture. But for a martian mission the controllers will be on the Moon. And that's a big, big difference.

Question: We know that Russia has lots of experience with life support systems because the MIR station was in orbit for many years. Is it possible to do a project like this without collaboration between countries?

Aldrin: The collaboration has already begun. While many people in the United States have been looking at going back to the Moon, what's been happening? In Canada they study robotic missions to the Moon or Mars. In Russia they plan, and soon will launch, a sample return mission, Phobos-Grunt, returning samples from a martian moon. And it carries Chinese and French collaboration. So who's ahead going to Mars? Not the United States. It's Russia and China with some Canadian involvement.

Question: Thank you very much for this interview. Could you add some words for our Starmus participants?

Aldrin: Everything that has been done in space was pioneered by Copernicus, Kepler, and Newton, who deciphered an understanding of the motions of the planets and the motions of stars in the galaxy. And of course from observations from Galileo's telescope, those first views of the moons of Jupiter, four large moons that orbit Jupiter. That inspired the thinking that the Sun is the center of the solar system rather than Earth. And that Earth is a sphere rather than being flat. We've come a long way in a short time.

WE HAD MADE IT! THE EAGLE HAD LANDED! MANY HAD THOUGHT IT IMPOSSIBLE. EVEN IN THE SCIENTIFIC COMMUNITY, SOME THOUGHT THAT UPON LANDING WE WOULD SINK IN AND BE ENVELOPED BY DEEP LAYERS OF MOON DUST. BUT WE DIDN'T. CREDIT: NASA.

LEONOV IN OPEN SPACE, 18 MARCH 1965. CREDIT: NASA.

ALEXEI LEONOV

OPENING THE DOOR TO SPACE

Alexei Arkhipovich Leonov is one of the greatest cosmonauts in history, having achieved a great milestone on March 18, 1965, when he became the first human to perform a spacewalk in orbit. Born May 30, 1934, in Listvyanka, Kemerovo Oblast, Soviet Union, Leonov was attracted to flight early on and was one of 20 selected as part of the first cosmonaut group in 1960.

Originally scheduled to walk in space on the Vostok 11 mission, that flight was canceled and instead Pilot Leonov, along with Commander Pavel Belyayev, launched on Voskhod 2, the mission that included his historic spacewalk. This daring maneuver lasted 12 minutes and 9 seconds as the spacecraft orbited Earth, and Leonov was attached to the craft by a tether stretching some 5 meters in length. In the vacuum of low-Earth orbit, however, Leonov's suit inflated, and he had trouble reentering the spacecraft, having to open a valve to release pressure so that he could squeeze back inside the airlock.

Leonov was selected to command a Soviet Soyuz mission that would orbit the Moon, and also selected to be the first cosmonaut to land on the Moon, but both missions were canceled. In 1975 he commanded the Soviet portion of the Apollo-Soyuz mission that was the first joint mission between the United States and the Soviet Union. From 1976 through 1982 he was chief of the cosmonauts and deputy director of the cosmonaut training center, before retiring in 1991.

Leonov is an accomplished astronomical artist, an activity that deepened his friendship with the great science fiction author Arthur C. Clarke, and he has written several books about his space-related activities.

ALEXEI LEONOV AT STARMUS.

Every human being has his or her own story. Mine begins when I first went out into space. I hope to be remembered as the first person to perform a spacewalk, with a 99 percent probability of never coming back and becoming Earth's first human satellite. I was afraid.

It was 1965. I was in complete darkness, absolute darkness — no lights and no torches. Besides, I had no footing; I could only cling with my hands, or just one hand. One of my hands was holding a camera, so I had just one hand to support myself. Under those conditions, I was supposed to reel myself into the airlock; I don't know how I could have possibly managed that, wearing my spacesuit and being unable to move freely in it. But somehow I managed it; I couldn't have failed. I realized that if I went back into the spaceship feet first, it would be impossible to drag myself inside. It was a huge problem.

I started to count the time — 30 minutes of my life. You see, nobody can help me in this world. If there is God, he will help, but no one else. Pasha, Pavel Belyayev, could drag me inside, but not before I made the effort myself.

So I made my decision. I had to report on everything to Earth. The great engineer Sergei Korolev had told me: "I need to know when your song is over." It was men's talk; quite straightforward. I will sing then! And I said nothing! To no one! I reduced the pressure and got into the zone where nitrogen boils. I was almost to a state when your feet swell up like rubber gloves, your eyes sink, and your head becomes too big for the spacesuit — a man completely deprived of mobility.

And there I was, not knowing what to do. I didn't want to speak to anyone on Earth. Just think of me telling the whole world that I'm in trouble! It was an open channel — everybody was listening! What's up with this man? He is unable to go into the spaceship! Just imagine how simple it would seem — to enter a ship!

That's why I kept silent. I reduced the pressure twice. Now, this was becoming serious. I looked at myself: my eyes were not sinking, but they were about to do so.

BELYAYEV, LEONOV AND KOROLEV AFTER THE VOSKHOD 2 FLIGHT, 1962. CREDIT: ALEXEI LEONOV.

ARTHUR C. CLARKE WITH LEONOV IN 1978.
CREDIT: ALEXEI LEONOV.

LEONOV WITH GENERAL TOM STAFFORD,
1975. CREDIT: ALEXEI LEONOV.

Should I go further and take more risks? It was a very tough decision. The clock was ticking away. And we hadn't had any training for this type of maneuver!

And then I made up my mind. I took my video camera. Yesterday in Krasnogorsk I gave a talk and said they were in debt with me. Back in 1962 they gave me a video camera, and it recorded everything I did, and then I gave it back to them, but I did so by risking my life. I could have left it behind and go using both my hands quite safely. But I thought of all those people who had worked on the camera and produced it for me, a whole factory, and how was I going to return and say I had left it behind? So I held onto the ship with my left hand, put the camera inside with my right hand, and pushed myself into the ship. As the rocket designer Boris Chertok said afterward, I just pulled the ship onto myself like a pullover. All this happened in just a matter of seconds.

That was a completely new method, and I tried it out on myself on the spot. The authorities were about to exclude me from the party for that. Of course, severe punishment was awaiting me: I had failed to follow the instructions. First, I hadn't reported anything. Second, I had changed the whole procedure for an unknown and untried method. This is a very serious fault in technique. But when I explained everything quietly and clearly to Sergei Korolev and the others, everyone was silent, waiting for Korolev to pronounce his sentence. And he said: "The fact is, Alexei is right!" And everyone clapped. That's it — I was right!

I think Korolev was an amazing person. The way he endured the tortures of the Soviet regime was incredible. They submitted him to such severe physical suffering, but he never ever spoke up. He died because his trachea was damaged during an "interrogation," and an operation couldn't repair the damage.

One of the most interesting episodes of my life is related to the movie by Stanley Kubrick based on the famous book of Arthur Clarke's, 2001: A Space Odyssey. In 1968, during the Vienna Congress, the premiere of this movie took place. Clarke and Kubrick, the author and director of the film, were both present at the premiere. The movie certainly impressed us greatly and is still very impressive due to its extraordinary camera work and large-scale images. The sound was in stereo; it sounded as if it were happening right there, in the hall. It was the first time stereo sound was used.

The movie begins with an image of a prehistoric man skinning his prey, a dead tapir. The man strikes the tapir on the head with a huge bone and then throws the bone up into the air. The bone bounces, spinning, and transforms into an enormous orbital station. All this happens to the sounds of a Viennese waltz. The waltz helps to create a beautifully arranged scene representing the bridge between ancient, profoundly prehistoric times and the present day.

The accompanying sound for the scenes where astronauts are working in the open space is merely their heavy breathing. Almost no music; no other sounds. In fact, there is some music, but it becomes almost unperceivable with that sound of heavy breath.

Afterward, Clarke said to everyone who was there: "I'll tell you a secret. We couldn't work out what sound we should use for the scenes of astronauts working in the open space. Then I came up with the actual recording of Alexei Leonov's work in outer space, and that was it — it turned out to be exactly what we wanted."

Since then, we have been good friends. Afterward, he used an illustration from my album The Space Lift for the design of his novel, The Fountains of Paradise. He treated me not like an astronaut but like someone with a different mentality. He was an extraordinarily interesting person. When he wrote his 2010: Odyssey Two, he asked me to review the book. It was intended for the magazine Tekhnika — molodezhi (Technology for Teenagers). I wrote half a page, though never managed to finish the novel.

Before he finished his 2010, I met him and he said: "You know, there is a secret I want to tell you. What would you think the super-spaceship is called in that novel of mine?" "I have no idea, Arthur," I said. "It's called 'Alexei Leonov'! What do you say to that?" And I said: "Well, I'll do my best as a ship." He was stricken by that phrase. He said he expected any response from me, but not that one.

In that novel, Clarke shows great fondness for the Soviet astronauts. In the end, the highest authorities called me and demanded explanations: "How could you write a review of that book? Do you know that it's the crew of the spaceship 'Alexei Leonov'?" "So what?" I said. "And their commander is Orlova!," they said. "Who is Orlova?" I asked. They said: "She is a dissident. The whole crew are dissidents: Ternovsky and all others." Then I said: "I have a question. Have you ever shown me the list of dissidents? I thought Orlova referred to Lyubov Orlova, the famous Soviet actress. I thought she was the character of the novel."

And then I said: "But look, there is so much fondness toward our country and our astronauts in this novel." Clarke had not depicted the Americans very favorably. The story unfolds at this "Alexei Leonov" ship. And when I opened the first page, there was the dedication which said literally the following: "To two great people: Alexei Leonov, astronaut and artist, and Andrei Sakharov."

This novel was published in Tekhnika — molodezhi. Then the authorities stopped the publication and fired Vasya Zakharchenko, the editor-in-chief. Some 10 years passed before we could start publishing that novel once more, and again in the same magazine. We did not change anything in the novel. Nobody would know whether those characters were dissidents or not. What matters is that the novel was written.

I have met Arthur C. Clarke many times. For his 80th birthday, we had a ceremony in his honor in England. He didn't know I would be there. He was sitting on the stage. An image appeared on the screen: a man in the open space. He was watching the screen. At that moment I came out on the stage from behind the screen and halted in front of it. The lights went on and he saw me. He said: "How did you get here from there?" I said: "As in the movie The White Sun of the Desert — you did a take, you called me, so I came." He was quite dumbfounded.

On his 90th birthday, I was with him again in Sri Lanka. We congratulated him and gave him a brilliant show. They love him very much back in Sri Lanka. Well, they used to love him; unfortunately, he is not with us anymore. But he has left us his library, his research center, though damaged by flooding. So that is the story of my relationship with Arthur C. Clarke.

My relationship with American astronauts started even before the Apollo-Soyuz mission. In 1971 the Soyuz 11 crew of Georgi Dobrovolski, Vladislav Volkov, and Viktor Patsayev died on a mission. They were our backup crew; the original crew was to be me, Valeri Kubasov, and Pyotr Kolodin. But due to Kubasov's illness, 11 hours before the start, it was decided that they substitute the other crew on that mission. It was a tragedy when they died, and the authorities in the United States discussed the matter extensively. They prohibited their astronauts from attending the funeral, but Tom Stafford assumed the whole responsibility himself and served as one of the pallbearers at the funeral.

There had been sadness, too. In 1970 Pasha, Pavel Belyayev, died following an operation. The Air Force Commander-in-Chief, Pavel Stepanovich Kutakhov, called me and said: "You know, this American general, Tom Stafford, has arrived. Please accompany him and take care of him." I replied: "I don't even speak the language." "It's OK," he said, "you are both pilots; you'll figure it out." And so it happened. For some three days, while the ceremonies went on, I was with Tom Stafford and we got to know each other well.

Even before that, in 1965, during the Athens Congress, the Soviet astronauts met the American astronauts. Pasha Belyayev and I represented the Soviet Union, and Gordon Cooper, Pete Conrad who afterward died in a motorcycle accident, and Deke Slayton represented the United States.

Deke Slayton was a war veteran. He had flown B-25 bombers, taking part in European operations, and bombing Berlin. He was a real man; very faithful to us. He was the director of flight operations but he didn't fly. He had some heart problems.

SOYUZ-APOLLO CREW BY THE BUST OF KOROLEV. DEKE SLAYTON, ME, TOM STAFFORD, VALERI KUBASOV, VANCE BRAND, 1975. CREDIT: ALEXEI LEONOV.

ASTRONAUT DONALD K. "DEKE" SLAYTON EMBRACES COSMONAUT LEONOV IN THE SOYUZ SPACECRAFT. CREDIT: NASA.

But he trained constantly and in the end, in 1975, he went on the Apollo-Soyuz Test Project as Commander of the docking module. Deke Slayton was a very sensible man.

The Apollo-Soyuz Test Project crew consisted of Tom Stafford, Deke Slayton, and a very experienced astronaut, Vance Brand. We used to call him Vanya Brand. I have just come back from Los Angeles, I called him and said: "Hi Vanya!," and he said: "Hello Lesha." And then there was myself and Valeri Kubasov. As I said, it was a good team.

The model for international cooperation was the crew of Apollo-Soyuz because we even have common children. I helped Tom Stafford to adopt two boys from a Russian orphanage. They are grown up now, doing their university degrees, flying. We meet at least twice a year: either I go to the United States or he comes here.

When the Soviet relationship with the United States was very tense, Tom Stafford gave a speech in the U.S. Congress and said that, "We need to work with Russia. I believe in that." When we had problems with the MIR station, he said they were mere technical problems which could be easily solved and the station could function correctly. In this way he defended us from criticism.

But let's return for a moment to this first meeting in Athens. Conrad, Cooper and Slayton didn't know a word in Russian. We Russians were more organized; we could say "all right." So we stayed there for about four hours. We drank a bottle of whisky, a bottle of brandy, and then something else. I don't know how we talked. But when we walked out of the room, we said to each other: "Look, they are sensible guys! We could fly with them!" And historians refer to this encounter as a model for very high communicative competence of the crew. It's difficult even to imagine the conversation between those five people, but after five hours there was perfect mutual understanding.

In 1965, Pasha Belyayev and I sat at the same table with Wernher von Braun and his wife Eva. We had an interpreter (as they were VIPs) and had a chance to discuss many different issues. Interestingly, he spoke of Korolev: "I don't know him," he said, but practice has shown that he is an extraordinary leader. I couldn't have done that in your context. I am not so good a leader as Korolev." Korolev was right to quit the research on V-1 and switch to R-1, a new model of the "Semyorka" missile, which is still functioning today.

He realized right in time that the V2 was not fit for serious work. It can be viewed as a medium distance missile. That Korolev recruited a most significant group of specialists of different areas. This contributed to creating the Semyorka missile that is still in use. "When I was in Germany, I had never heard of him," said von Braun, "though we were working in parallel fashion." Later on, I met von Braun in Huntsville. He said the same thing about Korolev, that he was an extraordinary leader. He didn't say "engineer" because it was clear Korolev had outsmarted him. Wernher von Braun was, of course, ahead of Korolev in engineering.

In 1961, Korolev started working on the N-1 missile. He intended it to be better than Saturn since the Saturn V used engines with low pressure in the cabin, which was not very efficient but reliable and safe. Korolev decided on high pressure in the cabin. Much work needed to be done to get rid of high-frequency fluctuations and so engineers discarded this option immediately. Of course the Saturn V completed all the missions it was intended for, and its last model was the two-stage type in the Apollo-Soyuz mission. That was the last mission of Apollo, and my last mission, too.

What if we had started cooperation between the Soviet Union and the United States in the 1960s? We would have achieved fantastic results with much less divided effort. Roger Chaffee and Ed White were members of the first American mission; White was the first American to perform a space walk. Gus Grissom, Chaffee and White, the crew of Apollo 1, died in the terrible launch pad fire. We had that experience back in 1961 when Valentin Bondarenko died in a test chamber fire. He was in a cabin with the same parameters as Apollo 1. After Bondarenko's death we decided to stop using that oxygen-rich environment and replaced it with a normal one. The Americans, however, continued to work in that direction, and three of their astronauts died because of it.

The Russian lunar program began very early too. In 1962 authorities decided to construct a craft for the implementation of a Moon mission. It was called Sever, meaning "north," and then was renamed L-1, L-2 and L-3. In 1964 the party and the government issued a resolution signed by Nikita Khrushchev. It was about organizing flights to the Moon, flights around the Moon, Moon walks, and returning triumphantly to Earth.

The first stage was to fly around the Moon. According to the results of the first three missions, they would choose the crew who would set foot on the Moon. Soviets already had the L-3 craft in mind, which was designed for one astronaut. Using it was risky, but the weight characteristics didn't allow for more. Engineers then created the Proton rocket to carry out this program. They considered the option of using the missile in conjunction with a spacecraft for reaching the lunar surface. Parallel to this, engineers also began constructing the N-1 rocket. It was a monster of 1,800 tons, with 30 engines totaling a thrust of 4,500 tons. They were Kuznetsov engines with a thrust of 150 tons each, and there were lots of them — 30 altogether.

At that time, Glushko engines already existed, with 600 tons thrust. It used a highly volatile, combustible mixture of fuel, and Pavlovich used to say: "We are not going to use those dirty motors." I think he wasn't against the quality of the fuel, but the personality of the missile constructor — who once had informed the KGB against him. As a result, he was sentenced to 10 years of hard labor.

So the first step was flying around the Moon. I was appointed director of the lunar program at the cosmonaut training center. After the general training was completed, two crews were selected: myself and Oleg Makarov, and Valery Bykovsky and Nikolay Rukavishnikov.

We began our work. What was it about? First, we were to be present at the assembling and electrical tests of the craft. Second, we would work out the navigation systems. Third, we would work out the system of manual piloting at escape

YURI GAGARIN WITH THE AUTHOR AT THE COSMONAUTS TRAINING CENTER, 1964. CREDIT: ALEXEI LEONOV.

velocity. The craft was installed on a centrifuge. In real conditions, according to real measurements taken by the crew, we found our location in space and composed the launching program coordinating it. It was done on a centrifuge. I reached about 196 centrifuge rotations with a 14g load factor, with the craft operating at escape velocity

MOSCOW PARADE 1965. PAVEL BELYAYEV AND
ALEXEI LEONOV. CREDIT: ALEXEI LEONOV.

COSMONAUTS YURI GAGARIN AND ALEXEI
LEONOV. CREDIT: ALEXEI LEONOV.

and two submergences.

Apart from this, I also worked on a system of reaching the lunar surface. We didn't have simulators. I graduated from the school of test pilots with a degree in helicopter piloting — otherwise I would not have permission to operate helicopters. A program was designed for landing a helicopter without an engine, which would be similar to reaching the surface of the Moon.

I conducted nine such landings, and they were very difficult and dangerous. Then the authorities stopped the program because it could end in a tragedy. Six craft were launched to fly around the Moon and all of them came back to Earth. There were problems related to two of them. First, the astro-sensor failed in one of the craft. We managed to solve this. The second problem was that the fifth craft upon jettisoning its heat shield, also lost its parachute lines, and the craft crashed onto Earth from 4,000 meters at 25 meters per second. Of course, it was all broken, but curiously enough, the optical equipment was undamaged. Afterward, we printed very nice Moon images from that cassette.

The last space probe (the sixth one) orbited the Moon and landed within 600 meters of the starting point. Time went by, and it became clear that a political resolution was needed to orbit the Moon. We were perfectly capable of that, but the nonsensical cautiousness of our government kept us from it. If Korolev had been alive, I'm sure we would have been the first to orbit the Moon, six months before the American mission of Apollo 8. They knew it and were afraid of it, but we couldn't reach the Moon before the Americans.

The N–1 rocket created big problems; actually, it never flew. The first accident happened in the 80th second of flight. It was related to the construction scheme. Other accidents followed and were due to engine problems. There were four launches and four accidents. They should have adopted the scheme suggested by the engineer Vladimir Chelomey, which suggested using four UR-500 rockets.

But the story wasn't quite over yet. Yuri Gagarin and I wrote a letter to the Politbureau asking them to accept our version of the program. Our Lunokhod was already pacing the Moon, so our government relaxed and said to themselves that they were able to manage things. Our argument was as follows: the Russians hadn't decided to quit the program entirely, so we should start with the Moon despite the fact that the Americans had already done it.

But alas, they didn't agree with us. Much later, they said: "We should have done what the astronauts suggested, they were smarter than we were." That's the story.

As far as the Moon is concerned, we could fly there by ourselves, without help from any other country. We had sufficient experience to carry out the program called Luna. We only needed the resolution of the government; that's all. And it was not over yet. We now had two powerful rockets called Energia that are more powerful than the Saturn V. Energia had performed two brilliant flights. Once it took a 200-ton block into orbit. The second time it carried Buran, the Russian space shuttle, into orbit.

The coming generation should focus on having a good government. Here's what I think of future prospects: first, the location for the Svobodny Cosmodrome was selected correctly. Given the current situation, we should calculate how much longer we are going to pay Kazakhstan for ongoing use of the Baikonur Cosmodrome; consider that we are now paying $117 million per year, and even so, we are not allowed to make very many changes there.

At the moment, Kazakhstan is governed by a most intelligent man, Nursultan Nazarbayev. But we do not know who will come next. Anything is possible. Maybe they will start looking for a more profitable alternative. It's simple. The Kyrgyz sold the Manas transit center to the United States. In this very same way Baikonur could be sold to any country. Or, in any case, they will revise the clauses of the contract related to rent payment.

In Russia, the Ulyanovsk Vostochny Airport is the best by all parameters. The climate there is absolutely great. It is a place where people can live decently, and, the whole place should be designed according to the principles of resort architecture, so that people can settle down there. The buildings must be built in a completely different way, the way that the Americans build them: they offer land for free or with subsidies and then people go constructing their own houses. They live there while they are using it, then if they wish, so, they can stay.

No one wants to live in Baikonur. It is a prison, and it was constructed by the government. If you look at Korolev's cottage, where he lived all his life — nine months in a year — you'll see it's a Finnish cottage, it would cost about 500 to 1,000 rubles. If you go in, you will see a bathtub on bricks and a rusty toilet bowl. That is the house of an extraordinary person who lived there. No air conditioning. The engineer of Baikonur, Vladimir Nesterov, was awarded prizes, but I would punish him; I would send him to prison for such attitude. These engineers were good at designing squares but weren't willing to think of the people who were going to live in five-story concrete buildings in those extreme weather conditions. What a disgrace!

In order to improve the future of space exploration, the whole system must be restored immediately. Schools must be founded to instruct young specialists. We cannot create anything worthy without them. You can paint whatever you wish — there are many ideas — but none of them is being implemented. There is a college, but it's only in the Energia research center. There are issues of specialists and issues of construction. I am going with a group to visit Vostochny this year, to see what they are up to. The minister of construction told me that nothing is being done. I asked him: "And what about accommodations?" He said: "There are five-story buildings left after the construction of the aerodrome — we will use them."

All I can do is keep my optimism.

ALEXEI AND NEIL AT STARMUS 2011 ON THE ISLAND OF LA PALMA.

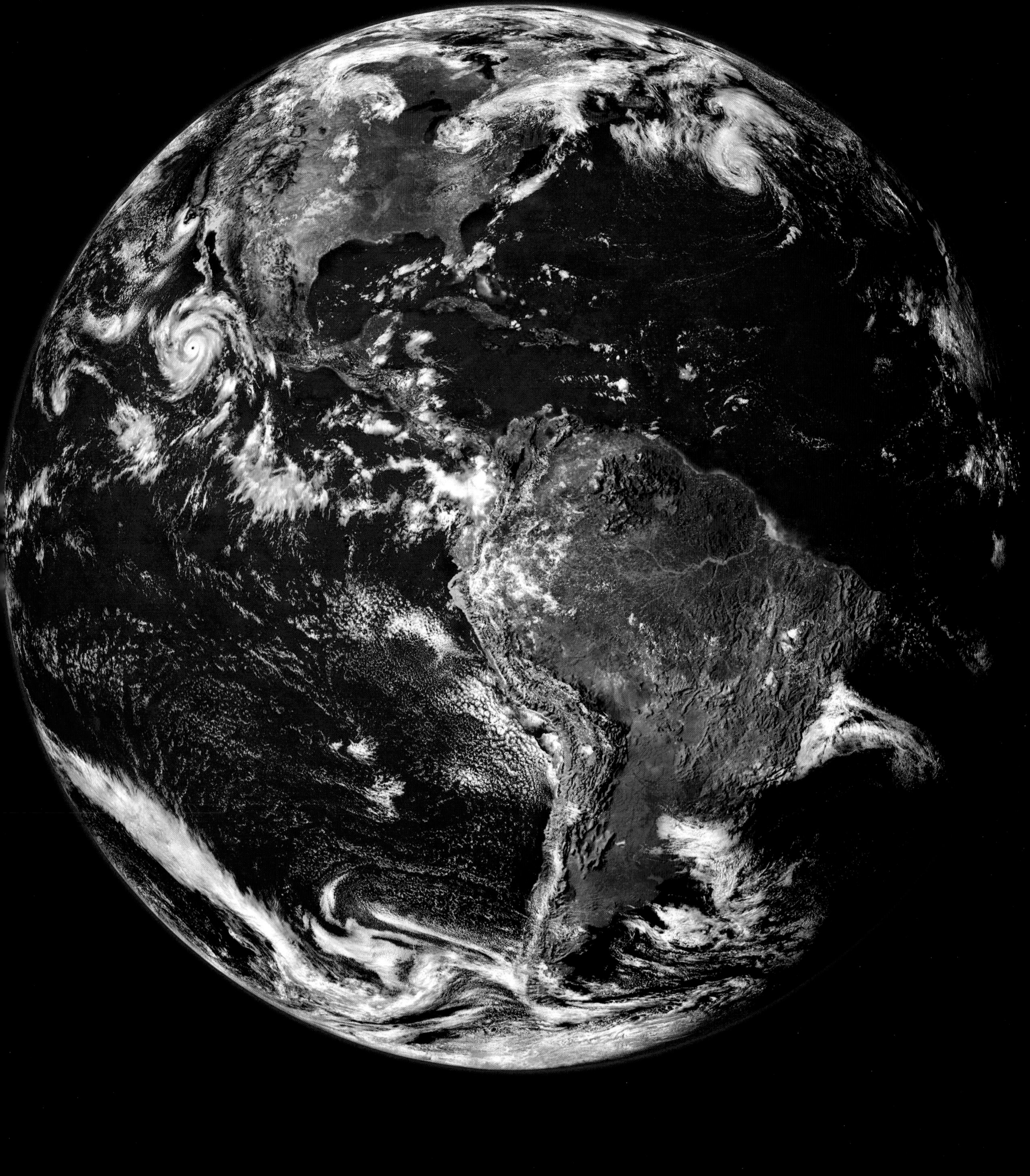

THE 'BLUE MARBLE'. CREDIT: NASA.

BRIAN MAY

What Are We Doing in Space?

Brian May is known throughout the world as guitarist, singer, and songwriter of the rock group Queen, one of the world's most famous and most successful bands of the modern era. Starting in 1970, the band's incredible success with May, singer Freddie Mercury, drummer Roger Taylor, and bassist John Deacon rewrote rock and roll history and is familiar to everyone in such hits as "We Will Rock You," "Bohemian Rhapsody," "We Are the Champions," "Killer Queen," "Radio Ga Ga," and many others. The group ended in its purest form with the death of Mercury in 1991, but continues on today with many activities.

Most Queen fans also know of May's involvement in astronomy. Born in London on July 19, 1947, Brian Harold May developed a strong interest in astronomy in his youth from reading a book written by Patrick Moore. He also developed strong musical interests and a fascination with animals and animal welfare, along with an interest in stereo photography. Astronomy would become a career track. He studied math and physics at Imperial College London and mostly completed a Ph.D. dissertation on zodiacal dust in the solar system — and then Queen took off.

Some 35 years later, May returned to finish his advanced degree, spurred on by Patrick Moore and by his astronomer-friend Garik Israelian. In 2008 he received his Ph.D. and since then has written two astronomy books in addition to his numerous musical activities, projects with photography, and extraordinary efforts with animal rights activism.

BRIAN MAY AT STARMUS.

I could be perhaps perceived as an ideal contributor to this Starmus conference, since I carry credentials from both music and astronomy. But in this company I feel very humbled. My qualification as an astronomer is an astrophysics Ph.D. from Imperial College, on the motions of interplanetary dust, and my credentials as a musician are 40 years recording and touring the world as a member of the rock group Queen, and as a solo artist. As an astronomer, I could very easily speak to you in depth and with confidence on the motions of interplanetary dust. As a musician, I could speak to you with some authority on what it's like to play an A chord at 10,000 watts in Wembley Stadium.

But the subject I've chosen to speak on today, and the subject that Garik asked me to speak on — because it's something we have spoken about many times over the years I've known him, is a subject I cannot approach with confidence. I approach it with some trepidation, because I cannot be an expert in this area. But also because I feel the weight of worry that what I'm contributing may sound negative, and almost ungrateful, in the company of our brilliant guests, men who have trod the Moon and space. Some of what I have to say is speculative, and I hope that our astronauts will be able to put me straight later on and tell me in which parts of my thesis I'm talking out of my hat.

I stand before you today, to address you neither as a musician nor as a scientist, but as a human being.

It will be entirely nontechnical. I suppose I have an unusual viewpoint, albeit not quite as unusual as our esteemed guest astronauts here, but because I have glimpsed the world from the extremes of the environments of pure art and pure science, and I've seen quite a lot of this world.

I've been absolutely enchanted by the talks at this conference. Enchanted, stimulated, and astounded because the speakers have all been able to answer so many questions about what we know about the universe we live in.

It has been amazing for me to meet the astronauts and learn from them how much they share this concern ... how much they care for the planet ... for the

WEMBLEY STADIUM AWAITS THE ARRIVAL OF QUEEN IN 1986 COPYRIGHT QUEEN PRODUCTIONS LTD.

animals ... for mankind, a mankind not split into fragments.

My mission here today is purely to frame a question. It's a question I do not intend to answer, but I hope to stimulate some discussion among the assembled company — most of you here are not only at the pinnacle of current thought, but influential in the world at large.

My question is: What are we doing in space?

There is more than one shade of meaning in this apparently simple enquiry. On the surface is the purely factual question of what is currently happening in the human race's exploration of the space around our planet — which has largely been answered already in this great conference — and very exciting it is too.

But my enquiry extends deeper to the question of what our motives truly are, in our further exploration, and ultimately to whether the motives on which we are acting stand up beside our picture of the human race in the context of the universe as a whole. In other words, to cut to the chase: now that the door to the conquest of space has been opened by brilliant scientists and engineers, and brave explorers, is the rest of mankind ready, or indeed worthy, to walk through that door?

And ... if we walk through, in bulk ... what will we take into space?

How did this begin? Amazingly, it is half a century since man first ventured outside the thin layer of life-giving atmosphere that surrounds our blue planet. In the 1950s and 1960s we saw two powerful nations, the U.S.A., and what was then called the U.S.S.R., who were in a state of so-called Cold War with each other, both pumping money and human ingenuity into building space rockets to take man into space. The first steps were very much like Jules Verne's projectile — a capsule shot into near space, and then allowed to follow its natural parabolic trajectory, in free fall, back to Earth. It was ascertained that a man could survive in the near vacuum

JOHN F. KENNEDY ARRIVING AT CAPE CANAVERAL IN SEPTEMBER 1962. CREDIT: NASA.

of space using microcosmic support systems inside metal containers, the first manned space vehicles, and even outside the capsules in the first space suits. Our venerable guest Alexei Leonov proved this by his personal courage.

So now it was clear that humans could journey into space.

What ensued was a Space Race, a rush to be the first nation to put a human foot on the Moon. Why? Was it in the spirit of exploration, of discovery, or pure human curiosity? Yes, all of these. We know that the two men behind American and Russian initiatives, Wernher von Braun and Sergei Korolev, had dreamed of a Moon landing all their lives. But if human curiosity was the only motive, why did the two nations not collaborate? What wonderful way to mend bridges it might have been, to work on such a noble project hand in hand. But of course they didn't. Why? Because the whole subtext of this endeavor was militaristic, just as it had been 40 years earlier for von Braun in Germany when he was developing V2 rockets to bomb London. (In Russia, Korolev was doing the same job.) The dreams were there, shared by the astronauts, the engineers, the astronomers, who worked on this project. But why did it get the billions of dollars it needed in funding, to make it happen?

Well, I don't think we can avoid the thought that it was because of quite different reasons. Not only did the conquest of the Moon look like it could give superior spying power, and firepower for the nation who got there first, but the prestige, the bravado, the impression of military might, would surely frighten all nations into submission. The power behind the two national efforts was, in fact, militaristic. I must stress that, by this, I do not mean that this was the idea of the armed forces. No, what I'm referring to is the military aspirations of politicians, which have to be carried out by armed forces who are often all too aware of the flaws in the reasoning of the politicians.

As we all know the race to set foot on the Moon was won by the USA. But from then on, one wonders what happened to the motivation, the power. Yes, there were more Moon landings; 12 people have walked on our Moon. But we are now 50 years on, and does it not seem incredible that the huge momentum of that time did not translate into a colonization of the Moon by now, half a century later?

Those 50 years have seen thousand-fold leaps in expertise, computer technology, the birth of the Internet. How come this outreach into space stalled? Buzz Aldrin told us in his address that after the clear objective of the first Moon landing had been achieved, it became harder to be clear about the objective and harder to keep the support for the continuing exploration going. Yes, that must have been so. But it's also tempting to theorize that the political "powers-that-be" did not see any immediate advantage in pursuing this path any further. They turned their eyes in other directions. And they were actually quite open about it.

John Kennedy spoke of man's ambition to explore the cosmos in the pursuit of pure knowledge, but the word "Star Wars" was coined to describe the ambitions of the development of unmanned weaponry in space instigated by President Ronald Reagan in 1980, the so-called Strategic Defense Initiative. And meanwhile, the mighty Saturn rockets no longer roared, and the Moon was left alone.

I can only guess, but I look at a recent failure of an application to study zodiacal dust to secure funds of about £10,000 to make further studies of its motions, and contrast it with the roughly $330 million that were allocated for NASA to hit Comet Tempel 1 with a projectile, and please don't tell me that military considerations have nothing to do with the decision making process. I don't doubt the sincerity of the scientists who pulled off this feat, but how jolly for the politicians to be able to demonstrate to the world that the United States can hit a target at 100 million miles!

The prime motivation for much of the money allocated to space exploration is evidently still tied up with the military, and with political power.

If it's true, are we happy with that? Does that make it the right kind of motivation? Is this what we will take into space? Through that door? Into the future?

Do we take military ambition? Do we take we take economic ambition? Politics, economics, and the military seem always to conspire. Do we take the greed and

SERGEI KOROLEV IN THE COCKPIT OF THE GLIDER 'KOKTEBEL'. CREDIT: NASA.

WEHRNER VON BRAUN. CREDIT: NASA.

THE EARTH AT NIGHT. CREDIT: NASA.

selfishness of big business into space? Will we rejoice, when we get off the lunar shuttle, in seeing a McDonalds sign? Kentucky Fried Chicken? Gucci, L'Oreal, hedge funds, insurance brokers?

But what else do we take into space? Well, probably a continuation of our present behavior, right?

We need new lands, do we? Earth is no longer big enough for us? Right? So, briefly, shall we look at the damage we have done already to our own beautiful planet — a planet uniquely perfectly suited to our needs, and the needs of all the creatures who, as Richard Dawkins has reminded us, each at the pinnacle of their evolutionary path, worthily share Earth with us?

Looking at our planet from afar, it looks so peaceful, clean, gentle, unsullied. It evolved over millions of years, with its flora and fauna, its delicate balance of independent emergent life. But this paradise, this Eden, is not showing us the hurt it has endured, in the mere couple of hundred years since man became all-powerful. It's hard to imagine, now, what Earth was like, just 300 years ago, before we covered it with roads, concrete and fast food chains.

It was literally teeming with life. It's said that when Captain Cook first dropped anchor in the Seychelles, there were so many turtles in the sea you could walk on them all the way to the shore.

It's said that when the last rail was laid on the first railroad across the United States, you could travel from coast to coast and there was never a time when you couldn't see buffalo.

Where do we even start to assess the impact we have had on our planet? Garik Israelian pointed out to me that, ironically, we have produced so much light pollution that most of us can no longer see the stars from where we live — so maybe we have to go into space to see them!

There are already thousands of pieces of debris whizzing around in orbit around Earth, the remains of spent rockets, and deceased vehicles, from large lumps of machinery, down to stray nuts and bolts — not great if they hit you at 17,000 miles per hour as you venture into space.

But let's look seriously at the mess we make right here, the pollution from humans and its effect on Earth.

Two days ago in this room, Buzz Aldrin said that getting to Mars will be good for us. We will learn to conserve and recycle on Mars. It will teach us to be better people. I can't help asking if it might be better if we learned to conserve and recycle and be better people before we colonize Mars? It's hardly necessary to point out every detail of the way we have treated our planet; how, in only 200 years, we have driven so many land animals into extinction, and are well on the way to doing the same to the creatures who live in the sea.

Those of us who are old enough to have been scuba diving for 30 years observe with dismay how much the seas have been impoverished in our lifetime. We see how we have stripped the planet of most of its vegetation, the very lungs of our world on which we depend for air. How we have pumped so much pollution into our atmosphere that we can't tell if we are causing global climate change or not.

Is this the kind of behavior we're going to take into space?

Every species of animal currently living on Earth, each a triumph of evolution, logically would seem to have the same rights to a decent life and a decent death, as us humans. But somehow, in the rush to propagate our species, the notion came into our heads that really, somehow, man was the only species that mattered. So we now calmly justify the expendability of every animal on the planet, in the name of advancing our own progeny. Suppose we find that intelligent life we're so excited about looking for *tomorrow*? How will we treat it?

At this moment, billions of animals — sentient creatures — are confined in degrading and ghastly conditions, many bred for nothing but to make the most profit out of food production. Cows, pigs, chickens, turkeys, many of them so hideously genetically manipulated that they cannot support their own weight. Animals that live a life of constant pain, only to be subjected to a violent, premature death, their tortured bodies heading out in shrink-wrap onto supermarket shelves. Read *Eating Animals* by Jonathan Safran Foer if you want the details.

Is this the kind of behavior we will take into space?

At this moment, billions of mammals, sentient, cognizant creatures, are confined in pitiful conditions, deprived of any sensory experience, tortured in the name of scientific research, medical research, the making of cosmetics, and other lame excuses. I have been working with the Hadwen Trust in the U.K., which has already demonstrated that progress in medicine may actually be accelerated by the replacement of all animals used in medical research, by eliminating pointless and irrelevant experiments, which are inconclusive because animals react differently from humans to most drugs anyway. The most tragic demonstration of this was Thalidomide, a drug passed by animal experimentation as safe for humans, leading to its prescription as a cure for nausea in pregnancy. The result was multiple birth defects, carving a tragic message in a whole generation of babies.

Is this what we'll take into space?

At this moment, birds are being bred in tiny boxes, to be released on British moors in a condition in which they basically can't fly properly, so they can be mown down by armies of men with guns in the name of sport. At this moment, gangs of men on horseback are lying about what they are doing out in the countryside, claiming that their packs of hungered dogs "accidentally" stumbled upon a fox and tore it limb from limb. Yes, they call fox hunting, even though it's now illegal in Britain, a "sport." They claim that torturing a wild animal to death in the name of sport is a "human right," even though this concept was roundly dismissed in the European Court in 2009.

Is this what we'll take into space?

At this moment, backed by the governments they have helped to install, farmers whose intensive farming methods have led to the proliferation of disease in livestock, and subsequently to the infection of the wild animals around them, are clamoring for the slaughter of the wild animals whose lives have been blighted by these diseases. The British government has recently announced its determination to cull our native badgers, despite the fact that scientific experiment has proved that culling of badgers will not even contribute to what they are trying to achieve, the control of bovine tuberculosis in cattle.

Is this disregard for the welfare of animals what we will take into space?

Just supposing we are lucky enough to find animal life out there, is this the way we will treat it?

This is how we treat the other species on the planet. But how do we treat our own kind?

Armstrong and Aldrin planted a worthy plaque on the Moon, a photo of which we saw this week, stating "We come in peace, in the name of all mankind." And I don't doubt for a second that this thought was in their hearts and minds. But what did we do, walking through that other door many years ago, the door that the gentle peace-loving pilgrim fathers opened to the other New World? We all but exterminated the indigenous population, the North American Indians, along with the buffalo with which they were interdependent. We enslaved the people of Africa because we thought they were less deserving than us of freedom and dignity. It's a shameful history.

Slavery was abolished by the efforts of William Wilberforce only a hundred and fifty or so years ago. Yet we all know that human trafficking is still rife. Young labor is imported to all Western countries, kept in conditions of no contact with the outside world. Children are abducted to be used for the pleasure of perverts in an industry which is spread out across the so-called civilized world. Children are made to work on toxic dumps, seeking out chemicals that will ultimately kill them, and then, worse, the people who keep them enslaved make them endure sexual abuse in return for pickings of the best toxic waste. We fight wars for territory, for political power, we call ourselves peace-keepers yet we use our might to make war in impoverished countries, often protecting regimes of questionable morals. We play God, attempting to change the leadership of countries to suit our own economic needs.

Our record of abuse to animals is matched by our record of abuse to our own kind.

So what will we take into space? All of this?

If we allow large numbers of men to go into space, who is to stop a country building a military base on the Moon? Or on a conveniently hard-to-monitor asteroid? And using it to bring about the next Hiroshima? The next act of destruction committed in the name of keeping peace, or spreading what we call democracy? Perhaps the next Hiroshima will be New York, or Moscow, or London. Suddenly the conquest of space takes on a huge, heavy overtone.

We all know the story of the meeting in Copenhagen, the story of the agonies of indecision of Oppenheimer and his colleagues, on whether or not to give the secrets of making an atomic bomb to their governments. We know what the result was. It is too late to take back the nuclear bomb from the politicians of the world. But it may not be too late to look at that door that leads into space — not to close it, but at least put some regulation on it, to stop the proliferation of man's foul temper, man's aggressive behavior out in the hitherto untouched cosmos.

Is it possible for scientists, artists, men of understanding and empathy, to take a moral stand, to take hold of the reins of future exploration of space, to make laws governing the further exploitation of lands outside Earth? To contain the evils we have wrought on our own world and behave decently out there?

Maybe the door needs to be held just ajar for a time while we turn our attentions to the millions of people on this planet who are starving, or dying of diseases which are curable, yet they cannot afford the cure. There are many who would question whether even one more rocket ought to be fired while there is still one child dying unnecessarily, while there are still people suffering torture because of their beliefs, animals suffering torture for our pleasure.

Is it a lost cause? Must we conclude that man, in bulk, is indeed unworthy to step off the tiny blue world, which he has all but destroyed in his folly?

I'm sorry if any of this has seemed negative.

I have actually agonized over whether I ought to give this talk at all. Nobody loves the pursuit of knowledge more than I do. I love the simple beauty of science that

BRIAN ON STAGE AT WEMBLEY, 1986.
COPYRIGHT QUEEN PRODUCTIONS LTD.

enriches our lives just as I love the simple beauty of music which feeds our souls. I was also a boy who dreamed of being a spaceman. Dan Dare was my hero, a fictional man of honor, courage and moral rectitude, just like the great men we have shared this festival with during these magical days, the real-life astronauts of our time. We have heard each one of these men express their determination that the future of space must be shared by all nations. Sitting in my room last night, I didn't want to be the one to doubt that the human race could pull it off.

But there is a huge positive side to all this. To be asking this question, at this time, is an opportunity. This could be a new start for mankind, and many of the people who can make a difference to the future are in this room. If you, if we don't ask this question, and take some action, to ensure that we get the right answer, who will?!

OK, for the last time, I ask the question, if we do open the door wide, can we, as concerned scientists, artists, and human beings, find a way to propagate just the decent, noble parts of our civilization?

Not cruelty, but empathy and compassion.
Not greed, but generosity.
Not conflict, but cooperation.
Not war, but peace, in which all men, all women, all creatures, share the glorious gifts of nature.
The glorious gift of life.
For now, in a sense, we are all participants at a new Copenhagen.
Thank you.

Brian May

BRIAN ON STAGE WITH TANGERINE DREAM AT THE STARMUS CONCERT 2011.

CHARLIE DUKE

JIM LOVELL

SECTION 2

SPACE ARGONAUTS

VIKTOR GORBATKO

The first explorers of space faced unseen vistas, technological challenges, and unknown dangers. The story of the early space programs and missions that overcame adversity inspire us today like few other moments in human history.

Early Soviet cosmonaut Viktor Gorbatko describes the early days of the Soviet space program, with colleagues such as Yuri Gagarin and Alexei Leonov, and his subsequent Soyuz flights.

The first incredible moments of a spacecraft orbiting the Moon form the recollections of Bill Anders, whose involvement in Apollo 8 is remembered with his capture of the famous "Earthrise" photograph and readings from the Book of Genesis.

Jim Lovell's gripping account of the emergency aboard Apollo 13, when an oxygen tank exploded and jeopardized the mission and the astronauts' lives, reminds us of the incredible daring and danger of space exploration, of pushing technology to new frontiers.

Apollo astronaut Charlie Duke describes what it was like to walk and drive on the Moon, to collect samples, to do research on an alien world.

BILL ANDERS

SOYUZ 24 CREW: YURI GLAZOV AND VIKTOR
GORBATKO. CREDIT: SOVIET SPACE PROGRAM.

VIKTOR GORBATKO

SUPERMEN OR PILOTS? THE FIRST SOVIET COSMONAUTS

Viktor Vasilyevich Gorbatko, born December 3, 1934 in Ventsy-Zarya, Krasnoar Krai, Soviet Union, is one of the most distinguished cosmonauts of the Soviet space program and was a Soviet Air Force pilot. In 1960 Gorbatko was selected, along with Yuri Garagin and Alexei Leonov, as a cosmonaut and began his training.

He worked on board the orbital station Almaz (a military space station under the cover of the civilian mission Salyut 5). Gorbatko was trained for the Soviet lunar program and was a member of the backup crew of Soyuz 2, which was cancelled. In 1968 he graduated from the Air Force Engineering Academy. In 1969 he flew as a research engineer on Soyuz 7 and later served as commander of the missions Soyuz 24 (1977) and Soyuz 37/Soyuz 36 (1980). He also served on the backup crew for Voskhod 2 and Soyuz 5, 21, 23 and 31. Gorbatko acted as Deputy Sports Minister and later lectured at the Russian Air Force Engineering Academy. Since 1993 he has been General Director of AA and AL in Moscow.

VIKTOR GORBATKO AT STARMUS.

I served in Moldova, in our Soviet Republic — such a wonderful place. Sunny Moldova. We were in camps: the main airport was under repair, so we were set up on the alternate airfield. We were navigating there. Unexpectedly, during the preparation for flight, the regimental commander said: "Go to the political supervisor." I went to him. I thought to myself, "what have I done?"

I came into the room. They greeted me. There were the representatives of the special department, except for the political supervisor. They gave me a paper. I signed, acknowledging that everything was a government secret, and I pledged not to betray it. When I signed the document, they ordered: "Now go to the regimental doctor."

I entered, and saw our medical books. There stood our doctor and Fedorov, the representative from Moscow, a lieutenant colonel. Afterward, he became the head of the department of hospitals. In the hospital, he worked only with cosmonauts who were already there and who had been selected.

They began to talk to me. Not a political supervisor, but the doctors: "What about your plans? What? When? How? At what altitude are you going to fly?" I answered: "What altitude? At the altitude that the airplanes fly — about 20 kilometers." They began to talk about higher altitudes. "What about 100 kilometers?" I wondered: "Isn't that a Sputnik?" "Yes. We suggest you. You have been recommended. We offer you the chance to undertake the mission. We'll send you to Moscow. But you can ponder it — it isn't necessary to give the response immediately. If you want to, you can first go to see your wife."

My wife was at home, about 200 kilometers from the airfield. Talk to her, I thought. But don't mention space; just mention the term "test pilot." Maybe, then, I thought for about a minute and blurted out, "I agree!" So everybody knew everything, but at home — nothing.

The first detachment was established from the fighter pilots. The first ships, Vostoks, were single-seaters. And it was possible to bail out during descent before the landing. In fact, the fighter pilot was a good place to draw on for cosmonauts. It combines all these professions: navigator, commander, pilot, operator. That led to the decision to employ fighter pilots.

Selection for the first detachment took place from fighting troops with recommendations from headquarters and agreement from the doctors, who worked with us. Several of us were recommended and directed to Moscow in order to pass the profound medical tests given in an aviation hospital. The first detachment is the one

**SOYUZ 24 CREW TRAINING.
CREDIT: VIKTOR GORBATKO.**

**SOYUZ 24 CREW TRAINING.
CREDIT: VIKTOR GORBATKO.**

who passed tests in conditions of 12gs in a rotating centrifuge. Only our group, who were in the first detachment. There were no 15g–20g tests. By the way, Anatoli Kartashov, who was recommended to be included among the first six, was expelled because of capillaries on his back, which began to break during the 12g test. He was expelled only for this reason.

So nobody was sent on the 12g overloads. And it was the right decision because overloads would take place in case of total breakdown. Normally we were subjected to 8gs. By the way, all the Vostoks were descending ballistically, and that's why overloads were not above 8g. The overload of 20gs happened when the delivery vehicle was broken down (Vasily Lazarev and Oleg Makarov were on board). This crew suffered 20g conditions because during the managed descent, the ship turned back-to-front. The overload then increased to 20gs.

In those days, secrecy was very high! For example, when we were entering the Zhukovsky Engineering Academy of Air Forces, as the first classes were forming, there were two people who had already flown — Yuri Gagarin and Gherman Titov. So there we were among common students, entering the academy, and there was much that we didn't see and hear.

The first detachment was filming a lot, but those exposed to mass media were those who had already flown. We were more focused on playing tennis and basketball. But sometimes you come across photographs and films and see yourself! Only when the Apollo-Soyuz program pushed forward did many things become known and become published. And then with the Intercosmos program. When it went on, the photos of the first and second crew were also published.

I took photographs in space during my second flight, when we were on the Almaz Space Station. It was called Salut-5 due to it secrecy, but in actuality it was Almaz-3. It was a military station. Basically, the Almaz program was a reconnoitering one. We were just working out the scheme; we were taking many pictures that were needed from Earth orbit. Of course, we took pictures only when the weather was fine, because pictures taken by unmanned aircraft were also accumulating. We took pictures of bases, airfields, ships in the sea. It was such a thing. Everything connected with military, but there were civilian shots as well.

The quality of the pictures was high. We had the so-called Agat device. It had a one-meter screen and definition also of about one meter. But it occupied half the station! We worked great with Yuri Glazkov. Secrecy was very familiar to us in the 1960s. Even Valya Gagarin had no idea that Yuri would be in space. At the time, I was at the central managing post in Moscow.

When I went out in the mornings, I turned on the radio. I had two little children. My wife began to say: "Why did you turn on the radio?" The radio woke up the children. And so I left early. She said: "It only later occurred to me — when they announced that the flight passed successfully." Radio announcers mentioned Gagarin's flight. For six years it had been prepared in secrecy.

We had a technical education, but secondary. Everybody had the diploma of a technical pilot. And later some attained an engineer's education. At first, we simply didn't have quite enough education. Engineering knowledge was needed, and that's why they were added.

Our Zhukovsky Air Force Engineering Academy gave us a lot. Back then, we had only our detachment and one for women, headed by Valentina Tereshkova. Do you know what diplomas we had? Pilot-engineer-cosmonaut. Only we have such diplomas: the first detachment of cosmonauts and the women's detachment. We entered in 1961 and left in 1968. But we hadn't normal terms, as normal students in normal universities do. We studied in one term, then passed exams, then had holidays, and then had a new term.

Sergei Korolev worked personally with every cosmonaut. Of course he took part, but he was not in preparation. He didn't participate, but he was present during the first six's exams. Exams were held directly on board a ship. Yuri Gagarin was the first who passed the exam on piloting a Vostok.

We had about 750 hours to pass in this term. The beginning was in September and it ended when we had the opportunity, not necessarily in January. We passed in April, May, even in June. When this term ended, then we had holidays.

The other students didn't know who we were. But you understood the situation when Gagarin, Titov, and others appeared. However, we were present at the classes together. Of course students guessed what group it was. Afterward, we had a separate group and separate lectures. Everything was separated. We did laboratory work. We went from Chkalovskaya to the academy in Moscow.

Those who didn't fly were not allowed to go abroad during this period. But Gagarin and Titov were allowed! And then, slowly, the others, too. For the first time, I was abroad, in North Korea, in 1969 and 1970.

The most impressive moment, of course, was Gagarin's flight. I was in the initial six, and I hoped to fly too. It created an impression of enormous happiness in me. We were all prepared for flight in outer space: Pavel Belyaev, Alexei Leonov, Yevgeny Khrunov, and me. Doctors lay off me!

I had a little peculiarity in my electrocardiogram, and the reason wasn't found. Doctors suggested myocarditis. First of all, I was taken off the preparations some two months before the flight. Second, they gave me a leave, and then another, and so on. But I rejected it. I wasn't going to miss my classes at the academy.

I began to ski intensively, even though I'm from the south. Skiing is not a pathway to the sauna! Physical training was key. When Leonov and Belyav had a flight, I was on rehabilitation in a hospital and was listening to programs about them. I was happy they were in space the last. I was in Moscow, at Lenin Hills for rehabilitation. They already finished their flight. The last evening I checked out, healthy. I proved that I was normal, that the diagnosis was faulty. The tonsils were guilty. They were removed, and everything went on normally.

But the first and the third flights were different. And the big difference was: Gagarin knew nothing. There were two flights before me, and I was told something. But you must feel it yourself!

Even such a moment! When you receive the command reveille, the first impression was overwhelming. You feel the rocket rise as if the chair was removed, and it hangs on in the air. That's all you feel!

Later, when we were already in orbit, we were in Earth's shadow. We left the terminator — it was already dark on Earth, but still sunny in orbit. The particles you see at the moment of separation, these particles of dust, in the beams of sunlight, look like stars near the ship! You think it's a nice how-do-you-do! You are surrounded by stars! Though you understand that actual stars are so far away when you look at them.

When you look down at Earth, the oceans, mainland, seas, pass by so fast, and you change the idea that Earth is big. It isn't so big because you can fly over it in 89 minutes. You can fly all over the world. It impresses too!

In general, the most beautiful thing from orbit is sunrise and sunset. Everything you see on Earth. You're struck by great happiness to be in a place where so few people have been.

THE AUTHOR WITH NEIL ARMSTRONG AND ALEXEI LEONOV.

BILL ANDERS' FAMOUS PHOTOGRAPH "EARTHRISE". CREDIT: NASA.

BILL ANDERS

The Early American Space Program

William Alison Anders, born October 17, 1933 in British Hong Kong, is the son of a U.S. Navy officer and took to a career of flying from an early age. Growing up in southern California, he was allured by a career in the skies and was graduated from the U.S. Air Force Academy in 1955, also earning a Master's degree in nuclear engineering from the Air Force Institute of Technology in Dayton, Ohio.

Becoming a fighter pilot, Anders spent his early years patrolling the skies during the Cold War. In 1963 NASA administrators selected him as part of the third group of astronauts, and by 1966 he was chosen as the backup pilot for Gemini 11. Two years later, on December 21, 1968, he served as lunar module pilot in the first lunar orbiting mission, Apollo 8, along with Commander Frank Borman and Command Module Pilot Jim Lovell.

As part of this historic mission, Anders took the famous color "Earthrise" photo from lunar orbit and participated in the celebrated reading from the Book of Genesis that was famously broadcast throughout the world.

From 1969 through 1973, Anders served as executive secretary of the National Aeronautics and Space Council. He participated in various business ventures and also served as chairman of the Nuclear Regulatory Commission, and is a retired major general in the U.S. Air Force Reserve.

BILL ANDERS AT STARMUS .

In order to understand how the lunar program came about, it's important to understand the background for Apollo. Back in the 1950s, the Soviet Union and United States were locked in a rather tough Cold War. Neither side trusted the other, both sides had nuclear weapons, and both sides were ready to deploy them. We had a strategy on both sides called "mutually assured destruction" — hardly a way to be comfortable. At least in the United States, we were digging bomb shelters and I wouldn't be surprised if in the Soviet Union they were doing the same thing, and with just cause.

I spent my early Air Force career chasing Russian bombers over Iceland when they invaded Icelandic air space, in what we nicknamed the "bear and the bison." Possibly, some of my cosmonaut colleagues might have been doing the same thing. Later, after Iceland, I was flying a modern high-speed supersonic interceptor that — believe it or not — had three nuclear-tipped rockets so that we could not only shoot down one plane at a time but we could also shoot down a whole bomber fleet.

In looking back, to think of a junior Air Force captain flying with these things under the wing over San Francisco kind of boggles my mind, but that was the Cold War. America had a real paranoia. We had Joseph McCarthy's congressional reviews. McCarthy implied that anybody who had even joined a labor union was a communist, and communists in that period of American history were considered dangerous. We had a real problem: Eisenhower (and later on his successors) worried about what was known as the "missile gap." If you had nuclear weapons and you wanted to get them to where you wanted them, one way was with missiles, and the United States was well behind the Soviet Union in that respect.

This was really brought to attention with Sputnik. This was an accomplishment that I don't think the Soviet Union — now Russia — really got recognition for. Sure, it surprised everybody, and it was a big motivation for our own program, but this little scientific instrument — weighing 85 kilograms, not very big, not terribly sophisticated by today's standards in both Russia and the United States — this was a major accomplishment. And it was a major shock in America.

That was aided and abetted four years later with Yuri Gagarin — a real step

TINY ONE-MAN SPACECRAFT, THEN CALLED CAPSULES, ORBITED THE EARTH IN THE MERCURY PROGRAM. THEY WERE CHECKED OUT IN A HANGAR AT CAPE CANAVERAL BEFORE BEING HOISTED UP AND MATED WITH A LAUNCH VEHICLE. HEAT-RESISTANT SHINGLES COVERED THE AFTERBODY. CREDIT: NASA.

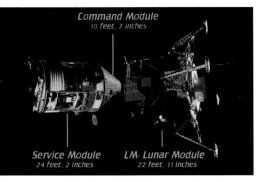

APOLLO 11 COMMAND MODULE DOCKED WITH THE SERVICE MODULE AND THE LUNAR MODULE. CREDIT: NASA.

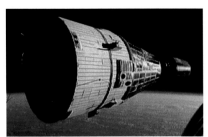

WALLY SCHIRRA AND TOM STAFFORD'S GEMINI VI-A SPACECRAFT, VIEWED BY ASTRONAUTS FRANK BORMAN AND JIM LOVELL ABOARD GEMINI VII. CREDIT: NASA.

forward in the history of mankind.

The reason we're here today is to celebrate a slightly delayed fiftieth anniversary of Yuri's flight. Yuri gets the major amount of attention. He's a hero of the Soviet Union, but my hat's off to the then Soviet Union and its partners in being able to accomplish this terrific feat, a major step for mankind in the exploration of the universe. Yuri was sent up on a very reliable rocket. He flew for 108 minutes in Earth orbit, came back successfully, and the rest is history.

In our country, our rockets were always exploding — they had a bad habit of doing that. I joked to my now friend Alexei Leonov that our Germans weren't as good as their Germans to start out with. Wernher von Braun made up for that in the long run. It was a pretty grim time in our country vis-à-vis manned spaceflight.

In 1961, that prompted President Kennedy to lay down a challenge that pushed America to go to the Moon in the decade of the sixties. People were aghast when he did that. Many thought it was impossible. Some of us in the program later wondered whether it was possible. Nonetheless, that is what started Apollo, if you will: the challenge to land on the Moon by the end of the decade.

Our engineers and space directors worked out a way to do that. I'm going to show you illustrations that will walk through the process. This one shows the one-man Mercury launched on an Atlas rocket that was going to show that humans could actually live and work in space. The lead doctor in the Soviet program, Oleg Gazenko, did that with animals, and of course Yuri proved it as well. To live, work and survive in space: there were a lot of theories that said it couldn't happen.

Then we went to the two-man Gemini to demonstrate our lunar orbital rendezvous technique, showing that we could actually join up with another spacecraft and dock with it, a precursor to Apollo. This illustration shows the lunar module docked with the command and service module. This little triangular or dixie cup-shaped piece is the part that came back and this is the part that serviced the front part and this is the engine that slowed us down in lunar orbit or sped us up to get us back. This is what Jim Lovell had a little problem with on Apollo 13. Whereas Gemini was launched on a Titan rocket, an ICBM, Saturn V was a ground-up design for which we must give Wernher von Braun and his team most of the credit in enabling the Apollo concept.

Here's a picture of a Mercury capsule: for one man, it was very cramped. The Geminis were even more crowded than the Mercuries. Jim Lovell had to share one with Frank Borman for two weeks. Didn't you come back engaged, Jim? But we won't ask!

Alexei Leonov brought another shock to our system, causing Americans to realize that we had a lot to learn. Alexei is outside the spacecraft before our program with Ed White on Gemini 4. We in the United States were considered well behind the very strong, aggressive Soviet program. This illustration shows Jim Lovell and others docking in Gemini 6 and 7. And then we move on to Apollo.

Here is the Saturn V, a huge rocket. It wasn't as big as the Russian N1, but nonetheless it was a big rocket: a first stage, second stage, third stage, and then the shrouds where we carried the lunar module. We didn't carry one on Apollo 8.

When fully fueled, this rocket weighed six million pounds, some 2.72 million kg. The first stage burned out in about two-and-a-half minutes and got us up to supersonic speed. Then we dropped it off and it fell back into the ocean. The second stage took us almost into orbit. The third stage burned a little bit and got us into Earth orbit. We went around checking the spacecraft systems and then reignited it so that it would take us up to about 35,000 feet per second (7 miles a second) and break us free, if you will, of Earth's gravity, sending us on the way to the Moon, if we were pointed in the right direction.

This illustration shows the third group of astronauts —I apologize to Jim Lovell, but I went everywhere in the Internet and I couldn't find a picture of the second group of astronauts. This is the third group of so-called Apollo astronauts. That's me at a somewhat earlier age. Buzz Aldrin spoke to you earlier. I didn't get one of you,

LIFTOFF FOR APOLLO 8. CREDIT: NASA.

ASTRONAUT GROUP THREE ANNOUNCED ON OCTOBER 18, 1963. THEY ARE (SEATED, LEFT TO RIGHT) EDWIN E. ALDRIN JR., WILLIAM A. ANDERS, CHARLES A. BASSETT II, ALAN L. BEAN, EUGENE A. CERNAN, AND ROGER B. CHAFFEE. STANDING (LEFT TO RIGHT) ARE MICHAEL COLLINS, R. WALTER CUNNINGHAM, DONN F. EISELE, THEODORE C. FREEMAN, RICHARD F. GORDON JR., RUSSELL L. SCHWEICKART, DAVID R. SCOTT AND CLIFTON C. WILLIAMS JR.. CREDIT: NASA.

DESERT SURVIVAL TRAINING IN NEVADA. CREDIT: NASA.

BILL ANDERS AND NEIL ARMSTRONG STANDING BEHIND PETE CONRAD AND DICK GORDON. CREDIT: NASA.

Charlie Duke, as you were so late in the program.

If we had to abort — and our orbits were a little more equatorial, if you will, than Soviet or Russian orbits — our spacecraft were designed to land on water, so we had to do survival training in a swimming pool. We practiced desert survival.

I don't think I'd dare wear that around the United States today. That was out in Nevada. This picture shows our jungle survival exercise. That's me being served a piece of iguana lizard. I was told that lizard tastes like chicken: I can tell you it tastes like lizard.

We did a lot of geological training. Some of us liked it more than others. It was one of my main interests. I was a rockhound (as they call it) when I was a kid. In fact, Garik's going to take me on a geology trip here before it's over. The geological training didn't do me much good because I didn't get close enough to look at the Moon in detail, but Charlie Duke will tell you a little about that.

We studied craters. At that time it wasn't then clear whether the craters on the Moon were due to meteoritic impact, whether they were volcanic, or both. So we went to about every crater we could find, most of them volcanic. Studying craters was certainly a lot of fun. We studied and trained in how to maneuver and walk around in lunar gravity, one-sixth g. There was a lot of thought that we might fall

JUNGLE SURVIVAL TRAINING. CREDIT: NASA.

over and not be able to get up. I didn't get to do it, but Charlie can probably tell you that it turned out to be pretty easy and, I think, a lot of fun if you watched these guys playing around on the Moon.

Eventually, I got out of the training program and was assigned to a backup crew with Neil Armstrong (opposite, bottom left).

This illustration shows me standing with Neil, Pete Conrad and Dick Gordon. I thought I had it made for an eventual lunar landing, but then—here's Jim Lovell with Buzz Aldrin, who spoke to you the other day, doing a tether experiment—then we picked a crew for Apollo (Chaffee, Grissom and White).

We all thought we were moving right along and then we had the Apollo 1 fire. That was really bad news, really a shock. I had to tell Pat White her husband had died. This was, in retrospect, a big mistake by our program management and design. We tested this thing at a hundred percent oxygen at a pressure of 15 p.s.i. Almost anything will burn in those circumstances and, sure enough, these guys had a spark and it killed them almost instantaneously.

That was the bad news. The good news is that this prompted a very big review of the Apollo spacecraft. I think my colleagues would agree that, had it not been for this fire, we would probably not have landed on the Moon when we did because we found all kinds of design features that just weren't good — manufacturing sloppiness. This allowed us then to proceed with hardly a problem after that. The nice thing about this is that my colleagues Jim Lovell and Frank Borman led one of the review teams, and the big bosses basically left the engineers and people like Borman no holds barred. If you found a problem, even if it was embarrassing, bring it up; we want to fix it. I'm not sure the more modern NASA does that, but at least that's what saved the Apollo program.

The other bad news for me was that Lovell and Aldrin did such a good job on their Gemini flight that they cancelled the one Neil and I were going to fly, but the booby prize was to get to fly on the lunar-landing training vehicle. Neil and I were among the first to fly that. (I didn't land on the Moon, Jim didn't either; Charlie did but he wasn't flying.) I think it would have been very difficult to do the lunar landing without the training in this. We all trained in helicopters in a 1g environment. But if you work out the mechanics, aerodynamics, stopping forces and all of that, they were different from 1/6-g. Just to learn to pitch up, stop and land in one 1/6-g, that made the difference. I flew it.

Valerie and our five kids came out to watch one morning. That afternoon and the next, Neil flew it. Unknown to both of us, the vehicle had a hidden defect. A sensor had gone bad, and Neil had one more take-off than he had landings. So we were now down to one lunar-landing training vehicle. I think only the commanders got to fly them after that. I feel fortunate. Charlie, you missed something by not flying that!

We pressed on and, in my case, the fire kind of shuffled the crews around. In my case, I was teamed up with Frank Borman and Jim Lovell on Apollo 8.

This illustration shows us in front of our Apollo mission simulator. One thing that NASA really invested in was ground-based simulators. It was amazing how realistic they were. I can't speak for the Mercury program, but I know what we had in Gemini. In the Apollo program, both the lunar module simulator and the command module simulator were amazingly authentic and we spent weeks there. In fact, they threw all kinds of problems at us. So much so that during the flight, I was a little disappointed. I thought I wouldn't get to show people that I knew how to fix this beast.

What was our mission? Well, initially, it was a high-orbit test of the lunar module. I'd been assigned one of the lunar modules and we were going to test that lunar module in high Earth orbit. Our Central Intelligence Agency believed that the Soviet Union was going to do a high-altitude flight around the Moon. There were unmanned tests of what later became known as the Zond program. Maybe Alexei Leonov can tell you a little bit about that later. So our people got nervous and were thinking that the Soviet Union was going to show us up again, plus the fact that my lunar module was way behind schedule.

JIM LOVELL AND BUZZ ALDRIN TESTING A TETHERED LUNAR LANDER. CREDIT: NASA.

JIM LOVELL, BILL ANDERS, AND FRANK BORMAN, THE CREW OF APOLLO 8. CREDIT: NASA.

THE APOLLO 8 PATCH. CREDIT: NASA.

BILL ANDERS CLIMBING OUT OF THE 16G CENTRIFUGE. CREDIT: NASA.

CENTRIFUGE TRAINING FOR THE APOLLO 8 CREW. CREDIT: NASA.

APOLLO 8 EGRESS TRAINING IN GALVESTON BAY. CREDIT: NASA.

I thought it was a brave management decision when NASA said "OK, we're going to swap these flights around," if Apollo 7 was successful (which it was, the first flight of the command and service module on a smaller version of the Saturn), they would send Apollo 8 on the first manned Saturn V away from Earth, break Earth orbit, and around the Moon. And not just around it, but into lunar orbit, to test the phases of the eventual lunar-landing flight.

The illustration I'm now showing depicts our patch. Jim Lovell's a real artist, and he designed it, so if you need a patch, talk to Jim. It basically lays out the trajectory of our flight, if you will, although we went around 10 times. There was a little bit of a concern, quite frankly, to all of us that we'd hardly flown this Apollo at all, and now we were going to go not just into Earth orbit, which would have been a challenge, but also into lunar orbit. NASA was good at bringing the families in, so they knew what was going on.

There was a squawk box, we called it, in the houses that had a five-minute delay, something like that on the voice transmissions. In case we blew up, they'd shut it off, with enough time so the families wouldn't hear the explosion and the screaming.

This illustration shows my wife Valerie and Susan Borman (I couldn't find one of your bride, Jim.), and there's our daughter, who is now the mother of three grown boys, checking out where dad and Frank and Jim were going to orbit the Moon.

We did a lot of training in the centrifuges. This illustration shows Frank in the commander's position and Jim and me over here on this side. Our program was designed to land on the water. We weren't nearly as big a country as Russia so we

APOLLO 8 WIVES VALERIE ANDERS WITH OUR DAUGHTER, AND SUSAN BORMAN. CREDIT: NASA.

hadn't a lot of land to land in. We were sort of short on it, but there's a lot of water out there and we had a big navy so our people designed this thing to land in the water although in theory it was capable of a kind of a crash-landing on the Moon.

The illustration shows balloons placed such that if the capsule tipped upside down, as it did when we landed, the balloons would inflate and flip the craft right side up.

Here's an illustration showing the Mission Control Center in Texas. Here's someone you might have heard of, Flight Director Gene Kranz, with the short hair. I think that's Fred Haise on your flight, Jim. They took over as soon as the rocket broke ground at the launchpad.

So here's our Saturn V out on the pad, fueled up and ready to go. Although I might look a little doubtful here, the crew is ready to go off to the pad. Since our spacecraft

PRELAUNCH. CREDIT: NASA.

GENE KRANZ, FLIGHT DIRECTOR APOLLO 8.
CREDIT: NASA.

had 5.5 p.s.i. oxygen once we got into orbit, we were pre-breathed on oxygen so that we wouldn't get the bends when the pressure was reduced. Shuttle programs and, I think, all Russian programs just breathe regular air, which is a lot simpler and smarter.

This illustration shows lift-off on the morning of December 21, 1968. This rocket is developing seven-and-a-half million pounds of thrust, which is lifting this six-million pound vehicle. So initially the acceleration, which starts at zero, is slow and the velocity is slow. The big F1 engines, gymballing back and forth, shook the top so much — way up here you can't see it — that I felt like a rat in the jaws of a giant terrier. The noise was unbelievable, thrashing back and forth, and I was watching

FRANK BORMAN. CREDIT: NASA.

JIM LOVELL. CREDIT: NASA.

APOLLO 8 LAUNCH. CREDIT: NASA.

the indications for the systems.

If something had been wrong, I don't think I could have done anything about it. If we had to abort, we couldn't communicate, it was so loud. Frank Borman told me later he was smart enough to take his hand off the abort handle. So for about 20 seconds we were basically an unmanned vehicle! We got away from the pad, picking up to close to supersonic speeds.

The illustration overleaf shows us staging, where we drop off the first stage and ignite the stage above it. Then, in eleven or so minutes, there's our trajectory by time camera, we're in Earth orbit. These are great views of the Earth, just beautiful, which we could see all the way to the Moon. There's Frank Borman at zero g. That's Jim Lovell doing star sightings. That's me just holding on.

ME HANGING ON. CREDIT: NASA.

THE FIRST STAGE OF THE ROCKET DROPS
AWAY. CREDIT: NASA.

ONE OF MY FAVORITE PICTURES IS THIS VIEW OF EARTH. CREDIT: NASA..

If you look hard, there's South America, the South Pole. The equator is right here. This "V" is what they call the intertropical convergence zone. There's the United States, of course. The intertropical convergence zone has recently acquired some infamy. This is where Air France 447 was torn apart, heading for Tenerife, which is about right here.

Earth, as we moved out, got smaller and smaller. We didn't see the Moon as we were going. We were told not to look at it. The spacecraft was oriented in a way that it was difficult to see it anyway. Since we went at a very New Moon, which meant that the Sun was behind the Moon, then we thought if we looked at it we might hurt our eyeballs. So we didn't get to see the Moon. Behind the Moon, on the back side, we were going backwards and we ignited our engine for four minutes to slow us down so that we were now basically trapped, if you will, by lunar gravity. So this engine definitely had to work just one more time to get us out of there.

The far side of the Moon is very rough with craters everywhere you look. The front side is much smoother. Geologists are still scratching their heads over that phenomenon. As you know, one side of the Moon is tidally locked. It wiggles a little bit but basically it faces Earth, and that side is the smooth side. There's the crater Tsiolkovsky — I hope I pronounced that right — named after the famous early Russian rocket scientist, sort of like Robert Goddard was in the United States. I believe this was actually taken by one of the Russian high-altitude probes that went behind the Moon and took the first earthrise picture in black and white. And of course the famous earthrise pictures that Jim Lovell keeps claiming he took, but that I was lucky enough to take on our fourth orbit!

APOLLO 8 FARSIDE VIEW. CREDIT:
NASA.

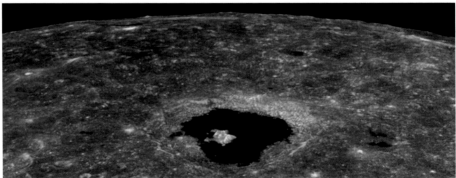

THE FARSIDE CRATER TSIOLKOVSKY. CREDIT: NASA.

On Christmas Eve 1968, we read from the first verses of the Book of Genesis. I can't speak for Jim or Frank, but at least I did it not for religious reasons but because those are pretty serious words whether you're a Christian, a Jew, or whatever. Most religions have a genesis story; we thought that this would help underscore the significance of humankind's first step away from Earth. Yuri's was the first step into space; ours was the first step away from Earth, hence that reading. We re-ignited our service propulsion system behind the Moon and got enough velocity to come home. The guidance was so accurate that we really didn't need to correct it at all to reach the tiny little slot coming back to Earth.

Someone asked me who was in control when Jim and Frank were sleeping and I said that Isaac Newton was in control because we were falling 240,000 miles all the way. We hit the atmosphere at about 35,000 feet per second. Unlike the Soviet program, which I understand had a bounce and then back in, we ploughed right on in, and the heat shield I think got up to about 6,000 degrees centigrade on the outside of the ionic cover. We would have burned up had this been solid material right against the surface.

We came in at night. I asked Jim and Frank, the old-timers, "What is this light?," and Frank said it was sunrise. I said if it's sunrise then we're flying right into the Sun because it's getting brighter and brighter. I felt like a little bug in the flame of a blowtorch looking back out.

This illustration shows the command module and these are chunks of the service module that had been jettisoned prior to re-entry, broken up in a photograph from the window of an airplane by a passenger down toward Australia.

We landed near Tahiti at night. It was a rough landing, we hit hard, flipped the spacecraft over, and we hung upside down in the waves. It was pretty rough. Jim Lovell and I were from the Naval Academy, but it was tough on Frank Borman, who was an army man and got seasick. Maybe that's why he never flew again! Maybe that's why I never flew again! Anyway, when the Sun came up, frogmen in helicopters shot some sharks that were circling around and deployed a big liferaft around the spacecraft. The aircraft carrier Yorktown showed up, and out we came. I think this was the most dangerous part of the mission, hanging by one wire from this helicopter. I think the best feeling was standing on that aircraft carrier deck.

And here's the steed that did it. That's quite an engineering design, and that spacecraft is now residing in Chicago. We got calls from the President, Lyndon Johnson, and parades in Chicago and New York.

What's the message from Apollo 8? We were blazing the trail for the subsequent Apollo flights, but I think Alexei — he wasn't on Apollo 8, but he certainly did a lot of other things — said it right: Earth is very small, very beautiful and very fragile. It's something we need to learn how to take care of. The fragility of Earth has gotten across to the environmental movement, but the smallness is still sinking in. With pictures like the earthrise and the Hubble shots, humankind has got to know that our home is not the center of the universe.

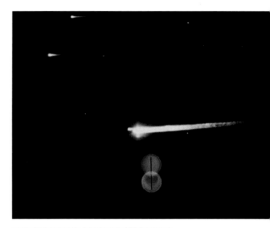

THE COMMAND MODULE STREAKING THROUGH EARTH'S ATMOSPHERE. THE SMALLER STREAKS ARE PIECES OF THE JETTISONED SERVICE MODULE. CREDIT: NASA.

COMMAND MODULE IN ITS LIFERAFT. CREDIT: NASA.

COMMAND MODULE BEING WINCHED ABOARD THE AIRCRAFT CARRIER. CREDIT: NASA.

CONGRATULATIONS FROM PRESIDENT JOHNSON. CREDIT: NASA.

"HOUSTON WE HAVE A PROBLEM". CREDIT: NASA.

JIM LOVELL

APOLLO 13: "HOUSTON, WE HAVE A PROBLEM . . ."

James Arthur Lovell did not guess he would be in for the most perilous moment in the Apollo lunar program when he first yearned to fly. Born March 25, 1928, in Cleveland, Ohio, Lovell moved at an early age to Milwaukee, Wisconsin, where he attended high school and became interested in rocketry and flight. Lovell attended the University of Wisconsin in Madison before transferring and graduating from the U.S. Naval Academy, and then commenced a career as a fighter pilot.

In 1958 Lovell became one of the test pilots selected as an astronaut-candidate for the Mercury program. Lovell was not a Mercury astronaut for medical reasons, but he did serve as backup pilot for Gemini 4 and made it into space in December 1965 as pilot of the Gemini 7 mission. He later flew with Buzz Aldrin on Gemini 12. As of 1966, he had spent more time in orbit than any other person.

Lovell joined Frank Borman and Bill Anders on the Apollo 8 mission, the first trio of humans to orbit the Moon, serving as the navigator and participating in the famous holiday reading from the Book of Genesis.

Scheduled to command Apollo 14, crews of Apollo 13 and 14 switched when it became clear that Alan Shepard needed more time to prepare. So on April 11, 1970, Commander Lovell lifted off on Apollo 13 with Jack Swigert and Fred Haise, and two days later a damaged heater coil in an oxygen tank sparked, turning the oxygen into a gas and causing an explosion, crippling the spacecraft.

The lunar landing was aborted, and it took the crew's best efforts to re-establish trajectory back to Earth. The situation created one of the most frightening and heroic moments of space exploration, exemplified in the famous line, "Houston, we have a problem . . ." and immortalized in the popular movie Apollo 13.

Lovell retired from the space program in 1973 and established several successful business ventures.

JIM LOVELL AT STARMUS.

Around the Moon . . . you are just 240,000 miles away. You can put your thumb up, you can put your thumb to the window, and behind your thumb is the entire Earth, and you can hide Earth from yourself and you realize how insignificant we really all are. How small Earth is. How Earth is, in reality, a spacecraft with limited resources and there are about 6 billion astronauts all trying to live and work together.

So that was really the impression I think that all three of us got from that. I'll continue now and just tell you a little bit about the other flights.

After Apollo 8 of course we had Apollo 9. Apollo 9 was going to do what 8 was supposed to do but Apollo 9 got the lunar module. They went up into Earth orbit with the lunar module detached, did various things to rendezvous and found out that everything so far was very good, all the ideas that we had about the two vehicles working together coincided correctly.

And then we had after that Apollo 10. Apollo 10 was the dress rehearsal to go all the way to the Moon. And sometimes people said if you're going that far, why don't you just land and that's always a question that people had.

But they went all the way to the Moon with the command service module and the lunar module attached and orbited the Moon, detached the lunar module, went down toward the landing and then, at about 50,000 feet, aborted — this was part of our training, to abort if something went wrong — came back up again, rendezvoused with the command service module, and came home.

And that was the final flight before we would actually attempt the lunar landing. And as we all know, Apollo 11 was the lunar landing. I think that Buzz Aldrin was here two days ago and he told you intricately all about that particular flight.

JIM LOVELL AT THE LAUNCHPAD OF APOLLO 8. CREDIT: NASA.

It's kind of interesting, I might give you a little aside. A lot of people in the world, and in the United States, didn't believe that we actually landed on the Moon on Apollo 11. They thought we faked it in West Texas someplace, merely to beat the poor Soviets to a flight. So we quickly got Apollo 12 ready and sent it, in November.

They landed in another flat area, because on Apollo 8 we were looking for suitable landing spots to give people the greatest chance of survival and these were the flat areas, we call them maria or "seas."

Apollo 11 landed on the Sea of Tranquility and then Apollo 12 landed on the Ocean of Storms. They in fact were so successful that they landed within walking distance of a Surveyor spacecraft that had landed about two years before. So they went over there and saw this spacecraft that had already landed, as a remote vehicle, two years before.

Well, by the time Apollo 13 came around, the scientists finally decided that, look, we have landed on the Moon and in reality, although Apollo 11 was a success in bringing back lunar material, that wasn't its real mission. Its mission was to prove that with the technology that we had, we could land on the Moon and bring somebody back safely.

But the scientists said "look, we've done that." We want to start looking at the science of Apollo. So they said we want somebody to land on the highlands of the Moon. The reflectivity is much brighter; the material might be different. We know there's ejecta lying on the surface, thrown up by volcanism in the early formation of the Moon, or by meteorite impacts, and that can tell us a lot about the interior of the Moon.

So Apollo 13 was designated to go to a place called Fra Mauro. Fra Mauro was a large crater in about the center of the Moon and we were going to land on the hills or the highlands surrounding that crater.

Take off on this flight was April 11, 1970, at 13:13 Central Standard Time. Now, in the United States, Apollo 13 is a very unlucky number, and right there I should have known something was going to happen.

The big Saturn V took off and as Bill has said, it is a three-stage vehicle to get first of all into Earth orbit to check both our command service and our lunar module before we would commit to the Moon. The first stage worked perfectly, jettisoned, and then we lit the five engines on the second stage. And about two minutes before it should have, this center engine of the second stage actually shut down.

Why? Do we have a crisis here? Do we have enough fuel? Do we have enough power to get into Earth orbit and then enough left over to give us the velocity on a proper course to go all the way to the Moon?

But fortunately the engineers over-built the vehicle, and we did. We got into Earth orbit, checked our vehicle, and on the far side of Earth, away from the Moon, we lit that third engine a second time, and it gave us enough velocity, and on the proper course, to coast all the way to the Moon.

That course is called a free return course. It's called free return because if something should happen to the spacecraft, for example if the engine for our spacecraft should fail on the way to the Moon and we were not able to maneuver, if something should happen like that, we would still be on a proper course going all the way to the Moon. And as we passed the Moon it would slow us down too, and turn us around, aim us back down toward Earth, on a course that would perhaps give us a safe passage through the atmosphere and a safe landing back on Earth. Every flight from Apollo 8 through Apollo 17 started out with this extra safety factor.

Well, about 30 hours after we had taken off, everything was fine, we got a call from the Control Center. And they said "Jim, if you want to land at this place Fra Mauro, you want the Sun in the proper position so that you can see the shadows of the rocks and the boulders on the surface." Because there's no atmosphere on the Moon, if the Sun is directly overhead, everything is completely washed out. You really can't see much. Then they said, "Well, we'll have to get you off that free return course."

Well, we examined our spacecraft to make sure they were okay, they were fine. Our two spacecraft now are married together, the lunar module called Aquarius and Odyssey, our command service module. We are doing all the maneuvering from our command service module, the lunar module Aquarius was powered down.

So we maneuvered to the attitude they told us to, lit that maneuvering engine, it worked fine and that was its test, and it moved us over to a new course to the Moon that we called a hybrid course to the Moon.

But now, now if something should happen to the spacecraft, for example if that engine we had just tested suddenly refused to operate, then we would be on a course that would again take us directly to the Moon.

The Moon's gravity, as before, as we passed the Moon, would slow us down and eventually turn us around and aim us back down toward Earth — but the closest point of approach to Earth would be thousands of miles out, much too far out to be captured by Earth's atmosphere for a safe landing.

Personally, I didn't worry about it. It was my second flight to the Moon, my fourth flight into space. Everything was familiar, the stars, the sights, the sounds, even the smells were familiar by this time, and we settled back for a very comfortable three-day voyage to the Moon.

About two days had gone by. I looked at my flight plan and it was time for a TV program to show everybody back on Earth what we were doing. I got the camera, my lunar module pilot Fred Haise went into the powered-down lunar module. I photographed him, all the things that he was telling people and just as I finished coming back down through the tunnel, back into our mother ship, there suddenly was a "hiss-bang."

The spacecraft rocked back and forth, lights were coming on, noise all over, jets were firing. Well, I looked up at my companion Fred Haise and he didn't know what was going on. I looked at my companion Jack Swigert, he didn't know what was going on, and then finally we got back into the command module and we settled down to try to figure out just what was happening.

About that time a light had come on that we had lost some of our electrical power. Before I could digest that piece of information, two more lights blinked on, warning lights, that two out of three of our fuel cells had just died.

Now a fuel cell is a device where we take liquid oxygen, liquid hydrogen and we combine them. We get electrical power and water. Our mission rules stated that if you lose just one fuel cell, the landing on the Moon is off. But one fuel cell alone would give you enough electrical power to get you round the Moon and back home safely. So at that time there was a wave of disappointment.

"You mean we can't land on the Moon? That's the only reason I'm here. I've already been here the other time . . . "

And then I drifted to about the center of the spacecraft, I looked up at the instruments that told me the condition of two huge liquid oxygen tanks stored away in the back end of the spacecraft in an area that we called the service module.

When I looked at the quantity gauge of one of those tanks, the needle read zero. And when I looked at the quantity gauge of the second tank, I could see the needle start to go down, ever so slightly, but something that you would never see with normal usage of oxygen on a flight to the Moon.

And that, ladies and gentlemen, was when the lead weight went to the bottom of my stomach. When I got that searing sensation of being in deep trouble and not knowing how to get out of it.

Then I drifted over past where our companion Jack Swigert was sitting, I looked out the window and I could see, escaping from right out of my spacecraft, at a high rate of speed, a gaseous substance.

And it didn't take much intelligence on my part to realize that the gas escaping, the needle on my second to last quantity gauge on the oxygen tank was one and the same and that very shortly we'd be completely out of oxygen.

And when that occurred, because we used oxygen to produce electricity in our

APOLLO 13 ASTRONAUTS FRED HAISE AND JIM LOVELL OBSERVE FEATURES OF A LAVA FLOW NEAR HILO, HAWAII, DURING A GEOLOGY FIELD TRAINING TRIP. CREDIT: NASA.

OBLIQUE VIEW OF THE LUNAR FAR SIDE FROM
APOLLO 13. CREDIT: NASA..

fuel cells, the last fuel cell would die.

We would lose all of our electrical power. And when that occurred, because we controlled and gimballed our rocket engine by means of electricity, we would lose the entire propulsion system.

We were in serious, serious trouble. We had, inside the spacecraft, a small oxygen bottle and a small battery, but they were to be used merely for the final plunge through Earth's atmosphere on the final stages of our flight back home.

Unfortunately, when the explosion occurred, we were some 200,000 miles from Earth. We were 90 hours from Earth because we had to go around the Moon to get back home again. And of course at the time of the explosion we were going in the wrong direction.

Believe it or not, the people down at Mission Control really could not believe what was happening.

We'd designed the spacecraft for two things. The equipment has to be very, very reliable; and with redundancy. We don't have one, we've got two, or three.

And when all three fuel cells died, when two oxygen tanks appeared to be disabled, when we lost the communications for a while, when the computer went offline, they said "Oh, wait a second. That all cannot happen at one time on that spacecraft. The odds are impossible. It has to be that the communication coming down through telemetry into the spacecraft was interrupted by a solar flare." They continued: "That's got to be what the situation is that's giving us all these false readings on our consoles about what's going on up there."

In the spacecraft, we knew what was happening. And by the time Mission Control also realized there was a real problem, Fred Haise and I met at that tunnel entrance and went into the powered-down lunar module to try to use it somehow, someway, as a lifeboat to get home.

For those of you who might not know about the lunar module, it's a very fragile vehicle. It doesn't have a heat shield. It's not designed to come home. It supports only two people. It's only designed to last 45 hours. It's only once you are in lunar orbit that you would power it up and then you land and explore, take off, rendezvous, dock, and then just throw the vehicle away.

And as it was only designed for two people I kept counting the crew — 1, 2, 3. I knew that we were in serious trouble. But we forgot about how long this thing was going to last. We got in and we turned on all the exotic electronic systems, the guidance system, the computer we needed — it used batteries by the way, it didn't use fuel cells — and we got started, and got everything powered up. And finally by this time, Mission Control realized that we had to do something. So they said:"Well, first of all, we think you'd better get back on that free return course."

I thought that was a good idea! I thought it was a good idea because, even though we were not successful on a landing back on Earth, it's much better to intercept Earth in some manner rather than being a permanent monument to our space program going out on a long 240,000 miles orbit right around and back, just about forever.

So I told them that everything was powered down on the command module; we had to use the lunar module for everything. They said: "OK, well use the landing engine of the lunar module, the one that we would normally land with — use that for the propulsion."

And I replied, "That's fine, we'll do that."And they said, "Here's the attitude to maneuver to get back on that free return course."

And when I started to maneuver, now using the little attitude jets of the lunar module, to get back on the course, I learned something that I've taken with me from the space program into private business: Always expect the unexpected.

When I started to maneuver to get to the proper attitude, instead of, say I wanted to maneuver down, it went on some wild gyration. If I wanted to go right it went left, if I wanted to go up it went down. What's happening here, why aren't my inputs giving me the proper response?

And then it dawned on me. We had attached to the lunar module a 60,000-pound dead weight: the command service module.

The command module was the only thing that had a heat shield, which we needed to get back through the atmosphere. The lunar module had never been designed with that dead weight attached. The center of gravity was way out in left field someplace. I literally had to learn, in a short period of time, how to maneuver all over again. When I put an input in, I had to know what the output was going to be. But ladies and gentlemen, you'd be surprised how quickly you learn when you're in a tight spot, and finally we got to the proper attitude, we lit the lunar module — or we lit the engine, it worked fine, moved us over to put us again on what we thought was the free return course.

Meanwhile, now we're very close to the Moon, about 25,000 miles away, and the Moon is filling up the entire window of the lunar module. We're past the sphere of influence whereby the Moon's gravity now has us and we're celebrating now. You cross the sphere of influence at about 2,000 miles an hour and then you start picking up speed.

Meanwhile, I am waiting very patiently for Mission Control to come up with some good ideas because I realize that the amount of water we had on board to cool all these electronic systems in the lunar module was not sufficient to get us all the way back home. And the oxygen, although we had it in the backpacks that we were going to use on the lunar surface, perhaps we could have tapped into that; and electrical power I knew was not sufficient to get us all the way home at the rate that we were using it. And finally, as the Moon kept getting bigger and bigger and bigger they came up and they said:

"We have a plan for you. We think that when the Moon pulls you around and you end up heading back down toward Earth, we'll have you light that lunar engine a second time and then perhaps we can keep it on long enough to speed you up to get you back into the atmosphere before the batteries die."

That was the most important thing. I said: "That's a good idea. We don't have a better idea up here." And they said: "Now wait a second. Be ready to copy because we are sending a crew down to the simulators to find out if these procedures work. If they do we'll send you up the instructions."

I replied, "I have my two companions with me because I know that when we go round the far side of the Moon we will lose communication with you." And so they said "okay" and a little while later they called back.

This time, they said, "Yes, these procedures appear to be okay, are you ready to copy?" I replied, "I am," and I started to copy the procedures thinking that my companions were also listening very intently in case I missed something.

And then I looked at my companions, and they weren't paying any attention. They were looking at the Moon. They had cameras in their hands. One guy was looking up shutter speeds, the other guy was looking up apertures.

I blurted out "Gentlemen, gentlemen, what are your plans here?" And they said: "Jim, when we go around to the far side of the Moon, we're going to take some pictures because, as you know, we never see the far side from Earth."

"If we don't get home, you won't get them developed!" I replied. They then said, "You've been here before and we haven't." So they got their pictures; I got the procedures!

Two and a half hours later, we lit the engines for a second time, kept the engines on for four and a half minutes, pushing us faster and faster and faster on the way home, then turned them off. Then we turned off all those exotic electronic systems that you would not be caught out there without: the guidance system told us our attitude with respect to the celestial sphere. We needed it for navigation, but it used up too much power.

Turn it off.

The computer: in its memory we had the information about the stars that we needed to navigate. Again, we couldn't afford the power.

THE HOME PLANET CAPTURED FROM APOLLO 13 DURING THE PERILOUS HOMEWARD JOURNEY. CREDIT: NASA..

THE CREW MEMBERS OF THE APOLLO 13 MISSION STEP ABOARD THE USS IWO JIMA, PRIME RECOVERY SHIP FOR THE MISSION, FOLLOWING SPLASHDOWN AND RECOVERY OPERATIONS IN THE SOUTH PACIFIC OCEAN. EXITING THE HELICOPTER WHICH MADE THE PICK-UP ARE (FROM LEFT) ASTRONAUTS FRED W. HAISE JR., LUNAR MODULE PILOT; JAMES A. LOVELL JR., COMMANDER; AND JOHN L. SWIGERT JR., COMMAND MODULE PILOT. CREDIT: NASA.

Turn it off.

The stabilization system, the autopilot for these two vehicles. We couldn't use those either.

Turn them off.

The only thing we had going now was the radio to talk to Earth and a little fan to circulate the atmosphere. Things were kind of quiet. And when things are quiet, you start to think. And maybe that's bad. Jack Swigert came to me and said:

"Jim I've been thinking; we might be exceeding escape velocity."

Escape velocity, perhaps for those who are not familiar with it, if I walk outside of this hotel and pretend the atmosphere is not there, if I could throw a baseball out into space at a little over 25,000 miles an hour, the baseball is not coming back to Earth. It's going to escape from Earth. And so if we miss Earth in some manner, that's the way we'll end up. But I said:

"Jack, don't you recall? We got back on that free return course." That course would guarantee us free passage through the atmosphere and a good landing on Earth.

Well how does it do it, on a lunar flight? Let's pretend, on top of the atmosphere, a short segment is flat. Coming back from the Moon we have to go inside a two degree, pie-shaped wedge with respect to the atmosphere. That wedge can't be any less than 5-1/2 degrees or any greater than 7-1/2 degrees. We have to hit inside that wedge to make a safe landing. If we come in too shallow, we skip out, like skipping a stone on water, and we're gone. If we hit it too steep, the sudden deceleration would make us a fiery meteor for a few seconds, and that would be it. We have to get into that 2-degree, pie-shaped wedge, and that's called the free return course. So I said:

"Jack, don't worry, we've got it made." I was wrong. I received a call from Mission Control, and they said: "Jim, we don't know what you're doing up there. We've been tracking you now for some time. It appears that you're no longer on the free return course," to which I replied, "Thanks a lot. We've turned off the navigation aids, we can't afford the electricity to run them. We're flying by the seat of our pants here."

Their reply was "Well, we understand that. Do you recall the flight of Apollo 8? And do you recall those emergency procedures that we had in the back of the flight manual, that if all the normal emergency procedures fail to work then you turn to the last page and try these?"

I next told them, "I do recall that on Apollo 8, I helped develop them there when we were training. But after Apollo 8 we tore them out of the manuals, because we wanted to save weight, we thought they were no good, useless." Their response: "You're going to have to use them now."

What that consisted of was for me to try to maneuver these two vehicles around, without the use of an autopilot, and get Earth in the window of the lunar module. Now you've all seen pictures of Earth from space, the daylight, the nighttime, the line between the two. On Earth we call it twilight, as it passes overhead. Out there, we call it the terminator.

In my lunar module I had a gun sight. Crosshairs. If I could somehow maneuver the vehicle around to put Earth in the window of the lunar module, and then put the horizontal line of my crosshair on top of Earth's terminator, I would then have the engine in a proper position to either steepen up or shallow out that angle on the way home depending on whether I had Earth's daylight at the top of my window or the nighttime, and if I lit the engine just at the right time. That is the entire procedure. For those of you who might want to go, you might want to take note. At the proper time I looked at Jack Swigert and I said:

"Jack, everything on the spacecraft now is off. Even the clock is not running. But you do have a wristwatch. You tell me when to start the engine, and you tell me when to stop it." I looked at Fred Haise. Fred was getting sick at the time, but I said: "Fred, I know that when that engine comes on, without an autopilot to help me, I will never be able to keep Earth in the window by myself. I'll take my backup maneuvering handle, keep Earth from going up and down too much, you take the backup handle and keep it from going sideways too much." He said: "Fine."

On the side of my console I had two buttons. One read "start" and the other one read "stop." These were direct electrical links between the battery and the engine. Normally, that link goes from the battery to the computer that does all the work, and then to the engine. We couldn't afford that.

At the proper time Jack hit the start button, the engine came on. I looked at Earth vertically, Fred looked at Earth horizontally. Fourteen seconds later Jack said "stop" and I hit the stop button. And then of course we waited until we could find out from tracking by the ground whether we had gotten back up into that quarter to come in and make a safe landing.

Well, ladies and gentlemen, I wouldn't be here today to talk to you if it hadn't been for my companions over here, but we did. We landed in the Pacific, just about where we should've landed had this been a normal mission. We got there a couple of days early.

READING THE NEWSPAPER ACCOUNT OF APOLLO 13'S SAFE RETURN ABOARD RECOVERY VESSEL USS IWO JIMA. THEY TORE UP THE VERY ELABORATE OBITUARIES THEY HAD ALL PLANNED FOR US. CREDIT: NASA.

CHARLIE DUKE

APOLLO: MORE THAN AN ADVENTURE

Born October 3, 1935, in Charlotte, North Carolina, Charles Moss Duke, Jr., in 1972 became the 10th and youngest person to walk on the Moon. Interested in flight from an early age, Duke graduated from the U.S. Naval Academy in 1957 and received a Master's degree in aeronautics from the Massachusetts Institute of Technology in 1964.

Duke became a naval fighter pilot and was stationed for some time at Ramstein Air Force Base in Kaiserslautern, West Germany. He also taught flight training and in 1966 became one of the fifth group of astronauts selected by NASA administrators. He served on support groups and as CAPCOM (capsule communicator) for Apollo 11. Duke finally embarked on a lunar mission himself with Apollo 16, in April 1972, for which he served as lunar module pilot and accompanied crewmates John Young and Ken Mattingly.

Long retired, Duke enjoys a variety of activities in and around his home in Texas.

CHARLIE DUKE AT STARMUS.

OPPOSITE PAGE: CHARLIE DUKE ON THE LUNAR SURFACE. CREDIT: NASA.

When the Apollo program was announced I was a young fighter pilot in Ramstein, Germany, flying F-102s. If you remember, we had 15 minutes of space experience in the United States and President Kennedy announced that we're going to go to the Moon. And as Buzz Aldrin says, we're going to land on the Moon and we're going to return safely. We all liked that part about returning safely!

At the time, I had no thought of being an astronaut. I laughed at Kennedy: "Yeah, sure — we're gonna make it. We've got eight years to do this. No way we are gonna make it!"

But it turned out that eight years and two months later, I was sitting in Mission Control talking to the astronauts when they landed on the Moon. So from an announcement of a program to the accomplishment of the goal of that program took eight years and two months. It was almost unbelievable to me.

Today, if a similar program was announced, we couldn't even write the proposal in eight years and two months! And much less get it done in eight years and two months. That's just the way things are today. Apollo was a political decision due to the Space Race. It turned out to be one of the greatest scientific endeavors of all mankind, I believe. We grew in our science knowledge, we grew in our ability as we learned, and I think that to be here with the two guys who were on Apollo 8, with Frank Borman, is a great honor. Because to me, Apollo 8 was the most dangerous, riskiest mission that NASA ever undertook. It was the second time we'd even flown the command module, and we were committing this crew to a lunar journey with very little experience on the spacecraft, with zero manned experience on the Apollo Saturn V.

So it was a very risky program, a very risky mission, but they pulled it off and we were on our way. Apollo 9, 10, 11 were all successful; with Apollo 12 we had a serious problem at liftoff; it was struck by lightning and they lost all their electrical power, their fuel cells dropped offline; but the Saturn vehicle was so sturdy it just kept flying, and flew them right up into orbit and they finally recovered their spacecraft and they went on to the Moon for a successful landing, as Jim Lovell related.

With Apollo 13, I was a back up, the lunar module pilot who was to back up Fred Haise if he had a problem, or if the crew had a problem — if they broke a leg, they got sick — we would take their place, John Young, Jack Swigert and myself. Well, if you remember those days, more than 41 years ago now, I came down with the measles and the NASA doctors were stunned. Astronauts don't get the measles; kids get the measles. But I had the measles and I exposed everybody to the measles on the two crews, and everybody had had the measles and was immune except for

ED MITCHELL, APOLLO 14, ON THE LUNAR
SURFACE. CREDIT: NASA.

FOOTPRINTS OF THE APOLLO 14
ASTRONAUTS. CREDIT: NASA.

Ken Mattingly. So they took him off the flight, which was a very big disappointment, and put in Jack Swigert, who I had trained with. But the beauty of our training, which Bill Anders alluded to, was so remarkable that in four or five days Jim Lovell said we were ready to go. With a crewman that they had trained with for less than a week.

Our training was so standard, and so thorough, that someone could step in — I wouldn't recommend it, but that's what happened — and so the backup concept on Apollo was very important. After Apollo 13 was over, I thought NASA made a very major decision, and a bold decision, to continue the Apollo program. We'd accomplished the goal, to land on the Moon, so why keep going? But they decided that we had these vehicles, we had the science, and we wanted to do the science, so let's continue the mission.

And so we started with Apollo 14, which landed where Jim Lovell and his crew on Apollo 13 were supposed to land, at Fra Mauro. They had two days on the Moon. This illustration shows Ed Mitchell here. They didn't have a car, like the later missions; they had this little mobile equipment transporter where they loaded their geology equipment. Here's a little movie camera that they had with them, here was the handle like a golf cart, and so they were able to pull this vehicle across the lunar surface with their geological equipment. They also deployed ALSEP, which was the Apollo lunar surface experiment package that contained a number of experiments. Apollo 14 featured two moonwalks, collecting a number of pounds of lunar samples, deploying their ALSEP package, and we were off on the scientific exploration of the Moon.

The landing sites were selected across the front face of the Moon to maximize the geological return and the sample return from Apollo. John Young and I suggested we could land on the far side of the Moon and see what it was like over there, but Houston said no way, we've got to be talking to you when you land on the Moon and so we're not going to let you land on the back side. So all the landings took place across the front face of the Moon, north and south of the equator, because that was the capability of Apollo.

This illustration shows footprints of the crew as they walked around the lunar surface. They covered more than 2 kilometers on foot, which was a pretty fantastic accomplishment for Apollo.

So to maximize the scientific return from the time on the Moon and the geological exploration, the last three missions, starting with Apollo 15, were called the J missions. Our lunar module had more batteries, we had more oxygen, and we had more cooling water. We had more consumables, if you will. We had more fuel. We also had a lunar rover. This was a vehicle that was designed by engineers at the Marshall Space Flight Center with AC Delco doing the electronics and Boeing the assembly of the vehicle. This illustration shows the high-gain antenna; it was pointed straight up at Earth. You had to have the vehicle stopped, on the Moon, and point it up and have the antenna aligned with Earth so that you had enough signal strength on the TV to broadcast a signal back to Earth.

On Earth we had three tracking stations — one in Australia, as Buzz Aldrin mentioned; one in Spain, in Madrid; and one in Goldstone, California, each with a 70-meter receiver dish. They could collect this signal strength to give you a reasonable TV picture. We had a color TV camera that we mounted on the front of the car. We just turned it on and an engineer in Mission Control controlled the camera. He could pan it around, he could elevate, depress; he could zoom in and out and focus. So he controlled the camera while we just went about our business.

The car was electric, with two batteries, 28-volt, 100-ampere batteries. Each wheel had its own electric motor. The tires were made out of wire, which was basically woven piano wire. When I saw that I said "this is the dumbest looking tire I've ever seen," but the guy who designed the tire knew the lunar surface, so as we drove along, the tire dug into the lunar surface and filled up with lunar dust, and so as you drove the tires were filled with dust. This gave us tremendous traction. This vehicle could climb a 25-degree slope on the lunar surface. It weighed about 500 pounds down here; up on the Moon, it weighed 80 pounds; but it could carry 1,100 pounds.

So just in the reverse of an automobile down here, we had a very lightweight vehicle but a very sturdy one. The controller was a handle that worked so that when you pushed forward you went forward, when you pulled back you put on the brakes. When you pulled left, the front wheels turned left and the rear wheels turned to the right, so you had double steering, and you pulled back to put on the brakes of course. If you wanted to go backwards you just flipped a switch, pushed the handle forward and the car went in reverse. But we had no rear view mirror so you couldn't see behind you.

THE AUTHOR, IN AN OFFICIAL NASA
PHOTOGRAPH. CREDIT: NASA.

JOHN YOUNG SALUTES THE FLAG. CREDIT: NASA.

So nobody wanted to back up this vehicle. But sometimes you got into a situation where you just did a U-turn, turned around and you were on your way. Sometimes you got in a situation where that didn't work, so John got out on his side, I got out on my side, we just picked it up and turned it around. Man I'll tell you, you felt like Superman up on the Moon! "Look at me Ma, picking up my car!"

John sat in the left seat. He was the commander, and he drove. I was in the right seat; I was the navigator. We had a set of maps that were supposed to get us from Point A to Point B. The maps worked if you landed in the right place. Fortunately, we landed in the right place, within a couple of hundred meters of where our intended landing spot was. That was very dynamic, by the way — in all the interviews I've ever given about what's the most exciting thing about being on the Moon, I say "the landing is the most exciting thing." Because if you don't make a good landing, it just spoils your whole day.

We had seatbelts so we buckled up our seatbelts because the drive across the Moon was very rough. It bounced a lot in this light gravity. Each wheel had its own independent system of shock absorbers with some dampers. On the back of the car we had a lunar tool carrier which carried a mobile magnetics experiment, with rakes and tongs and a penetrometer test and other things like that that allowed us to do a lot of geology away from the Apollo lunar surface experiments package.

We navigated on the Moon with a directional gyro. The Moon has remnant magnetism but no magnetic field. So how do you align a gyro? Well we just assume the shadow is west. And when we landed, the Sun was about 15 degrees above the horizon in the east and so you could see the craters as you came in; you could tell the surface was tilted toward you or away from you by the albedo of the surface. So John was flying, I was talking him down and we came in and landed, as the other crews did, on what was sort of a neutral looking Moon. By that I mean not too bright,

THE AUTHOR IN THE SUIT ROOM PREPARING
FOR THE APOLLO 16 MISSION. CREDIT: NASA.

LOOKING BACK FROM APOLLO 16,
EN ROUTE TO THE MOON. CREDIT: NASA.

not too dark. It turned out we were within one degree of level. The Sun always stayed in the east. Sunrise to sunset, as you know, lasts two weeks on the Moon. Apollo was there for 72 hours, so it was always daylight. Always morning of the Moon day so the shadow was always pointing west.

So we drove the car, to point the vehicle front end down Sun, and we had a little line that we put over the directional gyro and we just turned it so that west was underneath the line at the top of the gyro. So that was our direction, and we had an odometer on the right wheel that gave us distance.

"So okay John, let's go 120 for 2.2 km and right to 140 for another 1 km," and that was supposed to be Point A. Well, Point A was, let's say, Plum Crater or Flag Crater, things like that. It's like going through the forest looking for a single tree. So as you drove across you wondered if that was really the crater you were searching for. Most of the time we could find the exact crater we were searching for, but in a few instances, we said, "Well, this is close enough so we're going to stop here."

This illustration shows me in my younger days, in my pre-flight suit. You've seen the Saturn rocket, and Bill Anders talked about the vibration. One thing he didn't say was that the windows of an Apollo craft are covered over at this point, at liftoff if you will, by a boost protective cover so you cannot see out except for one window which is in the hatch, and behind the center seat, which was very difficult to look back this way for me, to see out of that hatch. So you're basically going into space depending on your instruments and listening to Mission Control repeat, "you're go, you're go, you're go."

When the rocket lifted off it started vibrating. And I remember Bill and others saying "this thing's going to really shake." But I didn't realize it was going to shake as much as it did. It just never really registered with me, this shakiness. So as it began to shake I got a little nervous. I thought there was something wrong with it. John was our commander — he had all the flight instruments — and I was just watching the electrical system, the environmental control system, and things like that.

So as we lifted off, my heart was pounding, and later on I asked our flight surgeon "what was my heartbeat at lift off?" It was 144 beats per minute. And I said, "What was John's?" Now this was John's fourth flight into space — he eventually did six. He was the commander. I said, "What was John's?" He said "70." So you can see who the cool one was on our liftoff.

This illustration shows another view: here I am in the suit room getting suited up, breathing pure oxygen to eliminate the nitrogen in our blood. As I said, our liftoff was shaky, and if I remember, it took about seven seconds, eight seconds, to clear the tower. The first stage was from here down and lasted in our case for two minutes and 41 seconds and we had burned up four and a half million pounds of fuel in the first stage.

This illustration shows the view of Earth we had. We were about 25,000 or 30,000 kilometers away now. Here's the terminator, this is the Gulf of Alaska up here, the Arctic Circle here, down across the United States; this is the western United States, the Rocky Mountains, Baja California, the Gulf of California. Here is Los Angeles and northern California, the Yucatan Peninsula, down around the Gulf of Mexico, here's Florida. And Texas would be right about here; the northern part of South America is here, and here is the Pacific Ocean.

To me it was just a jewel of beauty hanging in the blackness of space. The brown of the land, the pure white of the snow and the clouds and the crystal blue of the ocean, and there it was, suspended in blackness.

As you can see from this picture and the others that you've seen, out in deep space the Sun is always shining, and as it is on Earth, when the Sun shines, you don't see any stars. And so on the way we didn't have any star fields, but we did have a telescope and as Jim Lovell demonstrated, you could see stars in the telescope which you could then align as your reference to give you the guidance you needed to fire the engine in the correct position. But just looking out of the window, we had no visual reference.

This illustration shows a view of the landing sites, not only ours but the Russian landing sites, which were all unmanned. Apollo 11 is here, this is our landing site in the Descartes Mountains, about 15 degrees east and about 9 degrees south. Apollo 17 here, Apollo 15 up here, the most northern landing spot; Apollo 12, Apollo 14. Apollo 14 was Fra Mauro and that's where Jim Lovell in Apollo 13 was supposed to land but of course didn't make it.

The elevation on the Moon? The mare were sort of representing sea level, and we landed about 7,000 feet above that in the Descartes Highlands. Our landing site was selected, as they all were, by a group of scientists who covered the spectrum of scientific knowledge in where would be the best place to land. Our only input as near as I could see was "can we land there?" Was it too rough, was it not too rough, and if we thought, "yeah, we can land there," then that's what they picked because it would maximize our scientific experiments.

When Apollo was announced, as we were developing what we would do if we landed, everybody said, "well, let's go and pick up some rocks." That's one of the purposes, to pick up rocks on the Moon. We were all fighter pilots, test pilots, and we could tell you the difference between a rock and a piece of dirt, but that was not sufficient, so they made us all geologists and most of us had the equivalent of a Master's degree in geology before we went on our missions. I say this in jest — it's just to hopefully draw a laugh — it's not really true. But lesson number one in geology is the most important. And lesson number one is to pick up every color of rock on the Moon! And on the Moon we had gray ones, black ones and white ones, at least in our landing spot. But there was a lot more to it than that of course, and it's a funny story but it's not a true story. We did a lot of good geology on all of our missions, bringing back more than 600 pounds of lunar material during the Apollo program.

The J missions were designed not for 30 hours on the Moon for two guys, but for 72 hours on the Moon for two guys. And as a result, we divided our time up into three 24-hour periods. We would have a rest period, we would wake up, eat, we would put on our suits, prepare to go outside, which took a couple of hours, we would open the door and I was on the right side of the hatch like a copilot would be on an airliner. Jim Lovell, the commander, was on the left side of the lunar module, and that was the crew. Lunar module pilot, which is sort of a misnomer, it's more of a copilot, and the commander on the left, and so when you got suited up ready to go the hatch was right here in the center. And so I reached down and unlocked the hatch and pulled it this way, so John, our commander, got out first. I closed the hatch, went over on his side, opened the hatch and then I got outside. And like Buzz Aldrin says, you didn't want to close it and lock it, you just wanted to leave it a little ajar so that you could make sure you could get back in OK.

So we would suit up and then we would go outside to explore. The longest excursion for us was like seven hours and forty minutes. We got back inside, took off our suits, recharged our backpacks, debriefed mission control, and then went to sleep for eight hours. We were six hours late landing in our mission because of a problem in the command module. We did have a main engine problem — the engine was not a problem but the control system on the engine was a problem — which was a redundant system.

So now we're down to one system, which was an abort situation, but Mission Control, after six hours, figured out the problem and gave us a workaround. And it showed to me on my flight the amazing capability of Mission Control. Every mission had a problem that Mission Control was able to overcome and enable us to land safely. They couldn't land Apollo 13, but we got them back safely with the input from Mission Control.

So my hat is off to those guys and gals in Mission Control. They did a fabulous job and showed the teamwork and training efficiencies that NASA had developed. So we were late landing, and they changed our flight plan. Instead of powering down,

LUNAR LANDING SITES. CREDIT: NASA..

THE VIEW FROM THE LUNAR MODULE WINDOW. CREDIT: NASA.

LOOKING WEST FROM THE LANDING SITE.
CREDIT: NASA.

THE SHADOW OF THE LUNAR MODULE.
CREDIT: NASA.

putting on our suits, and our backpacks; they simply said, "by the time you get back inside and get ready to have a rest period you're going to be 35 hours awake, so we're going to change the flight plan and you're going to go to sleep first."

This happened four hours after we landed on the Moon. Can you imagine trying to go to sleep four hours after you landed on the Moon? Your mind is racing like crazy, you're describing every rock you can see outside, and you're looking at all this fantastic scenery, and so we said, "Yessir!" Well, I didn't get too much sleep that first night, but as for the next two rest periods, you were exhausted because working in a space suit for eight hours is a real challenge.

This illustration (previous page) shows the command module, seen from my window as we separated in lunar orbit. You're looking down at the lunar surface. Jim Lovell described the probe part of the command module. His antenna's pointed at Earth. The lunar module here looks like it's upside down but there's no upside down in space. Ken Mattingly took this as we were looking out into space. These little rods here are electrical circuits, so when this little tip touched the Moon it turned on a light inside, which said "contact" and you shut the engine off and you dropped in the last meter or so. You didn't want to land with the engine running because if you landed on a big rock and plugged up the engine it would blow up. Again, not a good deal. So we shut down the engine while we were still in flight.

In the descent stage, the lunar rover was folded up and bolted to the side. When you got on the Moon, you got down this way, you got on your hands and knees and you backed out, rear end first, onto the porch, and then you climbed down the ladder onto the footpad. From the footpad to the door, to give you some idea, the distance is almost 5 meters.

We had landed now, in a place called the Descartes Highlands, it was a big valley called the Cayley Plain. To the south of us we had this massive mountain, it was called Stone Mountain; and we were able on the second day to drive the car up to this position here, and I have a slide for that later, that's about 4 kilometers away from where we landed.

So the lunar rover was a revolutionary step in lunar exploration. This illustration shows a view looking to the west, you can see it's washed out more because this is looking down-Sun. As you looked down-Sun it was brighter than when you looked into the Sun, because when you look down-Sun you were looking at the sunlit side of the dust and the rocks and the soils. So you're looking at the reflective surface of the lunar surface.

And here is more. The shadow of the lunar module; this is the radar antenna that Buzz Aldrin was talking about that he had left on, that caused his computer over-loads. Here I am saluting the flag. One of the reasons we have the "Moon hoax" people who think we really didn't land on the Moon is because they see a picture like this and say, "look at that, the flag's waving in the breeze. The Moon doesn't have any atmosphere, so how can the flag wave in the breeze? Plus, there are no stars in the sky so they faked this in a hangar in Arizona or somewhere."

Well, the flag is held out not by a 40-knot wind but by a curtain rod, and it's wrinkled because it was vacuum-packed for six months and when I got there I tried to straighten it out and I couldn't get the wrinkles out. I had no iron to iron it, so we just put it up with the wrinkles in it. And if you look at this similar picture 72 hours later, it still has the same wrinkles. So we all had our picture taken. You can see our footprints in the lunar dust. It's very, very fine like powder or talc, but it had very good bearing strength and as you stepped on it you never sank in more than a couple of centimeters.

Here's a picture of our rover. John Young is working on the antenna. When we landed on the Moon, Earth was almost directly overhead, so we rarely saw Earth from our landing spot, because when you look up you're looking at the top of your helmet. So to see Earth, you had to grab hold of the rover and look backwards like that, and look up, and there was Earth. It was a half-Earth in the sky and as we looked back, we saw a half-Earth, you saw a half-Moon; the Moon was moving toward full, and Earth to the reverse, waning.

By this time, we had set up our Apollo lunar surfaces experiments package, which contained two seismic experiments. It had a magnetometer, a mass spectrometer, and a heat flow experiment that unfortunately failed because we damaged the electrical connection between the central station, which was a power distribution station to the experiments, and also the data collecting point. And so we lost the heat flow experiment, which was the only failure we had.

Finally, Apollo 17 got it done, and this illustration shows the handle of the shovel that we used to collect rocks. We had hammers that we could put in our pockets. You can see the suits — we turned out looking like Mr. Clean but we started getting covered with Moon dust right away. And it was so fine that you could not brush it off. We had a brush; we tried to brush it off, but it was impossible. And so we collected a lot of dust, on the suits, in our boots, and so on, and so when we walked back inside we were covered with Moon dust. The floor of the lunar module was covered with dust. We didn't think anything about it, but when we got back into orbit, all the dust floated up into the spacecraft. And it was so thick. We didn't want to expose our environmental control system to this dust, so we stayed closed up in our pressure suits.

We joined up with Mattingly about an hour later. He took off the docking hardware, opened the hatch and looked in, and he said, "You're not coming in here." So he floated over this Dirt Devil vacuum cleaner and we vacuumed up the lunar dust and then he would allow us to get back into his command module.

This was the first stop on our first extra-vehicular activity. So as we kept going in Apollo we got smarter and smarter and developed more and more capability. Instead of 33 hours we were staying 72 hours; Apollo 17 stayed 75 hours. We collected 98 kilos of rock, but they collected well over 100 kilos; and so the mission expanded and expanded and expanded.

One of the things we were very disappointed about was that Apollos 18, 19, and 20 were cancelled. It was a political decision. There was some science to it but it was mostly political. Astronauts were very disappointed because we had the vehicles. The hardware was available, the lunar rovers were available, everything was ready to go — all we had to do was to train the crews and we could have gone three more

THE APOLLO 16 ROVER. CREDIT: NASA.

HANDLE OF SHOVEL USED TO COLLECT ROCKS. CREDIT: NASA.

SOUTH RAY PANORAMA. CREDIT: NASA.

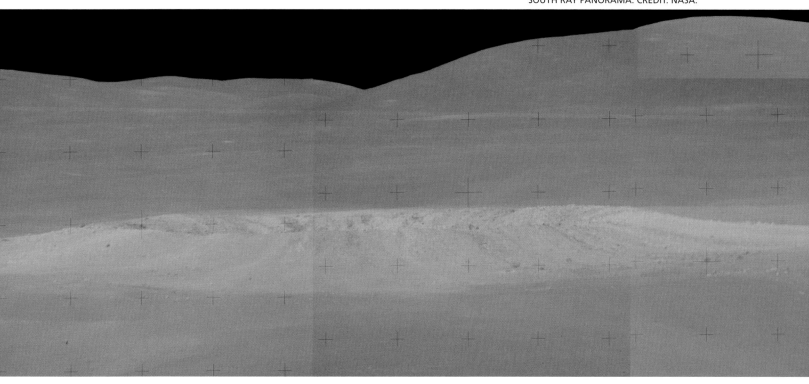

SOUTH RAY CRATER. CREDIT: NASA.

JOHN YOUNG WITH HOUSE ROCK ABOVE HIS RIGHT SHOULDER. CREDIT: NASA.

CHARLIE DUKE SAMPLING HOUSE ROCK. CREDIT: NASA.

times, but Apollo ended.

While we were on the Moon, NASA announced the space shuttle program, which is coming to an end next month. It's been a great program. Unfortunately, we don't have much to replace it with at this point.

I'll just run through a few more illustrations quickly. Here is a sample, you can see some white rocks back over here — this is what we call South Ray Crater, and it was about 8 kilometers away and was outside of our limit of travel. Five kilometers was our limit because if the car broke down you'd have to walk back, and that was as much as we thought we could handle.

Again, a picture of South Ray Crater as we look out to the northwest. This was a fantastic point up on Stone Mountain, I'm working on the lunar rover here. We're at about 300 feet or maybe 400 feet, a little over 100 meters above, the Cayley Plain out here, and back out over here is our lunar module. The view from up here was spectacular as we explored the flanks of the Descartes Formation.

Again looking back, this is now up at the top. John has come down and is looking back up toward the top of Stone Mountain. One of the larger rocks we visited, this rock is on the flank of North Ray Crater and was one of our last stops on the third day. That rock doesn't look very big, but on the lunar surface you're looking at objects you've never seen before, so big objects faraway look very similar to smaller objects close in. Your depth perception fools you. So I talked John into going to this rock. We started out and we jogged and we jogged and we jogged and by the time we got down there we realize that it's a big rock. We named it House Rock. It was about 15 meters tall and about 30 meters wide.

I'm standing there looking at this big rock and I've got this little hammer in my hand, and I hit it and a chunk came off about the size of a grapefruit. So like the commercial says, we have a piece of the rock.

This is a very moving picture for me. I had this picture in my suit pocket, on the last extravehicular activity, and so I walked out. (I had permission to do this by the way.) I pulled it out and I dropped it onto the lunar surface. That picture shows my family: our two little boys, my wife Dotty and me, and on the back of it we'd written "this is the family of astronaut Charlie Duke, who landed on the Moon in April 1972 and lots of love to whoever finds it." At this point the Moon's surface temperature was about 230° F, and plastic doesn't last so it begins to shrivel up. Within a minute of two it was just a little shrivelled ball. But anyway, it lasted long enough for me to get a picture.

And on the way home is a little picture of the Moon as we started home. This is the command module here and here is the view we had of this half Earth. Everybody has related, Jim Lovell related about holding up your thumb and underneath is Earth. Well, I didn't hold my thumb up, but I held my arm up like this in lunar orbit and sure enough, underneath my hand, was Earth. And at that distance, the thought occurred to me like it did to Jim Lovell, that there are five billion people under my hand. And I don't see the United States and I don't see Europe and I don't see Africa or any of Asia. You just see Earth, spaceship Earth, and we're all down here together. And we need to get along and we need to love one another and with technology we can help solve our problems.

And for a few years after that, I went around talking about that. But I had a big basic problem. I didn't even love my wife. How was I going to love you, or you? I had an explosive temper. I had an egocentric personality, and we were in deep trouble as a family. And I'm going all over the United States and all over the world talking about getting along. And I was a big hypocrite. But six years later, I had an encounter with Jesus. And that changed my life. It was a supernatural relationship — not a religion but a relationship with a person who changed my heart. I had peace in my heart. I began to love my wife and I began to love everybody on Earth. And I've been all over Earth sharing this love that I have for each of you. I have brown brothers, I have black brothers, I have white brothers, and I have yellow brothers — every race. I have a love for humanity that only came when I had this relationship. And so it was a tremendous change in my life.

And like Yuri Gagarin said, I haven't seen God, but I've seen the effect of God, at least in my life. I have seen the supernatural power of God at work in my life. I was driving down the highway one time. And in front of me was this big truck and off this truck bounced what I thought was a stick. A piece of wood but as it came toward my windshield I realized that it was a steel crowbar. And you could see the curvature of the crowbar; you could see the hook part of it. And when it got right here it just turned and went right over the top of my car. I can't explain it. But it happened.

I have seen the supernatural power of healing and so it's a relationship that I have experienced. I know many of you here have not had an experience and that's OK, we can get along, we can strive together. I tell you one thing; I love you. And I support your work and I support your science as we try to unlock the knowledge that's available to us with our minds. And so I leave you with that thought, that I have an emotion of love for each of you. It started with my wife and my family and it spread to everyone in this room and everyone in the world who I come in contact with.

So that's my story. That happened in the Apollo program and it's still happening today in my life as I travel. I am deeply honored and impressed with the opportunity to be here to speak to you.

Thank you very much.

ON THE WAY HOME. CREDIT: NASA.

THE DUKE FAMILY PHOTOGRAPH ON
THE LUNAR SURFACE! CREDIT: NASA.

RICHARD DAWKINS

MICHEL MAYOR

JILL TARTER

SECTION 3

Life in the Universe

The explosion of extrasolar planet discoveries of the last generation raises the question more strongly than ever — "How common is life in the universe?" Evidence suggests life was relatively easy to get going on Earth and that the Milky Way and billions of other galaxies are peppered with planets. So should life, even intelligent life, not be common in the cosmos?

Biologist and geneticist Jack Szostak explores the best ideas about the origin of life on Earth, describing how simple molecules led to complex compounds like RNA and the beginnings of life.

Evolutionary biologist Richard Dawkins describes the role of evolution in life on Earth and extrapolates that knowledge into other worlds in the cosmos.

Astronomer Michel Mayor, codiscoverer of the first exoplanet orbiting a main sequence star, updates us on the ongoing search for planets surrounding stars other than the Sun, a number now greater than 1,000, and what these planets tell us about our own solar system.

And Jill Tarter, director of the SETI Institute, unveils the game plan for future radio and optical searches for other civilizations in the galaxy. She reminds us that if we are to know other groups of intelligent beings, it will almost certainly be by their electromagnetic radiation and not by handshakes.

JACK SZOSTAK

GEOTHERMAL POOLS, WAI-O-TAPU, NEW ZEALAND.
CREDIT: JAMES SYMONDS

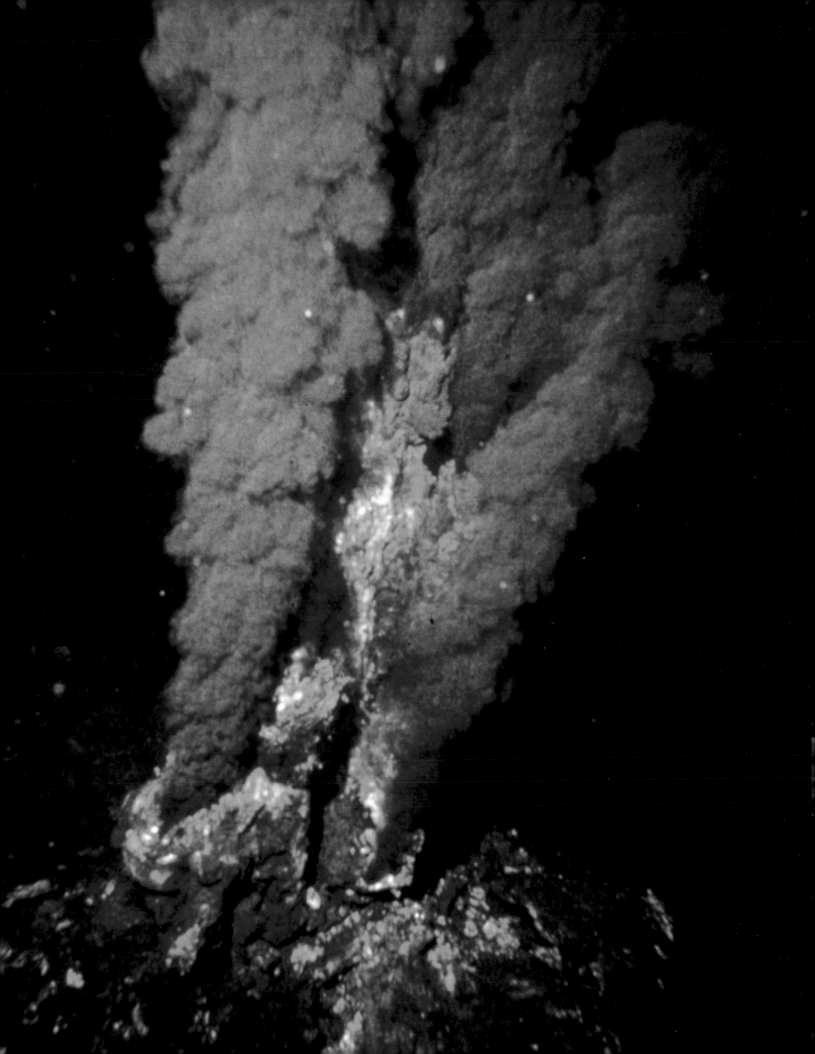

JACK SZOSTAK

THE ORIGIN OF LIFE ON EARTH

Born in London on November 9, 1952, Jack William Szostak is Professor of Genetics at Harvard Medical School and Alexander Rich Distinguished Investigator at Massachusetts General Hospital in Boston. In 2009 he was awarded the Nobel Prize for Medicine, along with Elizabeth Blackburn and Carol Greider, for the discovery of how chromosomes are protected by telomeres — specialized DNA sequences.

Szostak was raised in Montreal and Ottawa, Canada, and graduated at age 19 from McGill University with a degree in cellular biology. He finished his Ph.D. in biochemistry at Cornell University before undertaking research at Harvard.

Szostak's research is centered in genetics, and has been key to the progress of the Human Genome Project.

JACK SZOSTAK AT STARMUS.

OPPOSITE PAGE: BLACK SMOKER. CREDIT: OAR, NATIONAL UNDERSEA RESEARCH PROGRAM (NURP).

I'm going to discuss the current status of work on the origin of life. The origin of life is really a wonderful thing to study because it brings together so many different branches of science. Astronomers love this question, as do planetary scientists, chemists and biologists, because we're all interested in understanding this in a very broad sense — all the way from star and planet formation, to the changes that occur on young planets, the development of more and more complicated chemistry, and then the transition from complicated chemistry to simple biology, which really means the beginning of Darwinian evolution. Once Darwinian evolution is operating, we have a powerful explanation for the origin of more complicated forms of life.

To begin, I'd like to put current thinking about the origin of life into context by discussing the confluence of two major developments in science. The first is what I'd consider to be one of the transformative advances in biology, which is our developing understanding of how intensely and deeply colonized our planet is by life. This is something that was not appreciated until very recently.

This illustration is the iconic picture of a hydrothermal deep-sea vent: the temperature in the vent water is very high, everything is at very high pressure, and yet the entire environment of this geological feature is densely colonized with life. It was really an amazing surprise when these vents were discovered.

In the same timeframe we've learned that there is microbial life living inside porous or fractured rocks, all over the planet. Rocks with exposed surfaces often contain a thin green layer of photosynthetic cells (cyanobacteria) living in the pores of a rock. But we know from studies of deep mines that there is life in rocks kilometres down below the surface of our planet. There is also life in incredibly acidic and incredibly alkaline environments. For example, Rio Tinto in Spain has a pH below 2, yet is filled with diverse kinds of life. There is life in even more extreme environments than this, such as acid mine drainage sites, which are approaching concentrated sulfuric acid.

What these examples tell us is that once you have Darwinian evolution, life can adapt to new environments and it can colonize an amazing diversity of different places and different conditions. If you put that together with another major recent advance in science — the discovery of extrasolar planets — the implications are obvious. From the work of Michel Mayor and many other people, current extrapolations are that there may be as many as 500 million earthlike planets orbiting sunlike stars in our Galaxy alone. I think that, given the adaptability of life, it's almost certain that life could live on at least some of those planets.

The question is, does it? That's something I think we'd all really like to know. The answer to that question comes down to whether it's easy or hard for life to emerge from the chemistry of young planets. The answer to that, at this point, is clearly unknown. The most direct and satisfying way to answer the question would be through high resolution observations of extrasolar planets. It's clear that we're going to be making very intense efforts to look at the atmospheres of some of these planets in the coming decades, but it will probably be a much longer time before we have direct observational evidence to answer the question of whether or not there is life on any of these other earthlike planets.

In the meantime, what can we do? I think that we can get some interesting clues by just going into the laboratory and doing very simple experiments to try to understand all of the steps as we go from simple chemistry to more complicated chemistry, and then on to simple cells and from there to more complicated cells. If we can show from laboratory experiments that every step along that pathway looks relatively simple, I think it would be a reasonable extrapolation to say, yes, there probably is life in many places "out there."

On the other hand, it could be that there is one step — or several steps — that, no matter how hard we try, looks really, really difficult (in other words, very unlikely), in which case we would be driven to the conclusion that, despite the multitude of possible environments, we might be alone. That's what drives us to go into the lab and do the kinds of experiments I am going to describe.

There is a related question that I'd like to mention briefly. If there is life "out there" in different environments, is it going to look more or less like what we are familiar with, in a chemical sense? Would life on other planets use molecules like DNA and RNA to code for and mediate the inheritance of useful functions? Would there be molecules more or less like proteins to build the beautiful structures of life, to catalyze life's chemical reactions? Or could there be very, very different — or even moderately different — ways of building living systems?

Again, I think that we can potentially get some very interesting clues by going into the lab and doing relatively simple experiments.

How do we study the origin of life? What kinds of experiments can we do? How do we even figure out what questions we need to ask? There are two fundamentally distinct approaches to thinking about the origin of life. We can start at the top with modern biology, and try to reason down to what life looked like at earlier times, or we can start at the bottom with chemistry and try to work our way up to the beginning of life.

Let's consider the top-down approach first. There's a very simple explanation for why the origin of life has been so hard to think about logically for decades. Modern life — all of modern life, even the simplest bacterial species — is incredibly complicated. There are lots of moving parts, and a lot of information coded in the genomes of even the simplest cells. Modern cells have beautiful but complicated and intricate structures to control their shape and movement. Underlying that structural complexity, there is enormous chemical complexity. Even a tiny piece of a chart that describes all of metabolism would display dozens of chemical reactions. And all of these chemical reactions are speeded up by complicated protein enzymes whose amino acid sequences are coded in the cell's genetic information.

If we step back from the details and look at the underlying organization of modern life, we see that even this is complex. DNA is the medium for the archival storage of information, and that information is transcribed into RNA, a chemically very similar molecule, and the resulting messenger RNA (mRNA) codes for the synthesis of proteins, which do most of what goes on in modern cells. Other RNAs help to make those proteins, for example by catalyzing protein synthesis in the ribosome. In addition to the linear progression from DNA to RNA to protein (the famous Central Dogma), we know that you need DNA to make more DNA, and it turns out that you need certain RNA molecules to make other RNA molecules. And you need proteins to make DNA and RNA, and you even need proteins to make proteins. Everything in modern cells, at this level, depends on everything else!

How could such a system arise spontaneously? That conundrum stopped people cold for a long time. The correct solution was originally proposed in the late sixties by several very clever people, including Francis Crick, Leslie Orgel and Carl Woese, who said that life must have started with a single biopolymer, which must have been RNA, the central player in the Central Dogma. Nobody really paid any attention to their idea because it seemed so outlandish at the time.

But in the early 1980s, Tom Cech and Sidney Altman showed experimentally that that molecule in the middle, RNA, can catalyze — speed up — chemical reactions. That allowed scientists to look at early life in a completely different way. Instead of the complexity of modern life, we could think about an earlier, simpler kind of life in which cells would have basically two components: a cell membrane and — inside — some RNA molecules. The membrane could be made from soaplike molecules that would provide a boundary between the inside of the cell and the environment. It would also grow and divide, just like modern cells, but in a much simpler way. Trapped inside this primitive cell membrane would be RNA molecules that could replicate, so that they could transmit information to daughter cells. Most remarkably, those RNA molecules could do something, exactly what isn't clear, but something that would be useful for the survival or replication of the cell as a whole.

This next illustration shows what a primitive cell (or protocell) might look like. The primitive cell membrane forms a closed vesicle, which I'll discuss in more detail, and trapped inside the vesicle is some kind of genetic material. That genetic material could be RNA, but there's a huge debate going on right now about whether the first genetic material was actually RNA or some related molecule, perhaps even DNA. It may have been some related nucleic acid with a few chemical changes that made it easier to make, or easier to replicate. People in several laboratories are trying to work out possible chemical pathways leading to different genetic materials, so that we can have a better idea of whether RNA or something else was the first genetic material.

One thing that we have been doing in my lab is trying to build protocell structures similar to that shown in this illustration and actually watch them growing and dividing. We also, of course, need to think about what kinds of molecules would make up the components of the protocell. What's the membrane going to be made of? What's the genetic material going to be made of? Let's step back a minute and think about when all this happened and at what stage in the development of the planet all this occurred, so that we can have some idea of what kinds of biological building blocks might have been available.

The next illustration shows a rough timeline for the origin of life on Earth. We know the time of formation of Earth quite accurately (approximately 4.56 billion years ago, abbreviated Gya). There is still considerable debate about when the surface cooled down sufficiently to allow for liquid water, but there is some evidence that it might have been much earlier than the 4.2 Gya suggested in this illustration, possibly within a hundred million years, or even less, of the Earth-Moon impact. At the other end, the first really solid evidence for bacterial life is three-and-a-half billion years ago. So there's almost a billion-year window — at least 800 million years — between having water and land on the primitive planet and having life.

Lots of interesting chemistry had to be taking place during that time, leading to the synthesis of more and more complex molecules, the building blocks that would eventually come together and assemble into the first cells. At some point the pre-RNA world developed RNA catalysts, which enabled Darwinian evolution to get going. What we'd like to do is to fill in some of this rather vague pathway with

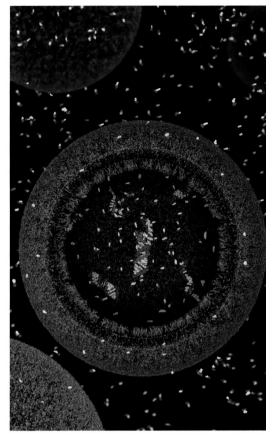

PROTOCELL MODEL, CONSISTING OF A MEMBRANE VESICLE WITH ENCAPSULATED NUCLEIC ACIDS. CREDIT: JANET IWASA.

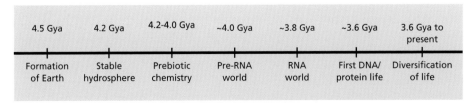

4.5 Gya	4.2 Gya	4.2-4.0 Gya	~4.0 Gya	~3.8 Gya	~3.6 Gya	3.6 Gya to present
Formation of Earth	Stable hydrosphere	Prebiotic chemistry	Pre-RNA world	RNA world	First DNA/ protein life	Diversification of life

ROUGH TIMELINE FOR THE ORIGIN OF LIFE ON THE EARLY EARTH. CREDIT: JAMIE SYMONDS.

SATELLITE IMAGE OF THE ASH CLOUDS FROM THE PUYEHUE-CORDÓN CAULLE VOLCANO. CREDIT: NASA.

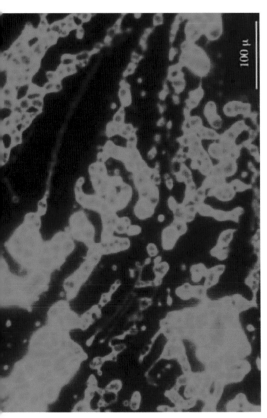

SELF-ASSEMBLED VESICLES COMPOSED OF MEMBRANE-FORMING MOLECULES GENERATED IN A SIMULATED HYDROTHERMAL VENT EXPERIMENT UNDER HYDROTHERMAL CONDITIONS. CREDIT: JACK SZOSTAK.

specific and realistic processes. Part of the difficulty is that we know so little about the conditions on early Earth, which is why this field is being driven forward by the efforts of planetary scientists, as well as biochemists and biologists.

At a chemical level, what we'd like to understand is the simplest building blocks, molecules like water, nitrogen, ammonia, carbon monoxide, hydrogen — all starting materials that we can more or less agree were present on the young Earth — started to react with each other to form the more complex building blocks of biology? Fatty acids (the building blocks of membranes), nucleotides (the building blocks of DNA and RNA), amino acids (the building blocks of peptides): how were these made, and how did they all come together to make the first cells?

The beginning of this field was Stanley Miller's dramatic 1953 experiment, in which he took various mixtures of gases and, by putting energy into the system through spark discharges, found that, over a period of days, the mixture of gas generated a tarry mess. Amazingly, it turned out that that material contained a great variety of compounds, including most of the amino acids found in proteins. So making amino acids actually looks really simple. For a long time that biased the field; people were thinking about proteins, so the likely availability of amino acids was fantastic. This happened long before we knew that RNA was the central and most important molecule to be thinking about. To me, it now seems that the most important thing going on in those experiments was not making amino acids per se, but making one of the intermediates that then goes on to make not only amino acids but lots of other things as well. That key intermediate is cyanide. Cyanide is a very reactive chemical and in a series of reactions it can generate all kinds of interesting molecules. It's one of the central feed-stocks for making the nucleotides from which you would then make RNA and DNA.

That leads to the question of whether this could really happen on early Earth. To me, this seems fairly likely, based on the nature of modern volcanos. The next illustration shows the ash clouds surrounding the recently erupting Puyehue-Cordón Caulle volcano in Chile. There were incredible lightning storms around the clouds. On early Earth, when there was no oxygen in the atmosphere, such lightning discharges would have been generating a lot of cyanide in local areas, perhaps making it possible to build up enough cyanide locally to generate the higher-order building blocks needed for life.

We know a lot about the chemistry leading to nucleotides, but I don't want to get into the complicated technical details here; instead, I would like to discuss the molecules that make up primitive cell membranes. These are much simpler than nucleotides and it turns out that they can be made in lots of different ways. They can even be extracted from certain kinds of meteorites that contain a lot of organic compounds; the extracted molecules spontaneously form little bubble-like vesicles in water that could trap other molecules. In experiments with ices in the form of solid films of methane, ammonia, carbon dioxide and similar molecules, exposure to ultraviolet light has been shown to generate molecules that can spontaneously assemble into hollow membranous structures that can hold molecules inside.

In yet another example, membrane-forming molecules are generated under hydrothermal conditions similar to the conditions in a high-temperature, high-pressure hydrothermal vent on early Earth.

Although the chemical details are still being worked out, it appears to be fairly easy to generate molecules that form these beautiful membranous structures.

It's interesting to speculate about the kinds of early Earth environments that might allow for the formation of fatty acids. Consider the hydrothermal vents that you would find in a geothermally active area, such as Yellowstone Park in the United States, or the geyser fields of Iceland.

Going deep underground, where it gets hotter and hotter, and the pressure is higher and higher, there are metals like iron and nickel, in the form of their oxides and sulfides. On the surfaces of these crystals, hydrogen and carbon can get together as the surface catalyzes the formation of linear hydrocarbon chains with oxygen at the end, after which they can be brought up to the surface of Earth by the flowing water and then concentrated in various geochemical scenarios. These molecules are basically soap (that's really all it is). If you shake these soap molecules up in water, with some salts, some buffer (such as amino acids, for example), they form really beautiful structures, as shown in this next illustration by assembling into sheets that close up and can hold large molecules like RNA inside.

These vesicles have very interesting and unusual properties. One property is that there's a lot of motion. When you see a picture they just look like fixed and rigid, but in reality they are very flexible and all of the molecules that make up the membrane are constantly moving around. Surprisingly, they're rapidly going in and out of these membranes and flitting from the inside to the outside — and all these motions happen very quickly, on a timescale of a second or less. These structures are very, very dynamic and that turns out to be completely critical to how they behave and why they're a good starting point for primitive cell membranes.

Another very interesting property of these vesicles is that they last a long time, even though the molecules they are made of come and go very rapidly. In the next illustration, you see red and green vesicles. They're labeled with a dye that doesn't move between vesicles. This picture was taken a day after the red and green vesicles were mixed together. We know that the molecules that make up any particular vesicle get randomized by exchange between vesicles every second, and yet the individual structures last for days, weeks, even months. They retain their identity even though the molecules they are made of are constantly in flux and being exchanged. So, just as in our bodies, where the molecules that make us up are different from year to year, here, the vesicles are made of different molecules on a second-to-second time scale.

To think about how a primitive cell would assemble, we need to imagine some way of bringing genetic materials into these membrane vesicles. That can happen spontaneously: when a membrane sheet closes up to form a vesicle it can just enclose whatever is in the solution. If there's some RNA in the solution, some of it will get trapped. But it turns out that some very simple minerals can make this process much more efficient. The next illustration is a pretty picture from work in my lab nine years ago when we were studying the role of clay in assembling these cells. There is a particular kind of clay, called montmorillonite, that forms from volcanic ash. The same volcanic geochemistry that generates cyanide and other chemical building blocks also makes a lot of ash, some of which will settle into the ocean, react with seawater and turn into clay.

Amazingly, that clay can help make RNA, in a process that was studied years ago by Jim Ferris. What we found was that that clay can also help membranes to form. In our experiment, we made small particles of clay with a dye-labelled RNA on the surface of the clay particles, and used that material to help vesicles to form from fatty acids.

In this illustration you can see that the RNA on a clay particle is trapped inside a giant vesicle, along with lots of other little vesicles, all made due to the influence of the clay. Remarkably, the clay helps make genetic molecules, helps make membranes and helps to bring them together. It's very suggestive that this simple, abundant mineral could really help to bring together the components for making primitive cells.

Based on the experiments with clay, it looks like bringing membranes together with RNA is fairly simple. The next problem we have to think about is how such a structure can grow and divide. A technical problem in working with vesicles is that these structures are very heterogeneous. They're not all the same size, and they usually have more than one membrane. If you shake up fatty acids in water, what you get is a complete mess: there are giant vesicles, there are tiny vesicles, there are vesicles with smaller ones inside (look back at figure showing "soap" bubbles).

If you wanted to look experimentally at how these kinds of structures could grow, it would be very difficult. If every vesicle grew a little bit, you probably couldn't tell;

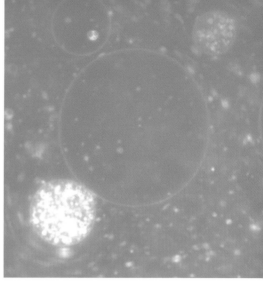

SELF-ASSEMBLED VESICLES COMPOSED OF OLEIC ACID. CREDIT: MARTIN HANCZYC.

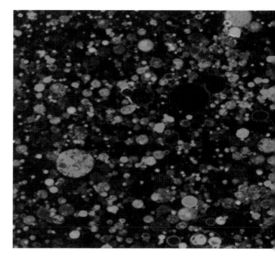

TWO POPULATIONS OF VESICLES, LABELLED WITH RED AND GREEN DYES, PHOTOGRAPHED ONE DAY AFTER MIXING. THE VESICLES HAVE NOT FUSED AND MIXED, RATHER, THEY HAVE MAINTAINED THEIR SEPARATE IDENTITIES. IMAGE CREDIT: MARTIN HANCZYC.

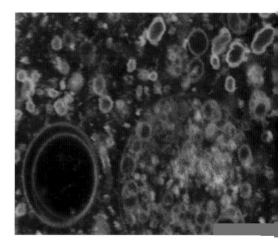

A CLAY PARTICLE COATED WITH ORANGE-LABELLED RNA IS TRAPPED INSIDE A LARGE VESICLE FILLED WITH SMALLER VESICLES (GREEN), ALL ASSEMBLED UNDER THE CATALYTIC INFLUENCE OF THE CLAY. IMAGE CREDIT: MARTIN HANCZYC.

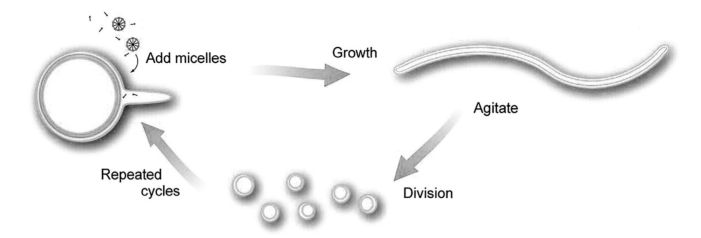

SCHEMATIC DIAGRAM OF A CYCLE OF VESICLE GROWTH AND DIVISION. AN INITIAL LARGE SPHERICAL VESICLE BEGINS TO GROW BY FORMING A THIN FILAMENT, AND EVENTUALLY TRANSFORMS INTO A LONG FILAMENTOUS STRUCTURE, WHICH EASILY DIVIDES DURING GENTLE SHAKING TO GENERATE DAUGHTER VESICLES. CREDIT: TING ZHU.

the mixture of vesicles would look just the same. We were stuck with that problem until a few years ago when a really brilliant student, Ting Zhu, joined the lab. He said, "I know how to make vesicles that are pretty much all the same size." Ting's idea was to get rid of the giant vesicles by squeezing the whole mess through a filter with small holes in it, and then get rid of the small vesicles by letting them float away through even smaller holes in a second filter. I was fine with the first step, but told him the second step would never work, because it would take far too long to be practical. Fortunately I was wrong, because Ting came back the next day to show me a beautiful picture of vesicles, all about the same size, about four microns across.

Once we could make vesicles like this, we could do a very simple experiment. We could add food to this system, in other words more of these soap-like fatty acid molecules, and just watch them grow. We thought that since we were starting with small spherical vesicles, they would just grow into bigger spheres. We also thought that, if the surface grew faster than the volume, they might get a little bit stretched out. That's not what happened. What happened was a complete surprise. Within a few minutes we could see thin wavy filaments emerging from each spherical vesicle. The nascent filaments gradually became thicker and longer, and over time the initially spherical vesicles grew into long branched filaments. Nothing that was trapped inside had leaked out; all the contents were still there.

That surprising result led to many fascinating questions. How does this happen? What conditions allow this kind of growth to happen? But more importantly, this phenomenon has solved what had been a very difficult question, which is, how could division occur? It's very hard to make spherical vesicles divide into smaller spheres; it takes a lot of energy to do that. But all you have to do to make a long filamentous vesicle divide is shake it gently and it will spontaneously divide. As a result a primitive cell might be able to divide into daughter cells just as a result of gentle wave action. We have made videos of the division process, in which we first see a strange transition from a smooth filament to what looks like beads on a string, which then snaps in response to motions in the fluid, resulting in smaller daughter vesicles. This process is illustrated schematically in the final illustration.

Steps in the origin of life seem easier if there's more than one way for that step to happen. So it's very satisfying that there is another way that division can happen that is totally different. This is driven by photochemistry — a series of chemical reactions started by light, and it results in a different kind of division. In this process, a filamentous vesicle transforms into a long string of beads and eventually the beads separate from each other, so that lots of daughter vesicles are generated. Again, there are many interesting questions to be asked about how this happens, but the encouraging thing is that protocell division, which initially looked like a very hard problem, now looks pretty easy. To summarize, we can start with fairly large vesicles, grow them into filaments, and easily make them divide into multiple daughter vesicles, which in turn can grow larger, and we can go round this cycle again and again and again.

At this stage, we have seen that one component of a primitive cell, its membrane, can grow and divide in a simple, robust fashion. The remaining big problem is how to get the genetic material to replicate, without enzymes (since there were no enzymes before the origin of life). Returning to the protocell diagram (the second figure), we have a model of a primitive cell consisting of a membrane and some genetic molecules on the inside. As the membrane grows, the genetic molecules get copied, so that when division occurs the genetic molecules get distributed into the daughter cells.

Now we're back where we started and the cycle of growth and division can be repeated indefinitely. I want to emphasize that the point of this repeating cycle is not just growth and division, but getting evolution started. The reason why that would happen is that information is coded in the sequence of nucleotides that make up the genetic molecules, whatever they are — RNA, DNA or something else. As they go through the process of copying and replication, mistakes are inevitably made, so lots and lots of different sequences will be generated over time. At some point one of those sequences may be able to do something that is good for the survival of the cell as a whole. The progeny of that cell will gradually start to take over the population, and the genetic structure of the population will start to change, which is the hallmark of Darwinian evolution. What we'd love to see in my lab is the spontaneous emergence of Darwinian evolution, or in other words, a chemical system beginning to act like a biological system.

To build a protocell capable of evolving, we have to think about what its genetic molecules would be, and about how they would get copied. What kind of chemistry could drive the copying of simple genetic molecules, or even complex ones like RNA? This is a problem that has fascinated people for decades now. The late Leslie Orgel made exciting initial progress in this field, but eventually, over a period of twenty years, he became convinced that the chemical replication of RNA was simply not plausible. As a result he came to favor the idea that there might have been a simpler genetic molecule that came before RNA. People are still debating this idea, but it's a hypothesis we can test by doing experiments. For example, we can make molecules that are a little bit different from RNA, essentially trying to make versions of RNA that may be easier to copy.

That's the kind of chemistry we're doing in my lab now. Another possibility is that the first genetic molecules were DNA, which is a lot more stable than RNA. It may be harder to make and harder to copy, but it lasts longer if you do make it, so maybe we got started with DNA. There are many other alternatives, many molecules that could in principle act as genetic polymers, so we have to make them and test their properties and think about how they could have formed on early Earth.

I mentioned before that the common clay mineral montmorillonite can help to assemble strands of RNA. This clay consists of many thin sheets stacked on each other, so it has a very large surface area. If the right building blocks (activated nucleotides) are present in the environment, they will stick to the surface of these thin clay sheets. These monomers can then join together and they can grow into fairly long chains of RNA through the catalytic effect of the clay surface. The really big, interesting and hard question that we're focused on is, how would these strands of RNA get copied?

Finding the right chemistry and conditions for RNA copying is one of our current goals. We'd like to start with RNA chains and watch the activated building blocks find their pairing partners on the sequence and gradually build up a complementary strand, making a double helical product. We can do a limited amount of RNA copying, but we can't do it fast enough and we can't do it accurately enough at this point. Those are the challenges for the future. I would like to emphasize again that we need these complicated molecules because they are the molecules that take care of inheritance. RNAs that carry out functions that are useful for the cell, e.g. that help it to replicate, or help it to survive, must replicate so they can be passed on to future generations of cells. That is why understanding the chemistry of RNA replication is such a big part of understanding how life began on early Earth.

Knowing just what we know now about the growth and division of vesicles, and the chemical replication of RNA and similar molecules, we're at a point where we can start to make some deductions about the kinds of environments that could allow primitive cells to reproduce on early Earth. Although this is a little bit speculative, it's very interesting to think about what the chemistry may be telling us about the environment. The next illustration shows a model, a theory, of what a primitive cell cycle might have looked like. At the beginning of the cell cycle some genetic molecule, maybe RNA, trapped inside a membrane vesicle.

Over time, the nucleotide building blocks cross the membrane and diffuse to the inside and copy the RNA strands. Then, in order to progress further, the two strands of the double helix have to come apart, and the only reasonable way of doing that is by heating them up. It appears that we need an environment that's fairly cool for the copying chemistry to work, but we need a high temperature to get the strands apart. An environment where this might be possible is a shallow pond in a very cold location, possible at high altitude, or in the Arctic or Antarctic, but also — as was probably common on early Earth — a volcanic environment.

Geothermal heating in this pond would result in plumes of hot water rising from vents then mixing with the cold pond water. As simple cells get entrained and rise through this plume of hot water, they get heated up, allowing the RNA strands to separate and more nutrients to flood into the cell. Once the cells return to the

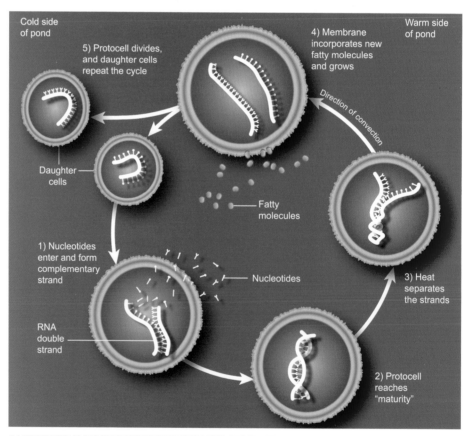

A HYPOTHETICAL ENVIRONMENTALLY DRIVEN CELL. MOST MEMBRANE GROWTH AND RNA COPYING OCCURS AT LOW TEMPERATURES. OCCASIONALLY, THE CELL IS CAUGHT UP IN A PLUME OF HOT WATER EMITTED FROM A GEOTHERMAL VENT; THE BRIEF EXPOSURE TO HIGH TEMPERATURE ALLOWS THE STRANDS OF DNA DUPLEXES TO SEPARATE, AND ALSO ALLOWS FOR AN INFLUX OF NUTRIENTS. CREDIT: JAMES SYMONDS.

surrounding cold water, the cycle of copying, growth and division could occur again.

Speculation about the environment for the origin of life inevitably leads to new questions. Is this a geophysically plausible model? That question is driving me, a chemist and biologist, to talk to geologists about where we might find environments like this. One interesting Earth environment is found in the Antarctic lakes that are permanently covered with ice. The lakes remain liquid because of geothermal heat, and in at least one case there are beautiful stromatolites growing on the rocky surface. This is not exactly what we need since there are no plumes of very hot water, but it is quite conceivable as an environment for bacterial life on early Earth.

A more geothermally active environment such as Yellowstone National Park may be even more relevant, since there we see dozens of hydrothermal vents pouring streams of hot water into a cold lake. In the long run, I think that combined studies of geology, chemistry and biology will drive us to a more and more detailed understanding of a complete pathway for making the chemical building blocks of biology, assembling them into protocells, understanding how such simple cells grow and divide and begin to evolve, and even deducing something about the environments in which all of this could have happened.

I want to end by touching briefly on a topic I mentioned at the very beginning.

Could there be forms of life very different from what we're familiar with? We know that there are environments within our own solar system where there are different liquids, for example the polar regions of Saturn's moon Titan are dotted with vast seas of liquid methane and ethane. There is very interesting organic chemistry going on in the atmosphere of this moon, and consequently many people are planning missions to explore this environment in more detail. Just seeing lakes of a liquid that's not water makes you wonder what's happening there.

Could there be chemistry there that could lead to simple living systems, or even part way to life? To address this question, we would like to know whether it is possible to make membranes in that kind of solvent. It turns out that the late Professor Kunieda in Japan made membrane vesicles in a solvent (decane) that is chemically quite similar to liquid methane or ethane (but physically easier to handle). So making membranes seems physically possible, but we don't know if it could be done with molecules found on Titan. An even more challenging and interesting question for chemists to think about is whether it would be possible to make genetic molecules that would function in such a very different environment. That's an area where almost no work has been done, but there is tremendous potential for interesting experiments.

I hope I've convinced you that we can do very simple things in the lab that can begin to tell us how some of the steps on the pathway from chemistry to life could have happened on early Earth. I think there are still many, many interesting questions along those lines that we'll be looking at in the near future. Much of this work has been done by the many talented students and postdocs who have worked in my lab over the years, with support from many different sources. Thank you for listening.

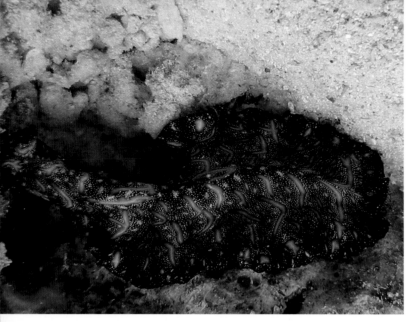

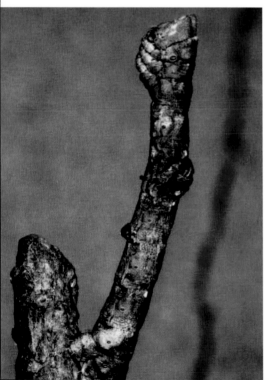

TOP LEFT: BEDFORD'S FLATWORM (PSEUDOBICEROS BEDFORDI). CREDIT: WIKIMEDIA COMMONS, JAN DERK.

TOP RIGHT: STORK IN FLIGHT. CREDIT: WIKIMEDIA COMMONS, RAJARAMAN SANJEEVI.

MID LEFT: CUTTLEFISH. CREDIT: WIKIMEDIA COMMONS, BORAZONT.

MID RIGHT: TREEHOPPERS, MEMBRACIDAE. CREDIT: WIKIMEDIA COMMONS, DIRK VAN DER MADE.

LOWER LEFT: STICK CATERPILLAR, PLAGODIS. CREDIT: PERSONAL COLLECTION.

THE ILLUSION OF DESIGN. CREDIT: STARMUS.

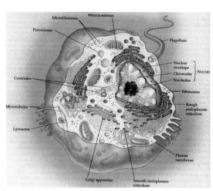

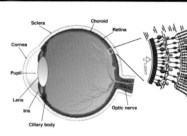

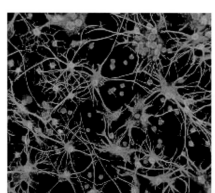

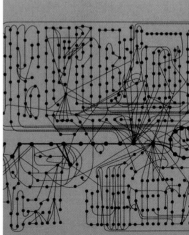

RICHARD DAWKINS

Born in Nairobi, Kenya, March 26, 1941, English ethologist and evolutionary biologist Clinton Richard Dawkins is emeritus fellow of New College at Oxford University in England. He is an accomplished researcher and celebrated author, having come to prominence with his 1976 book The Selfish Gene. Not only has he popularized the gene-centered view of evolution, but he has pioneered the idea of extended phenotypic effects — characteristics of an individual organism — not being limited to an organism's body. Dawkins' father was a civil servant stationed in Nyasaland (Malawi); the young Dawkins studied zoology at Oxford, graduating in 1962. By 1966 he received his Ph.D. and began teaching at the University of California in Berkeley before returning to Oxford in 1970.

Dawkins is also a celebrated atheist and has widely criticized creationism and intelligent design. His many bestselling books, including The God Delusion (2006), support his ideas on biology, genetics, and religion. The following is a transcript of his lecture, as it was spoken.

RICHARD DAWKINS AT STARMUS.

What a brilliant talk we have just listened to, just a beautiful, beautiful piece of science — and I've got the unenviable task of following it!

I want to move on a bit from the origin of life and use my biologist's intuition to try to speculate about whether we can make any educated guesses about what extraterrestrial life might eventually look like once it has originated.

The most salient and impressive feature of life is the illusion of design. Living things are often very complicated, very beautiful, and look overwhelmingly as if some engineer has designed them for a purpose. In this illustration you see some examples, just a more or less random collection, of living creatures: a flying bird, a swimming flatworm, a cuttlefish and a stick caterpillar. That thing sticking up in the air is not a twig; it's actually a caterpillar that has been shaped by natural selection, probably bird predation, to look like a twig in every detail. The things on the right are not rose thorns, they're bugs. They're insects. Once again, natural selection — bird predation probably — has shaped these things, has selected and eaten the ones that don't look like thorns, leaving the genes that tend to make bugs look like thorns.

And this illusion of design extends right into the minute details of living creatures. Consider the illustration opposite at bottom right: the living cell on the top left, a slice of brain tissue on the bottom left, bottom right is another rendering of what Jack Szostak has just shown us, the metabolism of a cell. You see how bewilderingly complicated it is, and that's going on in every single cell. Top right is the human eye, and once again you see this beautifully designed mechanism for seeing, for focusing an image on a retina: variable focus, variable stopping down and then the retina at the back with millions of — let's call them pixels. An odd little feature is that the photocells that are detecting the light are pointing backwards (they're pointing away from the light) and the "wires" that connect the retina to the brain run over the surface of the retina; that is not good design. That's what you'd expect according to a theory of historical accident.

Now we know, on this planet, what it is that creates this powerful illusion of design. It is Darwinian natural selection — evolution by natural selection — and it is an enormously powerful idea. I would define the power of a theory as what it explains divided by what it needs to assume in order to do the explaining. A powerful theory is one that doesn't need to assume very much in order to explain a hell of a lot. In the case of Darwin's theory, what it explains is everything about life, and what it needs to assume in order to do the explaining is actually nothing much more than accurate heredity. Once you've got accurate replication, that crucial step in Jack

Szostak's talk, everything else follows because accurate replication can never be perfectly accurate. There will always be imperfections; there will therefore be variation, there will therefore be competition that will inevitably lead to natural selection — assuming it doesn't die out altogether — and that powers the origin of everything else about life.

Does life on another planet have to be Darwinian? Can we imagine any other driving force to produce the illusion of design? Well, the only alternative that's ever been suggested in the history of science is the theory of Lamarck. Lamarck's theory begins with the assumption that animals are striving for something, striving to reach something, to achieve something. The second assumption is that the more that you use a bit of your body, like a muscle, the bigger it gets. So as the giraffe strives to reach the topmost branches of the tree, it stretches its neck, and the stretched parts are then inherited in the next generation. He believed, as most people did in his time, in the inheritance of acquired characteristics. So the evolutionary process was supposed to proceed by animals trying to do things, using certain muscles or bones as they did them. Those muscles that they used got bigger because they used them, and then those larger muscles or bones, whatever they were, were inherited in the next generation.

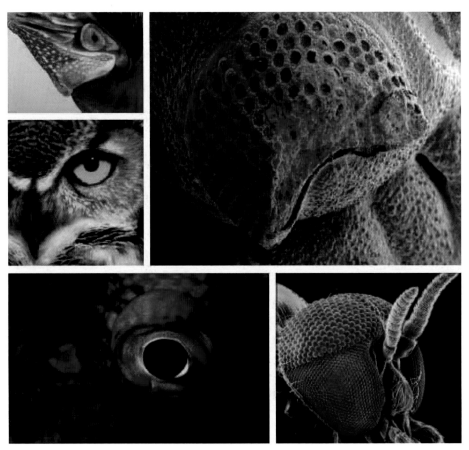

EYES FROM RICHARD DAWKINS' "ANCESTOR'S TALE". CREDIT: RICHARD DAWKINS.

Now, as a matter of fact, that doesn't happen. As a matter of fact, on this planet, acquired characteristics are not inherited, and that's often trotted out as the main objection to Lamarck's theory. But, actually, even on a planet where acquired characteristics were inherited, it still wouldn't work; it's still not a good enough theory to account for the evolution of complex life, and that's for two reasons. One is that with acquired characteristics there's no particular reason why there would be improvements: most acquired characteristics are actually disimprovements — they're things like broken bones, wearing out, scars, and so on. If we inherited acquired characteristics, we'd all be limping around on the broken bones of our ancestors, which we're clearly not. Even on a planet where that did happen, it still wouldn't provide the mechanism for progressive evolution.

The principle of use and disuse is also not good enough, is not man enough, to do the job. It's all very well to say that a muscle gets bigger when you use it a lot. That may be true, but that's not going to explain the fine intricate detail of something like an eye. The fine, sharp chisels of natural selection are good enough to provide the beautifully tuned organs like eyes and ears, but it's just not true that the more you use an eye the better it gets at seeing. There's no sense in which as photons wash through a lens the lens becomes clearer, or something like that. So we can reject Lamarck's theory not just on this planet but everywhere. It is an attempt at an explanation for evolution, but it's a bad one, and it's a bad one everywhere.

There is no other theory that's ever been proposed that would work. Intelligent design is not an explanation at all because it simply begs the question of where the complexity comes from. The whole point of what we're trying to do and what Darwinism successfully does is to explain complexity, statistical improbability, the illusion of design starting with primeval simplicity, which is easy to explain, and working up by slow, gradual degrees to complexity. That's what Darwinism does, and that's what intelligent design manifestly doesn't do because it starts with complexity, it starts with a designer, who's got to be supremely complicated and intelligent in order to start the process off.

So our working hypothesis will be that life anywhere in the universe has got to be Darwinian life. There remains the possibility that there are other theories that nobody's yet thought of, nobody's dreamed of, but we have to say that any theory that's going to be any good has got at least to share with Darwinism the property of deriving eventual complexity from primordial simplicity. If it can't do that, it's not the theory we're looking for.

Now, how likely actually is it that there is life on other planets? It was Enrico Fermi who famously once said at lunch with colleagues, "Where is everybody?" His colleagues, being very intelligent, immediately knew what he meant. He meant why have we not been visited by creatures from other planets, or why have we not picked up any radio transmissions from them? We simply don't know, as various speakers at this conference have said, whether there is life on other planets. We don't have enough data to narrow down the answer at all.

The possibilities are open all the way down, from extreme ("we are entirely alone in the universe," which some people believe), through various intermediates (such as "life tends to arise about once per galaxy" — still incredibly rare), to the other extreme ("life tends to arise on average once per star") — in which case we would have, I think, something like 10^{22} separate life forms in the universe.

Various people have espoused points along this continuum. Quite a lot of people think that we are alone in the universe — that life literally has arisen only once. That's fine, but just let me point out one corollary, one deduction, from that belief. If you want to hold that belief, that we are alone, it means that the origin of life is a quite stupefyingly improbable event. It's an event so improbable that people like Jack Szostak and his colleagues are totally and utterly wasting their time trying to come up with a plausible chemical theory for the origin of life because, if you want to believe we're alone in the universe, then what we are seeking in our theory of the origin of life is not a plausible theory, it's a highly, highly, highly implausible theory. We should be deeply worried if anybody comes up with a plausible theory if we want to believe we are alone in the universe.

Well, I don't know about you, but I found Jack Szostak's presentation extremely plausible, and that means that I am drawn to the view that there probably is quite a lot of life around the universe. On the other hand, since the reason for believing that possibility is the sheer number of planets, it remains possible that, although there's plenty of life around the universe, it's still seemingly rare because the number of planets is so large, and therefore the islands of life in the universe may be so spaced

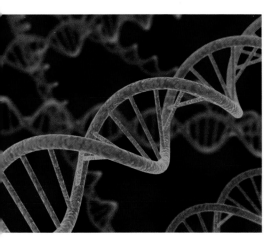

DNA. CREDIT: NATIONAL INSTITUTE OF
STANDARDS AND TECHNOLOGY.

out that the chance of only one of them ever encountering any of the others may be very low, which would be sad.

Encountering life bodily is vastly more improbable than encountering life by electromagnetic radiation from intelligent life forms, which is Jill Tarter's subject of course. If we were to be visited, a life form would have to home in deliberately and land on our planet, which would be an extremely improbable target. On the other hand, if that life form were to broadcast information by radio or by any other form of electromagnetic radiation, the message would radiate out in all directions, enveloping an ever-increasing sphere of targets, and the chance that we might be in this expanding sphere become great. On the other hand, the message is subject to deterioration by the inverse square law so that after considerable distances the signal would have dissipated and become indistinguishable from background noise. That problem can be overcome by beaming the signal, say, as a pencil-thin laser beam, but then we're back to the problem that the beam has to be very carefully aimed. We no longer have the advantage of broadcasting outward.

What kind of an event is an origin of life? Jack Szostak has covered that so well that I needn't go into it. The key event is the origin of a high fidelity self-replicating entity, of which the DNA is one example, and, as Jack Szostak said, there might be others, there might have been others originally, and DNA could have been a late takeover. Does it have to be carbon-based? Carbon has this property of forming chains and circles and complicated structures that are very well suited to life and so there's a sort of assumption that carbon-based life is relatively likely, but we could be wrong.

Carbon is capable of making big, complex molecules, in particular protein molecules, which have this remarkable capacity to fold themselves up, to tie themselves in knots, the three-dimensional shape of which causes them to have catalytic properties, literally because of their three-dimensional shape. The three-dimensional shape of a protein is determined by the one-dimensional sequence of amino acids in the chain, and that in turn is determined by the one-dimensional sequence of coded letters — nucleotides — in DNA. So it's theoretically possible to make a protein molecule any shape you like provided you only can work out the correct sequence of amino acids in order to do that, and then the protein will self-assemble, will take care of tying itself into the requisite knot to give exactly the shape that you want to have the right catalytic properties.

I liken a cell to a chemistry lab in which, instead of the bottles of chemicals all being neatly arranged on shelves, all the chemicals in the lab — hundreds of them — are tipped into one great vat, which would be a very irresponsible thing to do, except that, in living vats, which are cells, the presence of enzymes, the presence of specific catalysts, sees to it that the vast majority of reactions which could take place when you've tipped all your bottles into the vat don't take place, only one or two, only whatever is required for that particular cell takes place, and that's because of the specificity of enzymes. So it looks as though enzymes, specific catalysts, are immensely important, at least for life as we understand it.

And so the next question would be, "Does life on other planets have to have protein? Does it then have to have the protein DNA double act, the separation, let's call it, between the catalytic part of life and the replication part of life?" In our form of life these are well separated. DNA is a brilliant replicator but a lousy enzyme; protein is a brilliant enzyme but can't replicate itself. The possible solution, which Jack Szostak mentioned, is the RNA world; RNA, being a good replicator and a good catalyst, might have been the forerunner of both.

I think it's helpful to look at the properties of life as we know it and ask ourselves the question, "Which of these properties had to be true and which of these properties just happen to be true in our kind of life?" I've already mentioned Darwinian natural selection as something which I conjecture has to be true. I could be wrong. Darwinian natural selection depends upon high fidelity replication, hi-fi heredity. DNA is very, very hi-fi heredity and it gets that property from the fact that it's digital.

THYLACINUS, A DOG-MARSUPIAL. CREDIT:
WIKIMEDIA COMMONS.

But does heredity have to be digital? I conjecture that it probably does; our experience in digital encoding is more reliable, more accurate, than analog encoding, but we could at least think about the possibility of a form of life on some other planet which has an analog genetic system rather than a digital one. If it is digital, does it have to be a one-dimensional code, as we have, as DNA is, or could you imagine a two-dimensional matrix as the thing that is read off in the hereditary process? I've already asked the question, "Does it have to have protein?" "Does it have to have a polynucleotide DNA, RNA, or something like that as a separate replicator?" "Does it have to have sex?"

Probably not, because quite a lot of creatures on our planet don't have sex, and we don't fully understand precisely what sex is doing, so it probably doesn't have to have sex. Does it have to have separate cells? All the life that we know on this planet is either single-celled life, or, if it's large, is made up of lots of small cells. Could you imagine a life form that wasn't divided up into cells in that way? Cells have this remarkable property that a complete copy of the genetic information is present in every cell, which is somewhat weird, even in cells where it's not needed. Is that a necessary property of life or is that just contingent? Does it just happen to be true in the life that we know?

One way to answer this kind of question is that proposed by Stuart Kauffman, the distinguished theoretical biologist, who asked the question, "If we were to re-run evolution hypothetically, if we were to imagine evolution starting again, perhaps from the origin of life, perhaps from the origin of the first eukaryotic cell (that is, the first non-bacterial cell, the first cell of our kind, big cells with a separate nucleus and mitochondria, and things like that), if you re-run evolution a statistical sample of times, say, thousands of times in imagination — can't do it in reality — would you expect to get something like the same thing again, or would you expect every run of your re-run of evolution to give you a completely different kind of life?' And that's obviously germane to the question of how different life might be on other planets. If you could at least say that re-runs of life on this planet would tend to give the same answer, the same result after so many hundred million years, then that at least tells you something about the predictability of life generally — perhaps not much, but something.

Well, we can't literally re-run evolution — certainly not from the origin of life, certainly not from the origin of the eukaryotic cell — but we can do small examples of re-runs; for example, the mammals, the evolution of mammals, which started long before the dinosaurs became extinct. Mammals really came into their own and flowered after the dinosaurs went extinct about 66 million years ago.

It so happens that about the time the dinosaurs went extinct the great southern continent of Gondwana split up and you had separate evolutions going on in Australia, Madagascar, New Zealand, South America and even in Africa. The mammals evolved independently, or largely independently, in those places. The most perfect example is Australia, where the only mammals that seemed to get in in the first place were marsupials, and possibly only one species of marsupial, which is an interesting thought. This early marsupial gave rise to the entire radiation of Australian mammals at the same time as other mammals were evolving to a parallel radiation in Africa, in Asia, in South America and, to a small extent, in Madagascar.

What you see in the illustration opposite looks like a dog; it's not a dog, it's a marsupial, and what's impressive about it is that it looks like a dog; it behaves like a dog. It only went extinct in the 1930s — it looks like a dog and had a doglike way of life. This illustration shows another example. There are three ways of being a mole, totally unrelated, completely independent evolutions of the mole-like way of life, burrowing underground, eating worms and things like that. This illustration shows at top our European mole, below is the golden mole of South Africa, which is an afrothere — nothing to do with the real mole. It evolved the mole way of life independently. At the bottom is an Australian marsupial mole, which again evolved the mole-like way of life and looks like a mole, behaves like a mole, but is not a mole.

EUROPEAN MOLE. CREDIT: WIKIMEDIA COMMONS. GOLDEN MOLE. CREDIT: WIKIMEDIA COMMONS. MARSUPIAL MOLE. CREDIT: WIKIMEDIA COMMONS.

SKULL OF THE MARSUPIAL SABER-TOOTHED TIGER THYLACOSMILUS. CREDIT: WIKIMEDIA COMMONS.

FLYING SQUIRREL. CREDIT: WIKIMEDIA COMMONS.

PINK-WINGED FLYING FISH. CREDIT: PUBLIC DOMAIN.

There are also two ways to be a flying squirrel: a rodent and an Australian marsupial. They look and behave almost identically. These two approaches to the same way of life independently evolved in Australia and in the Old World.

And there are two ways to be a saber-toothed tiger: Thylacinus, which is a true cat, and Thylacosmilus, which is a marsupial (from S. America, not Australia).

Many creatures have amazing powers, such as the ability to inject poison. Jellyfish, scorpions, spiders, centipedes, insects, snakes, lizards, stingrays (among cartilaginous fish), sharks, teleost fish, stonefish — very deadly poison — even mammals. The hind claw of the male duckbilled platypus has the ability to inject poison, and among plants there are stinging nettles. So it looks as though hypodermic venom injection is quite easy to evolve.

Then there is electrolocation, something that is entirely foreign to us; we have no clue as to what it's like to be a fish that can detect objects by the distortion of an electric field emitted by the fish. This has evolved twice. There are two families of fish — so-called electric fish — that have evolved this ability. They produce an electric field and they measure, with little voltmeters all the way down the side of the fish, and compare the electric field, and from the distortion of the field they get an idea of what is in the vicinity — whether there's prey in the vicinity or whatever it might be. These two groups of fish have certainly evolved independently: one group in the New World, in South America.

Now there is an interesting and revealing difference between these two groups of fish. In order to do electrolocation at all, the fish needs its body to be dead straight. While it's swimming in a normal fish way, it would not be capable of doing electrolocation; there would be too much distortion anyway. So while they're electrolocating, these fish are straight. In order to swim while doing electrolocation, they therefore have to find a different way of swimming and the way they achieve that is by, instead of throwing the whole body into serpentine waves, they have one fin that runs all the way along the length of the body which does the serpentine waves. But, fascinatingly, in the South American family this one fin runs all along the ventral surface, and in the African family this one fin runs all the way along the dorsal surface. This again is sort of corroborating evidence that it's been independently evolved. But it's the same trick; the physics of electrolocation is the same in both.

You see what I'm doing: I'm trying to build up a picture for which things are easy to evolve by counting the number of times they've evolved independently and which things are difficult to evolve. How many times has true flight evolved? Apparently, only four times: in insects, they were the first to do it; in pterosaurs — pterodactyls — and the like, which were the next to do it; then in birds and in bats. Those are true flyers that can fly indefinitely using flapping flight. There are numerous other groups of animals which have evolved the ability to glide, in some cases gliding for considerable distances, and they're much more numerous.

These illustrations show a flying squirrel, and a flying fish, and there are lots more. How many times has jet propulsion evolved? Apparently twice, independently, both times in mollusks. Squid do it and they shoot backwards, so they shoot water out of a siphon at the front of the body very rapidly and they shoot very, very fast backwards, so fast that some squid have independently evolved the flying fish habit of zooming right out of the water and then coming down again a long way away. They do that by jet propulsion and swimming backwards. Scallops also have jet propulsion in a rather peculiar way. As they snap shut the valves, you might think they'd be swimming backwards, away from the "snap", but they're not. The reason is that the snapping forces the water out through little jets at the hinge of the two shells, which forces them forward.

How many times has the wheel evolved? Well, it's evolved in human technology, but even that took a long time. Famously, the wheel had to be invented, and it wasn't invented very early in human history. The only true wheel I know of in non-human nature is the bacterial flagellum. You know that many bacteria have a long whip-like tail sticking out of one end. They swim with this. This tail, this flagellum, truly rotates. You can see in this illustration the little molecular motor that turns it. It goes through a bearing, a true axle, it literally does rotate, and I think that's probably the only example of a wheel in nature. So we might say that wheels are not eager to evolve.

Some people have wondered, perhaps following science fiction speculations, whether something like humans, a bipedal brainy creature with eyes looking forward and with skilled hands, might evolve on other planets. Could it even have evolved twice on this planet? Some biologists have speculated that if only the dinosaurs had not been driven extinct by a comet or meteorite 66 million years ago, they might have produced something like a human. Many dinosaurs were of course bipedal; they walked along on two legs, so it wouldn't be that improbable that their freed-up hands could have been used for something. That is pure speculation.

Those who like science fiction will know that very often science fiction writers, perhaps rather unimaginatively, people their alien worlds with humanoid creatures, and they attract a certain amount of scorn for their lack of imagination. However, one reputable biologist, Simon Conway Morris, the Cambridge geologist, has gone on record as suspecting that something like humans is really quite likely to evolve. He seems to have an agenda behind that, but he actually has some quite good arguments. I thought I was pretty much alone in my enthusiasm for convergent evolution, but Conway Morris goes one better.

He points out, for example, that insects have a certain number of defining features: an articulated exoskeleton, compound eyes, a six-legged gait whereby three of the six walking legs are always on the ground at any one time, defining a stable triangle (two legs on one side, two on the other alternating), respiratory tubes known as tracheae (little tubes carrying air throughout the body, that carry the oxygen throughout the body and remove the carbon dioxide) and, in some groups of insects the development of complicated social groups like honey bees and ants.

All those features seem pretty strange, but Conway Morris goes through that list and shows that all of them have evolved more than once in different parts of the animal kingdom. Therefore, it wouldn't be surprising if insects had evolved twice. It wouldn't be that unlikely. He uses this as a sort of weak argument for why it wouldn't be that improbable that bipedal hominoids with big brains, forward-looking eyes and skillful hands might have evolved more than once.

I haven't yet talked about religion, but I thought I'd just better end up with it. There may be creatures so far advanced over us that, if we were ever to meet them, we would fall down and worship them as gods. But if there are — and I don't have any problem in believing that there are — they must have come about through some explicable process; if not Darwinian evolution, then some other process that does the same job, the same explanatory job, as Darwinian evolution, deriving complexity, and therefore the capacity to do clever things and intelligently design things, deriving complexity from original simplicity.

Complexity cannot be simply "magicked" into existence. You are not allowed just to postulate primordial complexity as your starting point. That's not science; that's cheating. Complexity, design, intelligence, purpose, goals: these things come late into the universe. They may have come many times into the universe, but they come after a long period of development, a long period of apprenticeship, of evolution. They cannot be imported early into your explanations because they raise more questions than they answer.

Supernatural explanations are not explanations at all. They are cowardly evasions of the obligation to explain, and I regard the obligation to explain as one of the highest obligations to which our species can aspire.

Thank you very much.

BACTERIAL MOTOR. ORIGIN UNKNOWN.

AN ARTIST'S VIEW OF THE FIRST MULTIPLANETARY SYSTEM DISCOVERED WITH THREE NEPTUNE-MASS PLANETS. THE HD 69830 SYSTEM IS ALSO REMARKABLE, BEING THE HOST OF A PROMINENT ROTATING DISC OF DUST AND ROCKS DETECTED IN THE INFRA-RED WAVELENGTHS BY THE SPITZER SATELLITE. CREDIT: LOVIS ET AL. 2009; EUROPEAN SOUTHERN OBSERVATORY.

MICHEL MAYOR

Extrasolar Planets in the Galaxy

Swiss astrophysicist Michel G. E. Mayor was born in Lausanne on January 12, 1942. He is an emeritus professor at the University of Geneva's Department of Astronomy, and still remains active in many areas of research. Mayor catapulted to great fame in 1995 when he and colleague Didier Queloz discovered the first extrasolar planet, 51 Pegasi b, orbiting a Sun-like star.

Mayor was awarded the Swiss Marcel Benoist Prize in recognition of his work and its significance for human life. In 2000, he was awarded the Balzan Prize and in 2004 he received the Albert Einstein Medal. In 2005, he was awarded the Shaw Prize in Astronomy. His team is responsible for finding about half of the exoplanets discovered to date using the Doppler technique.

He is a principal investigator of the HARPS consortium planet search survey, which has discovered a growing population of super-Earths and Neptune-like low-mass planets. Along with his colleagues Garik Israelian and Nuno Santos, Mayor was awarded the 2010 Ambartsumian Prize for Astrophysics.

MICHEL MAYOR AT STARMUS.

Even during antiquity, Greek philosophers discussed the question of the "plurality of worlds" in the universe as well as the possibility of the "plurality of inhabited worlds." More than 20 centuries ago, the Greek philosopher Epicurus expressed his deep feeling that other worlds should exist in infinite numbers in the universe.

Across the last two millennia, that question remained a philosophical discussion. More recently, the supposed existence of other worlds with living species has been at the root of numerous fictional works published during the 20th century. However, it's interesting to notice that prior to 1940, astronomers leaned toward extremely low estimates of the number of planetary systems existing in the Milky Way Galaxy: something between zero and a few. This estimation is fascinating, as the number of stars in our galaxy is larger than one hundred billion. That very pessimistic number was the result of the then-favored formation scenario of planetary systems proposed by Sir James Jeans. This scenario required a very rare event in order to form the gaseous nebulae needed to allow planetary formation to occur.

In Jeans' scenario, a dynamical interaction of very close stellar flybys was considered the main cause leading to the formation of gaseous nebulae. Such a close encounter of two stars can be easily shown to be extremely rare. With the abandon of Jeans' scenario in the 1940s, the old paradigm of planetary formation drastically changed and, immediately, the estimated number of possible planetary systems in the Milky Way jumped to billions.

In the modern view, the origin of the nebula needed to start the formation of planets is no longer the result of an incredibly improbable close encounter of two stars, but the result of the stellar formation mechanism itself. During the collapse of a turbulent and inhomogeneous molecular cloud, perturbations in the density are at the origin of stars that naturally become surrounded by rapidly rotating disks of gas and dust particles, forming a so-called accretion disk.

The existence of these disks, deduced from theoretical arguments, was first detected by the infrared radiation emitted by their dust. A beautiful confirmation of the omnipresent existence of these accretion disks was obtained by the Hubble Space Telescope in 1995. A large majority of young stars seen in front of the Orion molecular cloud exhibit a small dark halo, the dusty component of the accretion disks absorbing the diffuse luminosity of the nebula.

The most widely accepted mechanism of planetary formation was proposed by Russian astronomer Victor Safronov in 1969. In this model, coalescing dust in the disk leads to a slow formation of planetesimals that grow in mass and eventually

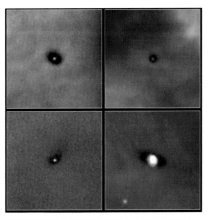

YOUNG STARS SEEN IN FRONT OF THE ORION NEBULA. THE HUGE MAJORITY OF THESE YOUNG STARS HAVE A FAST ROTATING DISC OF GAS AND DUST, HERE SEEN DARK AS THEY ABSORB THE LIGHT OF THE NEBULA. CREDIT: NASA, O'DELL AND MCCAUGHREAN, 1995.

A SMALL FRAGMENT OF THE INNER REGION OF THE MILKY WAY GALAXY, GIVING AN IDEA OF THE RICHNESS OF STARS IN THAT SYSTEM. HOW MANY PLANETARY SYSTEMS ARE HOSTED BY THESE STARS? CREDIT: EUROPEAN SOUTHERN OBSERVATORY.

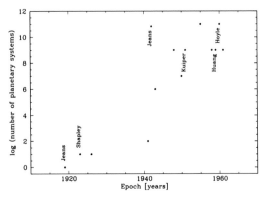

IDEAS ON PLANETARY FORMATION MECHANISMS HAVE DRASTICALLY CHANGED DURING THE 20TH CENTURY. READING THE PAST SCIENTIFIC LITERATURE, IT IS POSSIBLE TO APPRECIATE THE CHANGE OF PARADIGM THAT APPEARED IN THE MIDDLE OF THE LAST CENTURY. IT IS ONLY AFTER THE FORTIES THAT THE ASTRONOMICAL COMMUNITY ADMITTED THE POSSIBILITY OF A VERY HIGH FREQUENCY OF PLANETARY SYSTEMS. (DATA FROM DICK, 2001.)

create low-mass, rocky planets. In the regions of the disk distant enough from the star, the presence of ice particles makes the formation process more efficient and creates what will eventually become planetary cores. When one of these protoplanetary cores achieves a mass equivalent to about 10 times the mass of Earth, it causes a fast gravitational collapse of gas in the surrounding accretion disk, which completes the formation of a gaseous giant planet similar to Jupiter in our solar system.

That last phase of collapse can only appear during the few million years corresponding to the lifetime of the accretion disk. This means that the formation of massive planets can only take place if the initial growth of the accretion of ice particles and planetesimals is fast enough compared to the lifetime of the accretion disk.

Interestingly, this so-called core-collapse scenario was proposed only some 40 years ago. Following the scenario, planetary systems are direct byproducts of stellar formation and we can immediately expect that the vast majority of stars should host planetary systems. If we should have a very high occurrence of planets, the mass of these planets will vary from star to star. The most massive planets, gaseous giants, should be the least frequently encountered. The semi-major axis of Jovian planet orbits (at least at the epoch of formation) cannot be smaller than about five astronomical units (five times the distance between Earth and the Sun), the distance at which ice particles cease to sublimate and can therefore be used as building blocks. Such a semi-major axis corresponds approximately to an orbital period of 10 years.

Despite the expected high occurrence rate of planetary systems, directly detecting planets using imaging techniques on the closest stars is difficult, as the luminosity of a star is typically one billion times greater than the luminosity of a planet. Searching for a possible exoplanetary system, we are completely dazzled by the star's light. This is why all the first detections of exoplanets were accomplished using indirect techniques.

Two gravitationally bound objects show motions relative to the center of gravity of the system. The star, being much more massive than the planet, has an orbit that shows only a very small wobble. This stellar velocity along the line of sight (the radial velocity) will nonetheless exhibit small periodic variations, which can be measured. Analyzing stellar spectra from a very stable spectrograph reveals these small velocity variations thanks to the Doppler effect. The study of these velocity variations enables astronomers to determine a planet's orbital period, orbital eccentricity, and an approximation of its mass, from the amplitude of the signal.

In 1994, along with astronomer Didier Queloz, I initiated a systematic search at the Haute-Provence Observatory in the south of France to attempt to detect potential very low mass companions orbiting solar-type stars. At that time, we had an interest both for possible massive planets as well as for the suspected rare brown dwarfs. A brown dwarf is a very low mass star without nuclear reactions in its core. The lightest brown dwarfs could be just a few times more massive than Jupiter.

The mass range of brown dwarfs (which are believed to form, like stars, from the gravitational collapse of a cloud of interstellar matter) could overlap the domain of the most massive planets (which are supposed to form by the aforementioned accretion of dust and ice particles in an accretion disk). We selected a stellar sample of 142 solar-type stars chosen among stars in the solar vicinity under the condition that they were not known to be part of a double star system. We made the search using the new spectrograph (ELODIE) of the Haute-Provence Observatory. Every two months, seven observing nights with the 1.93-meter telescope were allocated to our program.

After only a few months, in the late autumn of 1994, we detected the first hint of a periodic variation in the velocity of one of the measured stars. We found a period as short as 4.2 days and yielded an estimated mass close to half that of Jupiter. A Jovian planet on such a short period, orbiting its solar-type host star at a distance of only 5 percent the separation between the Sun and Earth, appeared to be in serious contradiction with the predicted core-collapse scenario. To reject other possible physical interpretations of our observations, we chose to postpone the announcement of that incredible object by one year.

New observations at the beginning of the following observing season confirmed the stability of the period, of its amplitude and of the phase of the velocity variation of 51 Pegasi. The evidence was sufficient to be convinced that the observed velocity variation was caused by the gravitational pull of an orbiting planet!

The short period of the Jovian planet orbiting 51 Pegasi was puzzling. Soon after the announcement of the discovery of that first extrasolar planet in 1995, the short period dilemma was explained by the team of Lin, Richardson, and Bodenheimer. During the lifetime of the accretion disk, they postulated, the gravitational interaction of the young planet with the disk can induce a very efficient shrinking of the orbital semi-major axis, leading to very short orbital periods. This so-called orbital migration of planets is a key process needed to understand the amazing diversity in the orbital characteristics of exoplanets.

Since that first discovery, the number of detected planets has increased continuously. By the end of 2013, now, more than 1,000 exoplanets have well-characterized orbits. During the last 19 years, not only did we reach impressive numbers of new planets, but thanks to the design of more stable and sensitive spectrographs, we also had the possibility to extend our search to the domain of much less massive planets. A sensitivity gain larger than a factor of 100 has been achieved since the discovery of the planet orbiting 51 Pegasi.

Several gaseous giant planets have been detected in the years following the discovery of 51 Pegasi. These detections have revealed an amazing variety in the structure of exoplanetary systems. First, orbital periods are sometimes shorter than one day. Second, most gas giant planets with periods larger than a few months have quite large orbital eccentricities. In some cases, we can measure extreme eccentricities (for example the eccentricity of HD 80606 b is 0.93). Third, the maximum mass observed for exoplanets is not clearly established. A few planets hosted by solar-type stars have masses as large as 15 or maybe 20 times the mass of Jupiter.

Obviously, some ambiguity exists on the exact status of the rare very massive planets, as in this mass range we have an overlap with brown dwarfs. The lower limit for a brown dwarf formed by fragmentation of a collapsing cloud is probably of a few Jupiter masses. The most recent statistics indicate that 14 percent of solar-type stars host at least one gas giant planet (with a mass greater than 50 Earth masses and orbital period smaller than 10 years). Among Sun-like stars, about one star in seven is orbited by a gaseous planet in the range of above-mentioned characteristics.

A strong correlation of that rate has been observed with a star's metallicity. The stars with the highest concentration of heavy chemical elements in their atmospheres (three times the solar value) have one chance in four to be the host of a planetary system that includes a gaseous planet. At the opposite end of things, the occurrence rate decreases to about 5 percent for stars having only a third of the solar heavy-element abundance.

The development of spectrographs with an increased stability and sensitivity has allowed the detection of planets with much smaller masses. For example, the HARPS spectrograph installed at La Silla Observatory in Chile has demonstrated the capability to measure stellar radial velocities with a precision better than 50 centimeters per second. We can now detect a stellar wobble comparable to the velocity of a walking pedestrian! The direct consequence of that better precision is the capacity to detect and determine the statistical properties of planets with masses comparable to Neptune's, or smaller.

The important search for exoplanets carried out at La Silla with the HARPS spectrograph led to the discovery of an impressive population of compact systems composed with low mass planets. The characteristics of that planetary population are amazing. About 50 percent of solar type stars have planetary systems with

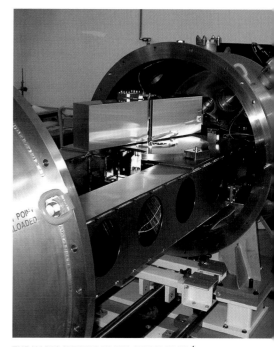

THE HARPS SPECTROGRAPH AT THE COUDÉ FOCUS OF THE 3.6M TELESCOPE AT LA SILLA OBSERVATORY IS PRESENTLY THE MOST PRECISE INSTRUMENT TO DETECT EXTRASOLAR PLANETS. ITS PRECISION ALREADY ALLOWED THE DISCOVERY AND CHARACTERIZATION OF THE HUGE POPULATION OF SUPER-EARTHS AND NEPTUNE-MASS PLANETS HOSTED BY SOLAR-TYPE STARS. CREDIT: MAYOR ET AL. 2003; EUROPEAN SOUTHERN OBSERVATORY.

low-mass planets on tight orbits, meaning less than 30 Earth masses and periods less than 50 days. (Mercury, by comparison, has an 88-day orbit.) More than 70 percent of these systems are multiplanetary. These planetary systems include Neptune-mass planets and planets with masses in the range of 1 to 10 Earth masses. (Planets in that range of masses have been called super-Earths). Strangely enough, these extremely frequent super-Earths are not represented in our own solar system and as such constitute a new planetary class.

I will mention a few enigmatic objects among that class. HD 69830, discovered in 2006, was the first system composed of three Neptune-mass planets. HD 40307, announced in 2009, was the first with three super-Earths. Already, today, a few planets with masses smaller than twice Earth's mass have been detected in the frame of the HARPS survey. HD 10180 was detected in 2011, a multiplanetary system with seven planets, most of them being super-Earths or Neptune-mass planets.

Now I'd like to describe the enormous contribution of planetary transits to the study of exoplanets. But already, we can mention the beautiful confirmation by the space mission Kepler of the existence of that rich population of very low mass planets with close orbits

Among these planets with close orbits, the probability of planetary transits is sufficiently large (a few percent) to allow the discovery of planets "simply" by searching for a periodic dimming of stars. If a planet similar to Jupiter passes in front of a solar-type star, we can observe a periodic dip in the stellar luminosity of about one percent — a transit. If an Earth-analog transits in front of a similar star, the dip will only be 0.01 percent. Several systematic searches are being carried out from ground-based telescopes as well as from two dedicated space missions (CoRoT and Kepler).

Among recent highlights was the first detection of a transit by an exoplanet. In 1999, two teams independently detected an exoplanet with a mass typical of a Jovian planet hosted by the solar-type star HD 209458. Discovered using the Doppler technique and with an orbital period of 3.5 days, this planet was a good candidate for a planetary transit search. Using the ephemeris determined by the radial velocity measurements, it was possible to predict the time of a potential transit if our line of sight were close enough to the orbital plane.

At the exact predicted time, during the night of September 9, 1999, the luminosity of the star HD 209458 decreased by a little more than 1 percent. The same phenomenon was also observed seven days later (two orbital periods later). The drop of stellar luminosity is obviously proportional to the size of the planet. Knowing the planetary mass from spectroscopic measurements and the diameter of the planet from the change in luminosity during the transit, we had the opportunity to estimate the mean density of the orbiting object. With a density of 0.3 gram per cubic centimeter, astronomers confirmed this transit object as a gaseous giant planet. For the last skeptics, this became the real proof than these strange "hot Jupiters" were indeed planets.

Following this first detection, several other transiting planets of Jovian masses and radii have been measured from ground-based observatories. However, Earth's atmosphere prevents a systematic search for very small transiting planets like those Neptune-mass or super-Earth planets. To detect them, we have to go into space. A first space mission, designed to study the acoustic modes from stars as well as planetary transits, was built and launched by the French Space Agency, CNES. As part of the results of this mission, we can point to the discovery of the transiting planet CoRoT-7b. With a period as short as 0.86 days, a radius of only 1.7 Earth-radii, and a mass of about 5 Earth masses, this planet is the first super-Earth for which it was possible to estimate a density. Within the error bars, the density is typical of a rocky planet. But its presence so close to its star means we should have a planet with a surface of melted silicates, at least on the hemisphere of the planet facing the star (the planet's rotation is expected to be synchronized with the orbital period).

When a planet transits in front of its host star, the luminosity of a small fraction of the stellar disk gets blocked. As the star rotates, a transiting planet will hide part of the velocity of the star and induce a small anomaly of its observed velocity. The detailed analysis of that anomaly (the so-called Rossiter-McLaughlin effect) provides an estimation of the angle between the orbital plane and the stellar equatorial plane. The orbital migration of a Jovian planet due to its gravitational interaction with the accretion disk at the time of planetary formation will most probably keep coplanarity between the two above-mentioned planes. At the beginning, the analysis of several Rossiter-McLaughlin anomalies appeared to confirm this expectation. But more recently, astronomers have found several planets with their orbital planes considerably inclined to the stellar equatorial plane. Worse yet, a number of planets have been even found on retrograde orbits with the planet rotating in the opposite direction to the stellar rotation!

These observations indicate that the migration expected from the interaction with the accretion disk is certainly not the key effect that explains "hot Jupiters." The physical mechanisms involved to explain the diversity of planetary system structures appear to be quite complex.

Planetary masses and radii can be estimated for transiting planets. Obviously, the relationship between radius and mass depends on the internal composition of each planet. Observations of transiting planets exhibit an amazing diversity of planetary internal structures. For example, we can notice the large scatter in the radii of planets having a few Earth masses. Clearly, not all of these objects are rocky planets. The internal composition of a planet is a fossil trace of its formation history and evolution. The accretion of ice particles or/and dust particles is linked to the migration track. When the shrinking of its orbit leads a low mass planet to be close to its star, we have to consider the possible evaporation of volatiles.

As a nice example of this complex game, we could think of a planet forming at a rather large distance of the star by the accretion of ice grains. If the accretion phase cannot form a core massive enough to gravitationally accrete the gas of the disk before the end of its life, the planet will end its formation phase as an icy planet, something similar to Uranus or Neptune in our solar system. If we combine this scenario with a strong orbital migration, we are at risk to have an icy planet close enough to the star to have its ices melted and end up as an "ocean planet." Those may be a frequent type of planet in the universe, while not existing in our solar system!

The careful analysis of spectra obtained while the planet transits compared to spectra taken out of transit have already provided lots of information about the composition of planetary atmospheres and — there, too — an impressive diversity.

It is impossible to close this talk without citing the beautiful results achieved by NASA's space mission Kepler. With a much larger aperture compared to its precursor, the CoRoT mission, Kepler has already identified more than 2,000 candidate planetary systems. The highlights of this harvest are the discovery of circumbinary planets (planets having an orbit external to a double star), planets with radii smaller than an Earth radius, and perhaps the mightily interesting multiplanetary transits. Several hundred planetary systems have been measured with several planets transiting the same star. Up to six planets have been detected hosted by the same star.

The comparison of the distribution of multitransiting planets with the statistics from Doppler detections allows an estimation of mutual inclinations of the various orbital planes. The result (within 1 degree) indicates the incredible coplanarity of these systems, a characteristic yet to be understood when we try to study the formation and evolution of these systems. The Kepler field on the sky corresponds to a rather narrow beam, with most of their stars being rather unfortunately faint. Kepler permits the determination of the planetary radii, but the physical interpretation of this rich data would be much enhanced if we could measure the mass of

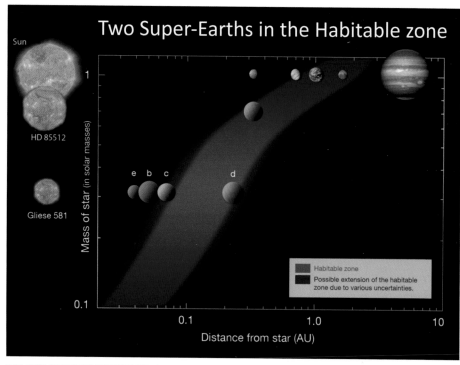

Two Super-Earths in the Habitable zone

THE BLUE STRIP IN THE FIGURE INDICATES THE REGION WHERE LIQUID WATER COULD EXIST ON THE SURFACE OF A ROCKY PLANET. THAT REGION DEPENDS ON STELLAR MASS AS THE STELLAR LUMINOSITY ITSELF IS STRONGLY DECREASING WITH THE MASS OF THE STARS. THE POSITIONS OF SOLAR-SYSTEM PLANETS AS WELL AS PLANETS OF GLIESE 581 AND HD 85512 SYSTEMS ARE INDICATED. THIS PLOT ILLUSTRATES THE PRESENT CAPABILITY OF THE HARPS SPECTROGRAPH TO DETECT PLANETS OF A FEW EARTH-MASSES IN THE SO-CALLED "HABITABLE ZONE". CREDIT: DIAGRAM KINDLY PROVIDED BY FRANCK SELSIS.

these planets.

The HARPS spectrograph installed at La Palma Observatory in April 2012 has already contributed to knowledge about the smallest confirmed planet detected by Kepler. Kepler 78b is indeed a planet similar to Earth with 1.86 Earth masses and a radius of 1.16 Earths. Its mean density implies a composition of iron and rock. The planet is a true hell, as its distance from its host star is as small as 0.0089 AU.

The flood of data acquired in the last 19 years will continue to contribute to our understanding of the physics of planetary system formation and in particular of our own solar system. However, we cannot ignore the most ambitious long-term challenge: the search for life in other places in the universe. Certainly this vertiginous question could already concern several places in the solar system as the planet Mars or the planetary moons Europa and Enceladus. But this important aspect will not be part of our present discussion. Is it realistic to detect life signatures on extrasolar planets?

A first step is to identify planets with suitable characteristics of the complex chemistry involved in the development of living organisms. Rocky planets located in the so-called "habitable zone" of their host stars are considered promising targets for future searches looking for life outside the solar system. A habitable zone corresponds to the stellar distance where liquid water could exist at the surface of a planet. This condition is certainly not sufficient to allow the development of life. For example, the mass of the planet is also critical, as a planet that's too small will not prevent the evaporation of its atmosphere. An orbital eccentricity that's too large is also an adverse condition, as the temperature in the atmosphere of the planet would fluctuate too wildly.

Other conditions probably have to be added, such as plate tectonics, magnetic fields, the absence of tidal synchronization, etc. However, it is already possible to identify planets with at least the minimum requirements for living chemistry — liquid water on their surfaces, masses sufficient to prevent the loss of their atmospheres, and orbits that aren't too eccentric. To these physical conditions, we have to add an observational condition. For any experiment designed to search for the signatures of life in planetary atmospheres, we must select host stars as close by as possible. Keeping in mind the huge luminosity ratio between the planet and the star, to have a chance to measure a planetary spectrum, the angular distance between the planet and its host star can't be too small. In addition, to get a well-defined spectrum, we need to collect enough photons issued from the planetary atmosphere. These conditions are only possible for planetary systems at limited distances, of the order of 50 light-years or less.

The number of transiting Earth twins at such close distances is probably quite limited. As all the ambitious space astrometric missions have been abandoned, the only technique with the capability to detect potentially habitable planets at close distances is Doppler spectroscopy. However, we are facing difficulties trying to detect stellar radial velocity wobbles as small as a fraction of a meter per second embedded in the intrinsic stellar variability. This intrinsic jitter, resulting from magnetic cycles, is of the order of 1 meter per second for the quietest stars. However, it could easily be 10 times larger for active stars. Despite that difficulty, already the HARPS spectrograph has allowed the detection of three super-Earths in their star's habitable zone — Gliese 581d, a planet of seven Earth masses hosted by a star of about one third of the mass of the Sun; HD 85512b, a planet of 3.6 Earth masses orbiting a star having a mass of 75 percent of the solar mass; and Gliese 667Cc, a planet of 4.3 Earth masses also orbiting a low-mass star at the bottom of the main sequence.

These early detections have been made because low mass stars are much less luminous compared to the Sun. As the habitable zone is closer to the star, the reflex motion due to the tiny planet is easier to detect. The low mass of the star is also a favorable parameter. We are still not at the level needed to detect a real Earth twin, but astronomers are quite confident that this goal is feasible. It's interesting to notice that these planets are at very limited distances from the solar system.

It's still difficult to estimate the occurrence of Earth twins in the habitable zones of solar-type stars. For the moment, the divergent values found in the literature are a good indication of our ignorance. If we consider estimates from the core-collapse scenarios as developed by different teams, low mass planets should be extremely frequent.

We are finding planets in many, many places. But we have only just begun.

7 OF 42 OF THE 6.1M ANTENNAS OF THE ALLEN TELESCOPE ARRAY AT THE HAT CREEK RADIO OBSERVATORY. CREDIT: SETH SHOSTAK.

LEFT PANEL: THE INEXPENSIVE 72" PRIMARY AND 36" SECONDARY MIRRORS OF HARVARD'S OSETI PROJECT AND SOME OF ITS CREATORS AND ELECTRONICS.
RIGHT PANEL: SHELLEY WRIGHT AND THE LICK OSETI INSTRUMENT THAT SHE BUILT. CREDIT: PAUL HOROWITZ AND SETH SHOSTAK..

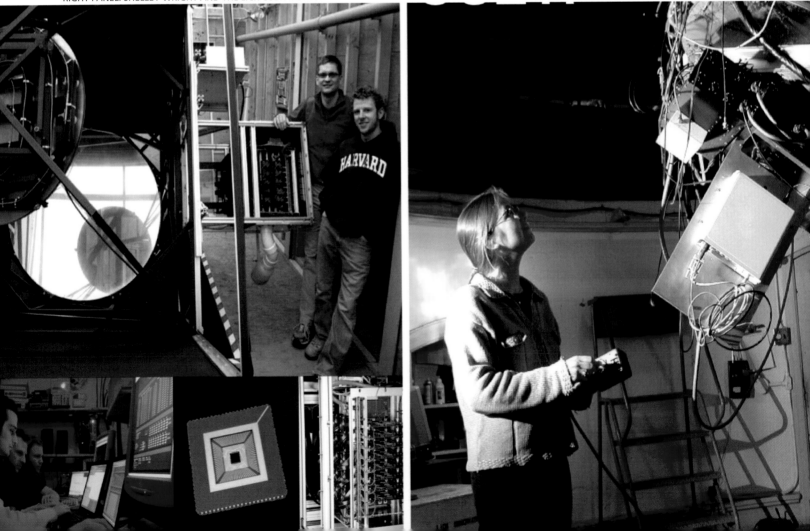

JILL TARTER

Intelligent Life in the Universe: Is Anybody Out There?

American astronomer Jill Cornell Tarter was born January 16, 1944, and is director of the SETI Institute in Mountain View, California. SETI, the search for extraterrestrial intelligence, is a field now is its current progressive state largely due to Tarter and her colleagues.

Tarter holds the Bernard M. Oliver Chair for SETI and is a Fellow of the American Association for the Advancement of Science and the California Academy of Sciences. In 2004, she was named one of the "100 most influential people in the world" by Time Magazine. She was awarded the Telluride Tech Festival Award of Technology (2001), the Carl Sagan Prize for Science Popularization (2005) and the 2009 TED Prize.

Tarter's astronomical work is described in Carl Sagan's novel Contact. In the film version of Contact, the protagonist, Ellie Arroway — a character "largely based" on Tarter — is played by Jodie Foster. Tarter has spoken around the world and has published dozens of articles about SETI to engage humans across the planet in this important search and to encourage young people (especially young women) to pursue careers in science, engineering and technology.

JILL TARTER AT STARMUS.

For many millennia, humans have been on a journey of discovery, seeking answers. Answers to questions about what is, and what ought to be. About who we are, why we are, and, of course, who else there might be.

Along the road, as part of our journey we've learned that our universe is vast. Our Sun is one of 400 billion stars in the Milky Way, which itself is one of 100 billion or more galaxies in our observable universe. And you've already heard from previous speakers that this wonderful playground for astronomers, these gorgeous objects we image in the sky and the physics that we have been unveiling as we study the cosmos, actually represent only about 4 percent of the total mass-energy of the universe. The other 96 percent consists of dark matter and dark energy – dark because we don't yet know what they are. Undaunted, we continue our journey.

Astronomers should be pretty humble people — although I haven't met any yet who are! So we blithely continue to ponder what we can observe, and we discuss dark energy and dark matter. "Dark" just means that we haven't a clue. That means that there are challenges, new things to be found out about the universe and potentially, one of those things is that we don't really understand gravity. In later presentations George Smoot and others will be talking about some of these pieces of the universe that we don't understand. I will concentrate on our attempts to seek answers to the question of whether or not we are alone in the parts of the cosmos we think we understand.

About 50 years ago, our journey of discovery took a technological turn and began using some new tools from radio astronomy. Frank Drake did the first SETI — search for extraterrestrial intelligence — radio search of two nearby stars, Epsilon Eridani and Tau Ceti. Back in 1960, Drake's Project Ozma observed these stars for a few hundred hours, using the Tatel Telescope of the National Radio Astronomy Observatory in Greenbank, West Virginia. Frank didn't find any evidence of extra-terrestrial technology; nevertheless, he learned something very important from a passing airplane. Sometimes terrestrial technology can seriously interfere with the search for extraterrestrial technology.

Today, SETI is a legitimate scientific exploration. Throughout previous millennia we've been asking the priests, the philosophers, the poets, the shamans, whoever we thought was wise: What should we believe about life beyond this planet? As a young graduate student, the thing that got me interested in SETI, and got me hooked for a lifetime, was the fact that I/we/you live in the first generation of humans who can in fact do an experiment to answer that old question, rather than resort to someone's belief system to find the answer. And so at the SETI Institute, what we're trying to do is substitute the verb "to believe" for the verb "to explore," and systematically look for evidence of someone else's technology. Although we call it the search for extraterrestrial intelligence the pragmatic reality is that technology is our proxy. We don't know how to find intelligence at a distance, so we're looking for evidence of distant technology.

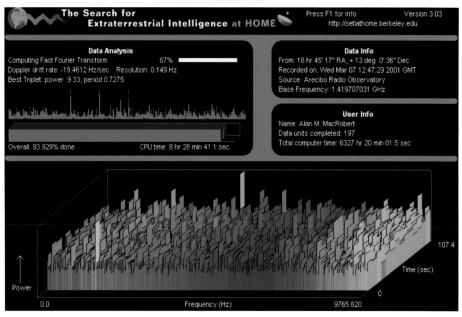

SCREEN SAVER FROM SETI@HOME. CREDIT: DAN WERTHIMER.

We now conduct SETI at optical wavelengths as well as the radio explorations that Frank Drake started in 1960. At optical wavelengths we're looking for very powerful, very bright, very short pulses of light — pulses that last only a nanosecond or so. Nature doesn't seem to be able to do that, but terrestrial technologies can do it with pulsed lasers and large telescopes. We could make very detectable signals of this type, even with our crude, very young, technology. With current fast, photon-counting diodes and meter-class telescopes as receivers, optical SETI observing projects could detect a petawatt laser focused by a 10-meter mirror at a distance of 1,000 light-years.

Lawrence Livermore has many such high-power lasers and our astronomers have built multiple 10-m class mirrors, so an advanced technology doesn't have to be very much more advanced than we are to be able to produce such detectable signals. We will not know if they choose to devote the necessary resources to transmitting signals unless we look. The Harvard University OSETI sky survey is systematically scanning 80 percent of the sky visible from Massachusetts, and OSETI instruments at other university observatories such as Leuschner and Lick in northern California and the University of Western Sydney in Australia are targeting individual stars looking for laser pulses.

We're also continuing with the radio searches that Frank Drake pioneered. We're using large scientific telescopes around the world. UC-Berkeley has a project called "SETI@home." It has been recording data at the Arecibo Observatory and allowing the volunteers around the world to provide their spare computing cycles to look for signals. It's been extraordinarily successful and is perhaps the best-known example of distributed computing. SETI@home pioneered the idea of individuals performing service computing in aid of scientific research, and today there are many different projects for users to choose from.

In addition to using telescopes belonging to scientific organizations, we are also now building our own radio telescope, specifically designed to do SETI and radio astronomy 24/7. This is the Allen Telescope Array, built in northern California. Allen refers to Paul Allen, the cofounder of Microsoft, who was brave enough to take a risk to fund all of the technology development and innovation that it took to create this telescope, and he has also funded the first phase of the construction with 42 antennas. From the beginning, Mr. Allen said that he wants partners in order to grow this telescope out to its full size of 350 antennas. We are actively looking for these partners. The nice thing about this ATA telescope, which is the first time we've ever built an LNSD — a Large Number of Small Dishes—array, is that you can begin to use it before it is finished. While we have only a small fraction of the eventual collecting area, the ATA has taken these small dishes of aluminium and steel and hooked them together with silicon-based digital processors in a way that is unique.

For the first time at the ATA, we have created a pan-chromatic, wide-field, snapshot radio camera. Because it is made from small dishes and is instrumented with innovative RF equipment that can receive sky signals over the entire frequency range from 0.5 GHz to 10 GHz at once, and because the digital signal processing backends consist of multiple spectral-imaging correlators, and beam formers with lots of spectral channels that can be used simultaneously, the ATA is an incredible panchromatic radio camera of a type that has never been possible before. Given the philanthropic support to grow the ATA out to 350 dishes, this telescope will improve in its sensitivity because it will have much more collecting area. It will also improve over time because it's really just a Moore's Law machine. While the ATA analog systems can provide data at all frequencies from 0.5 to 10 GHZ, the digital backends can swallow only a fraction of that bandwidth at any one time. Faster computing is a key to expansion. In fact we can get better every day by building better computer back ends for this telescope.

And LNSD is turning out to be an incredibly good idea if you want to build a large telescope at a minimum cost. A decade or two from now, another telescope is going to be sprouting like metal mushrooms in the deserts of either South Africa or Western Australia. The Square Kilometer Array (SKA) is an international project to build a telescope with a million square meters of collecting area. And we hope that, when the SKA gets on the air, it will take over from what we've been doing with the Allen Telescope Array and allow us to look even further into space for weaker signals.

Today, what we can do in our current program on the Allen Telescope Array, is detect a signal that is 2×10^{13} watts of effective isotropic radiated power. That effective power corresponds to the 2-megawatt transmitter that's currently on the Arecibo telescope, focused by that big thousand-foot dish. And we could detect signals that strong up to a thousand light-years away. That's where we are today and in the future we'll do bigger, better, faster, more sensitive searches. And we will enlarge the searches to include more types of signals, as we get smarter and our computers get faster.

From my point of view, one shared with my astronomical colleagues, we have the real privilege of understanding that we live on a fragile island of life in a universe that is full of possibilities. That's a perspective that I think we need to share with the world in order to help people to understand their cosmic origins and their commonality.

Obviously, one of those possibilities is other planets around other stars; other fragile islands of life. We've heard a little today and we'll hear much more tomorrow about how you find such planets. One way is to measure the reflex action that the tiny planet has on its big star. It tugs it back and forth on the sky just a little bit. More than 700 planets have been found and confirmed on the ground by watching the very tiny Doppler shifts in their stars' absorption spectra that can be interpreted as the induced motions of the stars, and by microlensing (another technique, that para-doxically never even sees the star, much less the planet). Prior to 1995, planets were

ARTIST'S CONCEPT OF MID-FREQUENCY DISHES WITHIN THE CORE OF THE FUTURE SQUARE KILOMETER ARRAY. THE OFFSET-GREGORIAN OPTICS OF THESE SMALL DISHES RESEMBLES THE ATA. CREDIT: SKA.

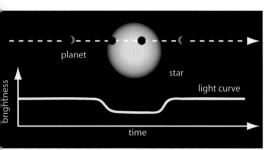

ILLUSTRATION OF THE REDUCTION OF
STELLAR FLUX DURING A TRANSIT EVENT BY
AND ORBITING PLANET. CREDIT: NASA.

a good theory, but the detection of 51 Pegasi changed everything. Today there is growing statistical evidence that the number of planets exceeds the number of stars — every star has at least one planet! Exoplanets have been one of the game changers that we've recently encountered.

The planets detected with ground-based telescopes are mostly massive planets, and many of them are in short-period orbits, because that's what instruments on ground-based telescopes find best. The job of the Kepler spacecraft, launched in 2009, is to find Earth-sized planets. Hopefully Earth-sized planets around a star something like the Sun, and at the right distance; the "Goldilocks zone" where there might be liquid water on the surface. We designate these as habitable planets.

Kepler works by detecting the transit of a planet across the disk of the star. When viewed by Kepler, some planets orbiting some stars will be properly aligned so that they pass in front of the star and in so doing will block a little bit of the star's light. If you are watching continuously, then for several hours you will be able to tell that the star has gotten dimmer, because of the shadow cast by the planet. This illustration makes transit detection look really easy, but it isn't. Jupiter passing in front of the Sun blocks 1 percent of the light from the Sun. Earth passing in front of the Sun blocks one part in one hundred thousand of the Sun's light. So Kepler requires really precise instrumentation, very accurate CCD movie cameras. Also Kepler has to look at a lot of stars simultaneously, because not all planets are going to be properly aligned to produce a transit.

Kepler looks where stars live, near the plane of the Milky Way Galaxy. Kepler stares at a hundred square degrees of the sky continuously. A hundred square degrees is 1/400th of the sky. To appreciate how big that is, put your arm up, straight up and the size of your hand is about a hundred square degrees. That's how much of the sky Kepler's looking at. Within that area Kepler is monitoring 170,000 stars. Those white rectangles in the diagram represent the 42 sensitive CCD arrays. Kepler's cameras are like your cell phone cameras, except that as opposed to 3 or 10 megapixels Kepler's cameras have 95,617,600 pixels. And they work! The first light image from Kepler, after the protective cover was removed from the lens, displayed a field of 4.5 million stars above the sensitivity limit of the CCDs. Kepler has been staring at 170,000 of those stars for a little over two years now. As the bright-colored circles in this illustration show, some of them actually have exoplanet candidates orbiting them.

As of February 1, 2011, based on only two quarters of data, the Kepler mission announced that they had found 1,235 candidate exoplants. Some 184 of them are giants, the size of Jupiter or greater. The bulk of them, 662, are the size of Neptune. There are 288 exoplanet candidates from Kepler that are a size that we don't have in our own solar system. They're bigger than Earth; these super-Earths are going to be fantastic to study, because they will help us learn a lot about how planets formed, and what they are made from. And lastly, there are 68 planets the size of Earth. Of those 1,235 planets, 54 are at the right distance from their stars to be potentially habitable, in the sense that they could have liquid water on their surfaces.

Jason Rowe of the Kepler science team has created a "Corn Cob" diagram to emphasize the differences among the Kepler systems and highlight the difficulties and rewards of the transit detection technique. The important details do not reproduce well in a small printed image, so I urge you to explore it at http://kepler.nasa.gov/files/mws/KeplerCandidates2326SunsRowe10000px.jpg.

In this illustration, Jason represents the stars by the big disks whose sizes and colors indicate their correct relative size and temperatures. Also shown is an image for the Sun, as comparison. The shadows of planets depicted in this figure are the relative sizes of the planets that have been detected in transit. Kepler is an amazing instrument and it's going to be showing us an enormous number of different ways to form planetary systems. To appreciate the difficulty of transit detection, look at an enlarged illustration of the solar disk — the big spot is Jupiter, the almost invisible spot is what Earth's transit would look like if we were in Kepler's field of view. It is really hard to overestimate how much having the ability to study this treasure trove of all these different kinds of planetary systems is revolutionizing what we think about the real world of planet formation.

I'm sure that many of you are familiar with a mechanical orrery. These elegant and beautifully crafted toys were the darlings of 18th-century natural philosophers; you turn the crank and all the planets and the moons go around with perfect order, illustrating Kepler's laws. I think that these lovely contraptions helped seduce us into thinking that everywhere else this same simple order was going to prevail. We embraced this unconscious bias before we actually got into the planet-hunting business. Al Cameron and others have constructed beautiful numerical models that told us that if planetary systems form at all, they all form with pretty much circular orbits, in a plane, the little guys (the rocky guys) on the inside, the big gas giants on the outside. Elsewhere, things would be pretty nice and uniform, just as they are in our own solar system.

Well, the real-world Kepler orrery of multiple planet systems isn't uniform at all. You can see it illustrated at http://kepler.nasa.gov/images/videos/orrery.mov. There are systems there that look nothing like our worlds! When I marvel at this animation, I think of the line in Contact when Jodie Foster says, "They should have sent a poet." We really didn't have any idea of the richness and diversity among planetary systems in the real world, and surely there is more to come. The Kepler orrery just emphasises how hard it is to make generalizations from a sample of one, and how we can fool ourselves concerning what we think we know.

Knowing the distances of the Kepler stars, knowing the size of that hundred degree square view, knowing the distribution of the general stellar population in the galaxy, allows us to predict from these early results that there will be something like 50 billion planets in the Milky Way alone, and 500 million of them could be habitable in the liquid-water sense. So this is a perfect time to be asking the scientific question, "Are we alone?" We now have many worlds to explore.

Most of my colleagues at the SETI institute, about 130 scientists and support staff, are interested in microbial life. They are trying to figure out how, using more advanced spacecraft a decade or two from now, we might be able to image a terrestrial planet in orbit around a nearby star and conduct a chemical exploration of its atmosphere. The goal is to see if there's disequilibrium chemistry in that distant atmosphere, just as there is here on Earth. Our atmosphere is marked by molecular oxygen from photosynthetic plants and methane from methanogens in the guts of termites and rice fields and gaseous cow farts (bovine flatulence).

Those two gases (methane and oxygen) are very reactive, and in equilibrium conditions they disappear by combining to form carbon dioxide and water. But the biology on the surface of this planet is so robust that it keeps our atmosphere well out of chemical equilibrium and uniquely marked with life. My astrobiology colleagues are trying to figure out how to look for life elsewhere. With our current, or planned, astrobiology toolsets, and assuming we eventually do find definitive bio signatures in the atmosphere of a distant planet, we won't know whether they are produced by microbes, or whether there might be mathematicians there as well. My team is interested in looking for the mathematicians!

SETI is a search for techno signatures rather than biosignatures. Whether or not SETI will ever succeed depends on whether or not there's anyone out there, and whether or not we are searching for the right technology. Our current technology is observable over interstellar distances; theirs might be as well. But we need one more thing for SETI to succeed. We need those technologies, on average, to last for a very long time; long in a cosmic sense. We are a very young technology in a very old galaxy. We've had relevant technology for a hundred years; the galaxy is 10 billion years old. Unless technologies last much longer than a hundred years there are never going to be any two of them that are close enough in space, and aligned in time (co-temporal), to discover one another. So longevity is the key to success in SETI.

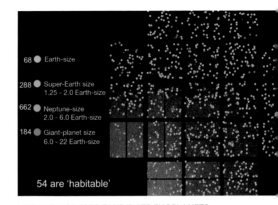

68 ● Earth-size

288 ● Super-Earth size
1.25 - 2.0 Earth-size

662 ● Neptune-size
2.0 - 6.0 Earth-size

184 ● Giant-planet size
6.0 - 22 Earth-size

54 are 'habitable'

LOCATION OF 1235 CANDIDATE EXOPLANETS DETECTED BY THE KEPLER SPACECRAFT DURING THE FIRST FOUR QUARTERS OF OBSERVATION. THE COLORED DOTS REPRESENT PLANETS OF DIFFERENT SIZE CATEGORIES. CREDIT: KEPLER MISSION.

But turn that around, and suppose we do detect a signal. Suppose all we find is a cosmic dial tone, no "Encyclopaedia Galactica," no information that we can decode, no extra-terrestrial salvation. Just a cosmic dial tone — just a proof that there's another technology out there. Physicist Phil Morrison talked about that potential and called SETI "the archaeology of the future." It's archaeology because that signal has taken a long time to get here because of the finite speed of light and the very long distances involved. But it's our future, because we could not have succeeded in detecting the signal unless technologies last for a long time. The successful detection of a signal tells us this amazing thing: it's possible to survive your technological adolescence, the unsettled state we are in right now. Today, we don't see a lot of other messages encouraging us that we can figure a way through our current challenges. That's what keeps me motivated to continue SETI searches, what gets me out of bed every morning: the archaeology of the future.

We've been doing SETI for 50 years and some people say to me, "In 50 years you haven't found anything; it's time for you to stop, nobody's out there." These people don't understand the magnitude of the search. In our exploration of the cosmic ocean, numerically a very good estimation of how much we've done versus how much we might have to do to have a good chance of finding a signal is to say that we've so far examined one eight ounce glass of Earth's oceans. If it were fish we were searching for, and didn't find one in our sample glass of water, we'd be unlikely to conclude that the oceans were devoid of fish. Instead we'd correctly conclude that we had not yet taken a large enough sample, and perhaps that we need to use bigger glasses. There's a lot left to accomplish with our explorations and our SETI Institute team is not daunted by the size of the remaining search. Exponential improvements in our technologies will allow us to build bigger glasses, dip them out of the cosmic ocean many at one time, and search them faster and in different ways.

Right now we do an extraordinarily good job of finding certain types of signal: Narrow band, frequency-compressed signals in the radio, or short-time pulsed signals in the optical. This illustration shows a signal, captured by the ATA, from the most distant human-made object. This is a waterfall plot showing the carrier signal transmitted from the Voyager 1 spacecraft now leaving our solar system and travelling into interstellar space. The power in that transmitter is only about 6 watts, like one small white Christmas tree light bulb, and it's coming from a long distance. What's plotted here on the horizontal lines is frequency, lots of narrow frequency channels; and the vertical lines are different time samples. This plot does contain a signal that your eyes may be having a hard time finding (it's indicated by the arrows), but our computers find the signal with great ease because we've told them that's the pattern to look for. The computer detection result is displayed as the white fluctuating line, its peak is highly, statistically significant. If we have guessed the right signal, our computer systems have a good chance of finding it.

But what if we've guessed the wrong signal? What if we're not yet looking for the right thing? In 2009, when I was awarded the TED prize (Technology, Entertainment, and Design), I got the opportunity to make a wish to try and change the world. And I wished that TED would empower earthlings everywhere to become active participants in the ultimate search for cosmic company. Now it might not be exactly obvious to you how this can change the world, but I think it can. Combatting faith-based science and magical thinking are critical to our future survival — getting a global community of citizen scientists passionately involved in the search can do just that.

So my action charge to all of you is: go home, take your LinkedIn, your Facebook pages, whatever you have as profiles of yourself, and make the first description of who you are the fact that you're an earthling. Let's start with that. Then let's try to capture and enthrall the younger generation, because these are the people whose perspective we have to change. Let's find a way to use the marvellous power of the human brain and eyes for pattern recognition to help us do our searches in ways we haven't been able to do before. By actively engaging the public in our search, we have a fantastic opportunity to tell the story of cosmic evolution and explain that beings made from stardust, as we are, may have been produced elsewhere. We humans are all the same when compared to them.

We're trying to build a global community that we call SETI Quest. It all starts with the wonderful ATA telescopes in northern California and donations of fast server hardware from Dell and Intel, plus resources in the cloud supplied by Amazon web services. We've published the code that we've built to do the SETI signal detection, over decades, as open source code on GitHub. We're trying to reach out to the open source community to say "gee, there are clever things in here, take it and go do with it what you want. Or help us make it even better." We're trying to reach out to the digital signal processing communities, mainly electrical engineering students at universities, to help us build new algorithms to find different kinds of signals.

And this summer, while we are enjoying the interactions here at the Starmus Festival, my team is supervising two interns from Google who are working with us at the SETI Institute to do just this. We're also trying to build a citizen science project in collaboration with the very experienced Zooniverse team. This project that will allow citizen scientists to work alongside our automated signal detection system, viewing live data, to look for things that we could be now missing. If they find something, they will cause us to move the telescopes in our next observing cycle to follow up on their discoveries. We want to involve people because we want to tell them the story of cosmic evolution. We want them to understand their intimate connection with the universe. We currently have a tablet-based, Android application that we're beta testing for this pattern recognition application. We need to learn how humans interact with our data as a way of helping us to develop the real-time application.

For my SETI team, it's a particularly exciting time. We know where to point our array; we have launched a two-year project to explore the Kepler worlds; we have plans to involve earthlings in the search; we're successfully building tools that will engage the world and improve the search; but we've run into a perfect funding storm. At this time there are serious challenges with science funding at the Federal level in the United States, and with the State of California, where we're located. The University of California can no longer provide the funds to operate the telescope that we built as a partnership. We're going to need support from everyone, and tomorrow we will be launching a crowdfunding web site SETIStars.org. It isn't comfortable for me to talk to you about our funding needs. But I'm doing it because SETI is really so important, it is in fact too important to fail. We've seen, over millennia, what happens when you take a small island and you carve it up into even smaller islands that war over perceived differences. In the end, we actually all belong to the single tribe of earthlings. We ought to be interacting in a way that celebrates the commonness of all humans, rather than fighting over the supposed differences.

SETI has this marvelous ability to hold up a mirror to the entire planet and say, "Look! When compared to anything out there, you are all the same." We need to trivialize the differences among us. If SETI projects never succeed in finding a signal, but manage to promulgate this change of perspective, then I think SETI will have been one of the most profound endeavors of humankind. I am reminded by a quote from Neil Armstrong. Neil was asked about how the Apollo program actually had benefited humanity, what had been the best thing about it? Neil responded, "But I would say that it will enlighten the human race and help us all to comprehend that we are an important part of a much bigger universe than we can normally see from the front porch."

SETI follows in the footsteps of the astonishing earthrise photo taken by Apollo 8 astronaut, Bill Anders, and the wisdom of Neil Armstrong; it can change the world in ways that will ensure our long-term future. That's what SETI can do. Thank you; join us.

We are finding planets in many, many places. But we have only just begun.

VOYAGER 1 SIGNAL 106 AU AWAY

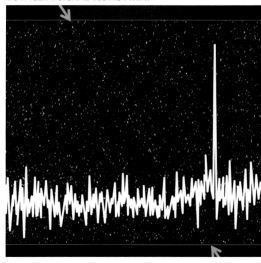

WATERFALL PLOT (FREQUENCY HORIZONTAL VS. TIME VERTICAL) OF DATA COLLECTED BY THE ATA SHOWING THE CARRIER SIGNAL FROM THE VOYAGER 1 SPACECRAFT FROM THE EDGE OF THE SOLAR SYSTEM (INDICATED BY THE ARROWS). SUPERIMPOSED IS THE RESULT OF THE STATISTICAL TESTS PERFORMED BY THE SIGNAL DETECTION SOFTWARE; THE PEAK INDICATES HOW READILY THIS WEAK SIGNAL IS DETECTED.

STARMUS GALLERY

Images from STARMUS 2011

Noel Carboni   Alex Cherney   Greg Parker   David Malin

THE ROUND TABLE DISCUSSION INSIDE
THE GRAN TELESCOPIO CANARIAS (GTC).
STARMUS 2011.

THE SONIC UNIVERSE CONCERT, STARMUS 2011. BRIAN MAY WITH TANGERINE DREAM - EDGAR FROESE, IRIS CAMAA, LINDA SPA, THORSTEN QUAESCHNING, HOSHIKO YAMANE, BERNHARD BEIBL.

ADAM BURROWS

KIP THORNE

SECTION 4

COSMIC SOUND AND LIGHT

The Milky Way Galaxy and indeed billions of other galaxies in the universe are filled with interesting creatures — exploding stars, black holes, gamma-ray bursts, and the oscillating sounds of the cosmos.

Princeton University astronomer Adam Burrows describes some of the most explosive — and important — events in the universe in his descriptions of super-novae and gamma-ray bursts. It is in the former, in these dying massive stars, that the elements in our bodies were created.

The founder of Starmus, astronomer Garik Israelian of the Institute for Astronomy at Tenerife, delivers a unique perspective on the cosmos. Awash in a world of sounds on Earth's planetary surface, humans don't often ponder the sounds of the universe at large. But he shows us how we can appreciate the music of the cosmos in an enlightening journey into the acoustic universe.

Caltech's Kip Thorne, one of the world's greatest experts on black holes and gravitation, delivers a detailed exploration of the most mysterious citizens of the cosmos, black holes. These monsters of the deep seem to defy our intuitive common sense and hold answers to timeless questions.

GARIK ISRAELIAN

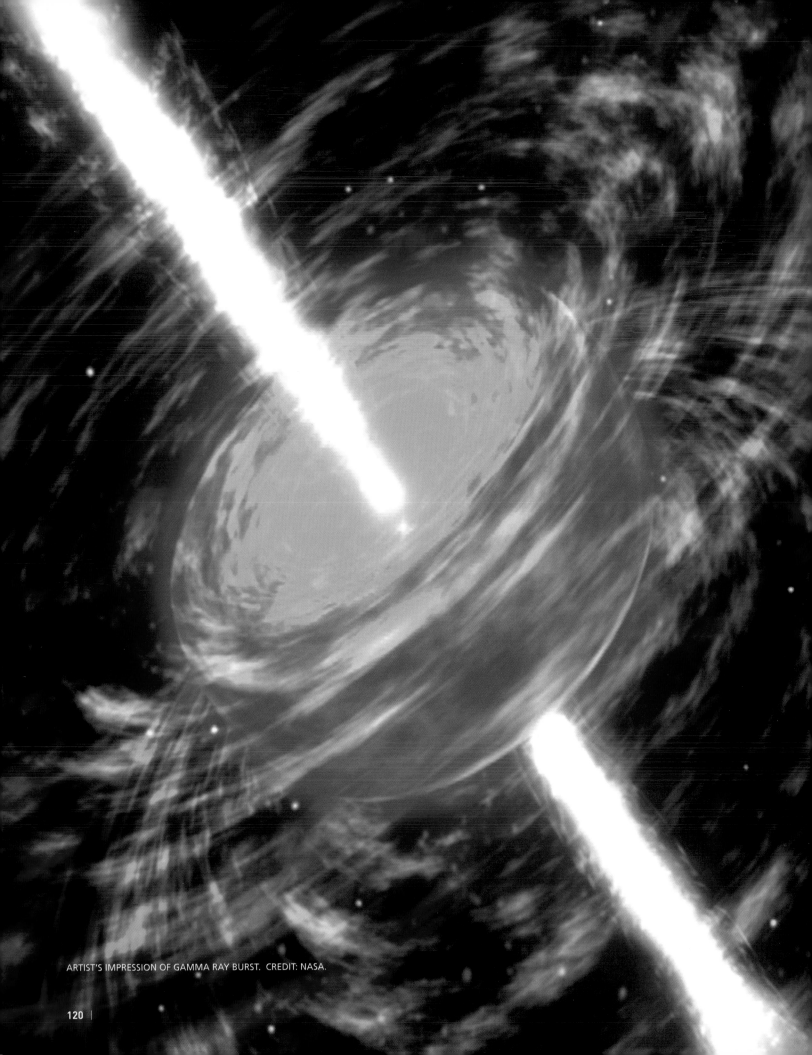

ARTIST'S IMPRESSION OF GAMMA RAY BURST. CREDIT: NASA.

ADAM BURROWS

Explosive Astrophysics: Supernovae and Gamma-Ray Bursts

Princeton University's Adam Burrows is a special breed of astrophysicist, working on an array of projects investigating high-energy objects. He is focused on examining the physical processes involved with supernova explosions, the end result of very massive stars that die with a great bang. He also investigates gamma-ray bursts, the extraordinarily powerful blasts that result from a variety of unusual causes.

Burrows is also focused on studying brown dwarfs, those very low mass objects that form an intermediate population between stars and very massive planets, and also the search for and understanding of extrasolar planets.

He is chair of the National Research Council Board on Physics and Astronomy, a member of the board of the Association of Universities for Research in Astronomy, and a board member of the Aspen Center for Physics.

ADAM BURROWS AT STARMUS.

When you look up at the sky you see stars. The stars seem not to change at all; they seem to be ever fixed. But that's an illusion. As Sami Solanki alluded to before, indirectly, when talking about the Sun, when you see the Sun it may seem fairly benign and quiescent, but when you look at it in x-rays it's quite violent. There are many, many explosions associated with it.

That should give you a hint of what stars are like in reality. If you speed up their evolution you note, theoretically and observationally, that in fact stars are born, they live, and they die. The star that we are familiar with, the Sun, will die fairly quiescently and leave behind a white dwarf, which has an interesting second life to be sure.

But there are stars more massive than the Sun, 10 or 20 times more massive than the Sun, that in fact will die quite violently. These stars give birth to neutron stars and black holes, and they'll launch what is known as a supernova explosion.

Those supernova explosions can be seen across the universe. They are the origin of most of the elements of existence. The calcium in your bones, the hemoglobin in your blood, the oxygen we breathe are all produced in this massive star context, and in the violence of the explosions themselves, to litter the interstellar medium and to contribute to the next generation of stars.

So supernovae are central elements of change in the universe. In the galaxies that we saw yesterday in profusion, every region of those galaxies has such violence associated with it that gives birth to the next generation and is part of the cycle of birth and regeneration in the universe.

In this talk, I explore the theory of supernovae, with some asides on observations, and it's going to be a talk that is not only at the confluence of much of 20th and 21st century physics, but also of mathematics and the computational arts. We're starting to glimpse an understanding of exactly how these phenomena occur.

And so, without further ado, I list the basics of why you should be interested in supernovae in particular. As I said, they are the origin of the elements, but they also inject energy into the interstellar medium. They roil and make it more turbulent, and so they are important agencies of the energetics of galaxies. They may even trigger some star formation. Indeed, the Sun's birth may have been triggered by a supernova.

They are a major source of cosmic rays that are irradiating you right now — high-energy particles that are part of the background radiation of the cosmos. As we heard earlier, supernovae can be used as cosmic yardsticks to measure the universe. This is one of the major ways we know that the universe is not only expanding, but seems to be accelerating. And so they're very, very important and they have

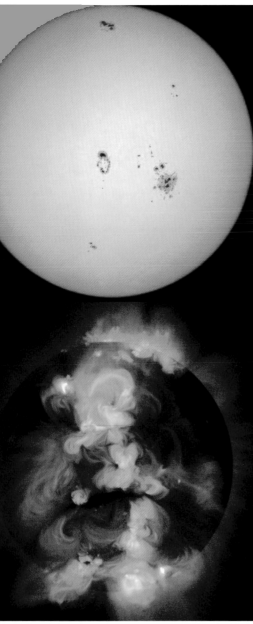

THE SUN VIEWED IN X-RAYS (BELOW) AND
VISIBLE LIGHT (ABOVE). CREDIT: YOHKOH;
NASA/ESA/SOHO.

very important secondary uses.

As I suggested, they also produce stellar corpses. Every star is going to have a
final state. Neutron stars can be in binaries; they can accrete matter from companions; they can give rise to x-ray bursts and be bright x-ray sources — quite exotic
phenomena. Black holes can behave similarly. And so, between white dwarfs, black
holes, and neutron stars, we have a whole population of final states to stellar
evolution.

This illustration is similar to what Sami Solanki showed concerning the Sun.
Above, you see the Sun in the optical, with sunspots, and those sunspots belie the
violence that underlies them. But this is nothing compared to the energetics that I'm
going to be talking about, the powers associated with supernovae and the gamma-
ray bursts that may be related. This is 22 orders of magnitude weaker than the
supernova phenomenon. It completely dwarfs our own understanding. Any of the
things that we are associated with, or that we understand from living on Earth, do
not equip us for the magnitudes involved.

So, this drama includes actors and players. The actors are massive stars that will
die violently. They will produce neutron stars that may be only 10 kilometers in
radius, but have a mass that may be 50 percent again as massive as the Sun — so
they are very dense. There are white dwarfs that are about the radius of Earth, but
about the mass of the Sun, again very dense, but not as dense as the neutron stars.
But then of course, as Kip Thorne eloquently describes, there are black holes in the
universe. Those that I'm going to be talking about are stellar-mass black holes, not
the super-massive black holes to which he alluded, but they are nevertheless as
exotic. There are many binary systems where you have close stars where the
interaction between them is central to what you see, and there are concepts such as
accretion disks and bipolar jets, jets that can emanate from these very compact
regions to give you phenomena that we associate with gamma ray bursts. So those
are the basic actors.

The players in the explosive aspects of the universe are listed here. I've left out a
few. There are x-ray bursts that happen on the surfaces of neutron stars, and there
are thermonuclear explosions. But they're too small to be included in this talk. And
Bob I apologize, there are novae explosions that happen on the surfaces of white
dwarfs, but they're also too small to be included in this talk.

What I'm going to focus on are two types of supernovae and two types of gamma-
ray bursts. The first is the so-called Ia supernova, which is very bright and is the
major one used to take the measure of the universe. It's a thermonuclear explosion
of a white dwarf that is replete with fuel: you take a white dwarf with carbon and oxygen, and you raise the temperature by some means, and you can ignite a thermonuclear explosion, converting that carbon and oxygen into iron and many other
species. This actually happens in the universe. It's a quite violent event and it leaves
nothing behind. The products are injected into the interstellar medium.

The second is the core-collapse supernova, and they occur more than once a
second in the universe. During this talk, there will be thousands of this type of
supernova throughout the universe. These do leave behind those remnants that I
mentioned before — the neutron stars and the black holes. There's quite a variety
here.

Gamma-ray bursts are quite exotic. They were discovered in the mid 1960s and
published as existing in the early 1970s. And they are of two types: one may be
associated with core collapse, but may be much more energetic and could be
announcing the birth of a black hole. Whether or not they are, they're associated
with bipolar jets. The other may be associated with binary neutron stars that are
close enough that by the gravitational radiation to which Kip Thorne alluded earlier
can come together and merge quite violently. I'm going to show some of the concepts associated with that a bit later.

When neutron stars merge they give off the gravitational waves that LIGO, the
Laser Interferometer Gravitational Wave Observatory, may be able to see. And so if

we see a gamma ray burst at the same time we see the gravitational radiation, then we have a smoking gun for the phenomenon. That would be fabulous.

So let me start with the Ia supernovae, and again, though I'm going to be emphasizing the theoretical aspects, there is beauty associated with these, and I'll touch on that as well. For people who want to understand the science as well as the art, let me list a few of the basic facts: you produce radioactive nickel in these contexts. Radioactive nickel is the progenitor to the iron that surrounds you. You produce nickel-56 and it decays into cobalt-56 and then to iron-56, the latter being the standard iron with which you are familiar. Because of that radioactivity, you heat the gas that is ejected and it's that heating to incandescence that powers the light of many of the supernovae that we see. If we didn't have this nickel, particularly in the Ia supernovae, you would not see the supernova. So the radioactivity is central to the phenomenon we associate with supernovae as observers.

The explosion and the light might last for months. The amount of energy is incredible, but I don't want to dwell on that. I'll let you contemplate some of these numbers, and as I said before, this type involves the complete disassembly of the object. This illustration depicts a supernova remnant, bounded by a blast wave. It's in fact a few light-years across, and we see many of these in the galaxy and in the universe. Those are the products. This is the early phase, the first 10,000 years or so after the supernova, and it is this material that's going to be incorporated into the next generation of stars. They look fairly different, but they can, by and large, be characterized by this outward-propagating blast wave, with energies that are 10^{28} megatons of TNT equivalent — if you can get your minds around that.

Now, when we do simulations of these phenomena, what we find is that there is a burning front. It's almost like taking a piece of paper and lighting the fire on one end and watching the flame move through it. But that flame is a thermonuclear flame so it's quite energetic. It's also the case that in a gravitational field that flame when propagating leaves behind material that is a little bit less dense. The net result is that that flame is mixed. It's a turbulent thermonuclear flame and that's rather exotic as well.

We're trying to simulate those sorts of things. So, we have instability and a nuclear phenomenon simultaneously, and we try to throw that on a computer and we get this, where instead of a nice spherical expansion we see turbulent bubbles. Each one of those bubbles is again burning the thermonuclear fuel, the carbon and the oxygen into iron and nickel and so on. And so theorists have tried to simulate this, where in fact the thermonuclear burning front might be only a few millimeters in thickness, but the star in which this is happening may be a few thousand kilometers in radius.

You can imagine it's a very difficult computational problem, to handle that range of scales. And so they punt. They try to do what they can.

And in the process of doing what they can they find structures like this, when they look on the small. The burning fronts can get quite corrugated, quite tangled and they are very difficult to simulate. On the large, this is what you'll see, a white dwarf disassembling into bubbles and this is just the early stage. I'll call your attention to that clock. That clock is moving in milliseconds, and so what's happening is that a star the size of Earth, by thermonuclear processes disassembles within seconds to inaugurate the supernova that lasts for months, and that you can see for 10,000 years. It affects its environment for millions of years, and the next generations. And this happens again and again and again.

Now there are a variety of mechanisms that people have suggested, all of which are thermonuclear in a white dwarf. One of them is an off-center ignition. This is the white dwarf star and you just set off a little bomb in the center because you want to see something happen; then, you see how it propagates, rising like a balloon, penetrating to the surface and starting to spread — all the while burning this thermonuclear fuel, incinerating the star.

In this particular case what happened was it wrapped itself around the star

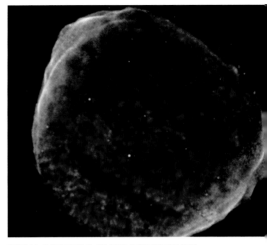

TYPE IA SUPERNOVA SN1006 SEEN IN X-RAYS. CREDIT: CXC, NASA.

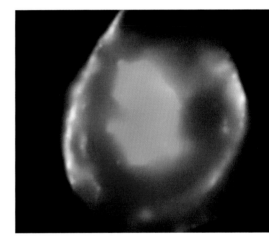

TYPE IA SUPERNOVA REMNANT: DEM 171. CREDIT: J. HUGHES, P. GHAVAMIAN AND C. RAKOWSKI (RUTGERS UNIV.) ET AL., CXC, NASA.

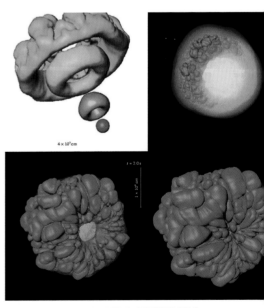

TURBULENT BUBBLES. CREDIT: MIKE ZINGALE, STONY BROOK.

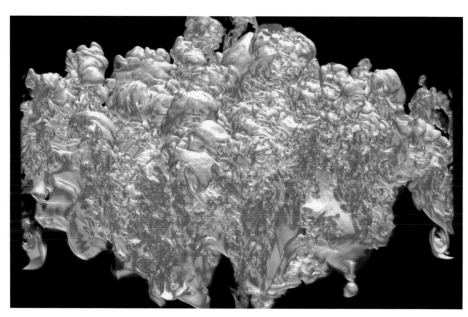

TURBULENT THERMONUCLEAR FLAME FRONT.
CREDIT: MIKE ZINGALE, STONY BROOK.

before the entire star disassembled, and at the back end it "clapped." The burning material hit other burning material so violently that it inaugurated an explosion on the inside. So you have a bubble rising, a surface wave going over to the backside, and then the violent initiation of the explosive detonation of the entire object — all in a second. The speeds we're talking about are 10,000 kilometers per second. Escape velocity from Earth is 1,000 times less than that. The amazing thing about what I'm saying is a lot of what I'm saying is actually true.

The other type of supernova, by far the most prominent, is that associated with the death of massive stars, so-called core-collapse supernovae. Again, there are some facts associated with them that are very similar to the Ia supernovae, but you do leave behind a remnant. Most often a neutron star, but at times a black hole, and we'd like to know when the black hole is formed and when the neutron star is formed. These are still things we don't understand. Again, they are the major sources of elements, but one of the things that is quite fascinating to me, and to many of the theorists, is that what's happening in this case is not thermonuclear. It's associated with the collapse of the stellar core, which, because it doesn't have thermonuclear fuel, doesn't lead to a thermonuclear explosion. It continues to collapse, all the way to nuclear densities, and so the basic scenario is the following:

A massive star has been evolving for about 10 million years. It creates a core in its center, a very dense core — a white dwarf-like object. That white dwarf achieves the so-called Chandrasekhar mass, above which it cannot support itself against gravity and it collapses. If it were made of thermonuclear fuel that collapse, just like a diesel engine, would heat up that material and it would explode.

But without thermonuclear fuel it continues to collapse, and that collapse takes a second, just as in the other case. So imagine the drama. A star has been around for 10 million years. It creates a core in its center, that when it becomes critical, collapses in a second, and sets off a supernova. The whole object is dying, in one second. And it sends out a blast wave through the star that will take an hour to a day to get to the surface. Then, it'll go through the entire display of a supernova, partially powered by nickel, throwing away all this material in a quite violent event.

The progenitors of these sorts of things might look like this next illustration, Eta Carinae in our own galaxy. It may be a binary of massive stars, and it has a nice bipolar structure. It hasn't exploded, but it erupted in 1843. People would like to think that maybe this is the precursor of a supernova only about 7,000 light-years away. That's a small distance for these things. You don't want to be too close.

On an H-R diagram of luminosity vs. surface temperature such as Garik Israelian showed yesterday, the evolution of these supernovae develops something like this

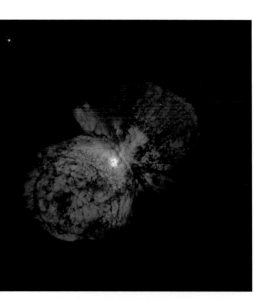

ETA CARINAE. CREDIT: NASA/HST.

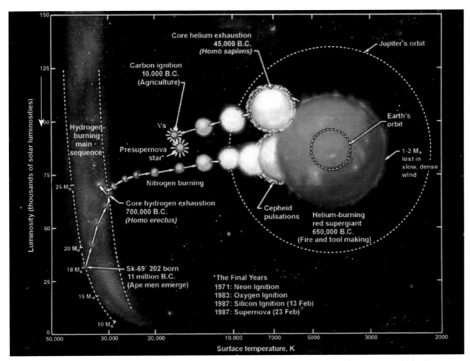

HERTSPRUNG RUSSELL (H-R) DIAGRAM. CREDIT: STAN WOOSLEY.

— high luminosities, high temperatures on the left hand side. The star might be sitting here, and the star, like the progenitor for Supernova 1987A, which exploded in 1987, about 8,800 days ago, would have evolved like this.

It would have been a blue supergiant; it would have expanded to the red, then gone to the blue. There are various associated curiosities, such as when SN 1987A happened, Homo Erectus was emerging, taming fire and making tools. After this, the outer material evolves independently of that central core. The central core is where the action is. The rest of the star is oblivious to the fact that it is going to die. And when it does, it explodes. I show here the luminosity vs. time in days. This is just an example — a blast wave propagates through the star, it hits the surface and you

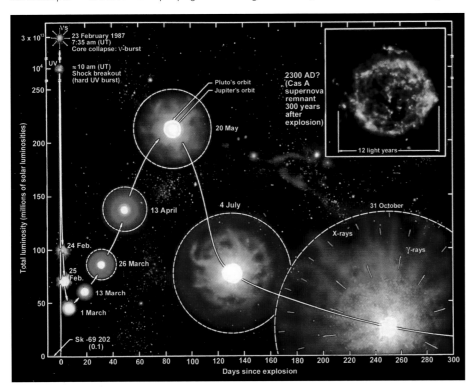

CORE COLLAPSE SUPERNOVA LIGHT CURVE: SN1987A. CREDIT: STAN WOOSLEY.

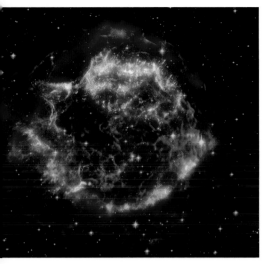

CAS A REMNANT IN X-RAYS. CREDIT: NASA/
JPL/O'KRAUSE (STEWARD OBSERVATORY).

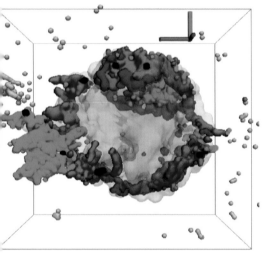

CAS A REMNANT. CREDIT: DELANEY ET AL.
2010.

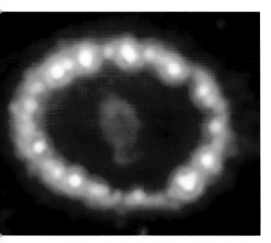

HUBBLE IMAGE OF SN1987A. CREDIT: NASA/
HST.

get a big ultraviolet flash, and then it follows a light curve that can last for very many months.

A supernova, when it goes off, can be as bright, or nearly as bright, as the entire galaxy in which it resides.

An example of a supernova remnant created in a core-collapse supernova is given here. This is Cassiopeia A. It went off less than 400 years ago in our galaxy. It has many, many structures in it — we see the blast wave here, the so-called reverse-shock there. One of the most interesting things about this object is that in fact the elements that are created and that have been ejected are ejected aspherically. They're not distributed very uniformly. Another thing that's interesting is this little dot at the center. That's the newly born neutron star, and we see it in the x-ray. Now, I said that the elements that are ejected are not ejected spherically.

This next illustration is a rendition of the data that people have taken of Cas A, where the green is iron and the red is argon, and you can do this for a number of different elements.

But you can see that there are structures that are emerging that are quite aspherical. That is an emerging, central theme. Explosive phenomena tend to be not only violent, but unstable — and material is broken up. To simulate things theoretically, you have to be able to go beyond the relative simplicity of one-dimensional spherical explosions and really bite the bullet — you must simulate in the full three dimensions of nature.

One of the things produced in a core-collapse supernova explosion is a pulsar. You have a rapidly rotating neutron star that has a magnetic field that is giving out radio waves, and can give off x-rays, gamma rays, and optical light. This next illustration consists of a movie of the central region of the Crab Nebula, and you can see pulsations (stills are shown here).

The movie (http://chandra.harvard.edu/photo/2002/0052) is not in real time. The pulsar is actually pulsating at 30 times per second. That rate is the rotation rate of this one-and-a-half solar mass object. So these things can rotate very fast. If Earth were rotating this fast, it would spin apart.

When Supernova 1987A went off, it not only excited a supernova, it excited the supernova community and its environment. In this time-lapse picture from the Hubble Space Telescope you can see the inner region and I want to call your attention to two things. One, it's not spherical in the inner region. Two, you see all these structures light up. That is the material that's going fastest from the blast, and it's hitting the ring that resides around the supernova, exciting it to fluoresce.

We're still watching this and we're going to be watching this for the next 50 years. It's one of the best examples of a core-collapse supernova that we've been able to study. It's the first supernova to go off in our vicinity that we've noticed since the invention of the telescope. In our vicinity is the crucial part. We see 500 or 600

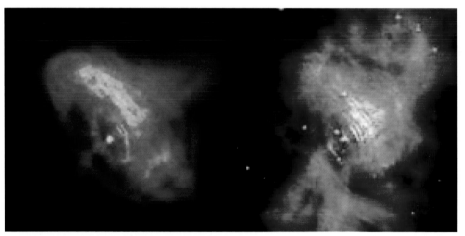

HUBBLE IMAGE OF SN1987A. CREDIT: NASA/HST.

supernovae a year as observers, and there's more than one a second, as I said, in the universe.

So let me get to the theoretical crux. This next illustration shows a cartoon of a massive star. What happens at the end of its life is that it creates a so-called "onion skin" structure where you have nested elements that are progressively lighter as you move out and heavier as you move in — hydrogen to helium; helium to carbon; carbon to neon and other species; and on to oxygen, silicon, and iron. That iron core eventually achieves the so-called Chandrasekhar mass. And it has a radius, again, just a little bit smaller than the radius of Earth.

When it reaches that mass it collapses catastrophically. This whole object collapses within about a quarter of a second. Do people know how long a golf ball is in contact with a golf club when you hit it? It's only 10 milliseconds. A few times that is all we have for this entire object to collapse and to form the proto-neutron star that will evolve into the neutron star.

So, when we do these simulations in two dimensions we watch the collapse. There is the bounce and there's the shock wave that's produced. Behind the shock wave there are instabilities. The radius here is only about 200 kilometers. So this is the belly of the beast, the inside where all the action is happening. You see instabilities aplenty, but notice something: that shock wave is not moving out. Theorists have yet to figure out how it actually explodes. When you do these simulations in two dimensions, you most of the time get that the shock just sort of sits there. That's a very unsatisfactory state of affairs. That's not a supernova. And so we've been spending the last few decades trying to figure out how to reignite this object because we can't figure out what we're doing wrong.

In two dimensions, so we're not doing the full 3D problem, you see the shock wave at the periphery and the radius is still only a few hundred kilometers. It's trying to explode, but it's being held back by all the material that's raining in. There's something holding it in. This being a simulation though, we let it go long enough that the inner oscillations were sufficient to generate sound waves aplenty. And those sound waves steepen into shock waves and it ignited into the supernova. When it ignited the supernova it was off center and it left behind a very rapidly oscillating object. I'll repeat this just to give you a sense of what the state of the art was just a few years ago.

I don't believe that this is the way things happen. And the reason I don't believe it, the major reason, is that we can now do 3D simulations. These computer runs are expensive. And in the 3D simulations we see something else. This is pretty exotic and I made a movie of it so I thought I'd show it. Remember what I said, that the shock wave seems to stall. Doing 3D simulations you can try to get a sense of what's happening. Those ghost-like particles that are flying in just represent the mass that's falling in. That's the accretion that's holding in the blast, and that blast wave is sitting there trying to get out and can't. But you see it's oscillating in all sorts of ways.

This particular simulation just shows, quite graphically, the basics of that phase. But what do you think is going to happen if you do a calculation that takes longer than this? This is a preliminary 3D calculation that shows you the character of what we're dealing with. Shown is the isosurface of material going at 5,000 kilometers per second. Everything inside is going more slowly and everything outside is going faster. You see how broken up that material is. It's a rather amazing context in which to try to do theory, but this is what we have to contend with.

When we put in more physics, this is what we see. It collapses and bounces, and very soon you get this turbulent convection. This turbulence is similar to the turbulence in the Ia context, the thermonuclear case — it's associated with the so-called Rayleigh-Taylor instability. The Rayleigh-Taylor instability is what happens when you mix salad dressing. Has anybody here ever done that? You have oil on the top and vinegar on the bottom, there's an interface, and when you change the effective direction of gravity it turns out that there's a heavy fluid on top of a light fluid and

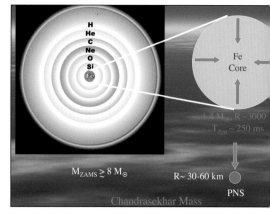

CHANDRASEKHAR MASS. CREDIT: ADAM BURROWS.

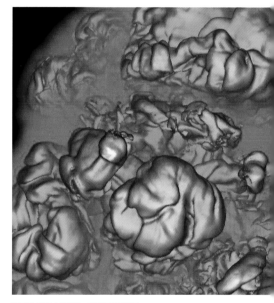

CORE COLLAPSE – MOVIE STILL.
WWW.ASTRO.PRINCETON.EDU/~BURROWS/

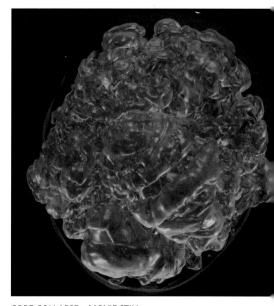

CORE COLLAPSE – MOVIE STILL.
WWW.ASTRO.PRINCETON.EDU/~BURROWS

nature tells you it's an unstable surface.

It's also the reason water falls out of a glass. Anybody ever wonder why water falls out of a glass? No. If you have a pump, a pump can support 10 meters of water. There are lots of pumps on this island. They can pull up 10 meters of water because of atmospheric pressure. Atmospheric pressure is holding up 10 meters of water. If the glass is only 10 centimeters high, that's much less than 10 meters. So atmospheric pressure should be able to hold in that water. It has more than enough pressure. But the water falls out. It's because the interface is unstable to the Rayleigh-Taylor instability. If there's any corrugation at the surface at all, that heavy water fluid on top of the light air fluid will have an unstable interface and that will fall. You should try it some time. Put a piece of paper there, a thin piece of paper, you stabilize the instability, and the water won't fall out. But if it does, don't blame me. But I recommend people try this out.

Structures like this are not only complicated, but they're beautiful. I find them so, and it's this type of object that is emerging into the rest of the star. So you can demonstrate the same sorts of things — I have a few movies that depict the characteristic structures — the roiling and boiling material, the shock wave, and in this particular simulation the explosion occurred fairly early. When we did this simulation in 2D it did not explode. So we're getting a hint that dimension, perversely, is central to the mechanism of the explosion. Nature does this effortlessly. We require

FORMATION OF GAMMA-RAY BURST. CREDIT: NICOLLE RAGER FULLER OF THE NSF.

the Department of Energy and their computers. And because I like this movie I'm going to show another one.

The surface again is a shock wave. This bubbling and boiling seems to be essential to the explosion. So one of the things that seems to be happening here, is in fact the following: when you get to these high densities and temperatures, you produce neutrinos in abundance. Very weakly interacting particles, but at these densities and temperatures they're produced in abundance, and in this phenomenon you get a big burst of neutrinos. Kip Thorne was boasting that they get 10,000 times the luminosity of the universe in gravitational waves. I can't trump that. But I can get a factor of five times the luminosity of the universe in neutrinos in this context. Neutrinos are easier to see than gravitational waves, but they're still tough.

And so what are we concluding? Those neutrinos not only take out energy, but they can heat up the material behind the shock. And what seems to be happening is that the efficiency of the neutrino-matter coupling, the neutrinos coming out there, is larger in 2D than in 1D. And it's larger in 3D than in 2D. And it's large enough in 3D to give us what we've seen since the Chinese were taking records. In this movie, the camera's rotating. The blast wave is emerging and what's left behind in the dissolve is a neutron star.

Those two types of supernovae have engaged astronomers for many, many decades. But there are new objects, gamma-ray bursts, that I want to end with. As I have said, one class may be associated with the massive stars. In both cases there seems to be a relativistic jet. You have material, maybe a few hundredths of a solar mass, maybe more, that is moving relativistically — very close to the speed of light, probably in both directions, emanating from a central object. How does that happen? There may be two ways that I think I want to talk about today.

In both cases, it may be that a black hole is formed. The gamma-ray burst emits mostly gamma rays. The average gamma-ray burst lasts for 10 seconds, but some are shorter, some are longer. That burst is brighter than a supernova in gamma rays, but it has about the same total energy — in kinetic energy and radiation.

We can simulate things like this, and with magnetic fields. If you have rapid rotation you can wind up the field lines and you can amplify them — there are different ways of doing that. We can make movies of these theoretical results and just watch what happens. Remember that collapse, bounce, and the shock wave, in this more exotic context, wind up the magnetic fields — see those magnetic fields in the process of being amplified. They amplify to such a degree that the magnetic stress is sufficient to blast, in a bipolar fashion, an explosion out of the poles. It creates in some sense, a tunnel-boring machine in two directions, but very energetic, that can be as much as ten times as energetic as a regular supernova. By the way, that shock in the movie is moving at 20,000 kilometers per second.

These jets then propagate through the star that's sitting there. It may take only 10 seconds for that jet to emerge after being produced in a process similar to what I showed earlier. When it emerges, and there's probably another one on the other side, the gamma-ray burst phenomenon starts. But it seems like there's something very interesting here. The jets have to be pointing toward us in order to see them. You can see something if they're pointing off to the side, but the average gamma-ray burst seems to need to point toward us within five degrees or so in order for us to actually see it. One of the reasons for that is that a relativistic jet beams its energy forward. By Einstein's theory, if it's moving very fast, very close to the speed of light, then it will beam its radiation and energy forward.

One could do other simulations. With rapid rotation, you can get all sorts of exotica, but I'm not going to emphasize the minor points. In the movies of the simulations you can witness the types of jets that might emerge. Now, this is what I found off the Internet, so I apologize for that, but it shows what may happen when those jets emerge, eating away at the star and leaving behind a black hole with an accretion disk that might continue to power it. Again, the only reason you see this thing, except for the underlying supernova that might be associated with it, is

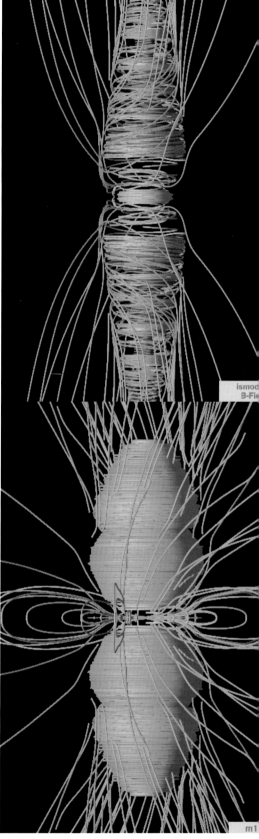

MAGNETIC FIELDS IN THE FORMATION
OF A GAMMA RAY BURST, MOVIE STILLS.
WWW.ASTRO.PRINCETON.EDU/~BURROWS/

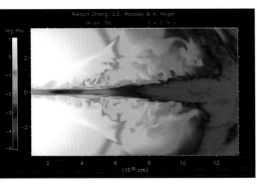

3-D SPECIAL RELATIVISTIC HYDRO SIMULATION OF A COLLAPSOR JET – MOVIE STILL. HTTP://COSMO.NYU.EDU/~WQZHANG/MOVIES

SHORT HARD GRB MODEL. MOVIE STILL. WWW.ASTRO.PRINCETON.EDU/~BURROWS/

because the beam may be pointing toward you. And if it is, and it's in our galaxy, it would be a very bad day! Anything in its way, at those distances, is going to be sterilized. Earth would be killed. Fortunately, in our galaxy, these things happen maybe once every million years.

Now there's a satellite in space, the Swift satellite, that can trigger on gamma-ray bursts and then tell people on the ground to go look at them. It sends telemetry down to telescopes that will then slew to the gamma-ray bursts; and what they see is not just gamma rays, but infrared and optical emission. Those gamma-ray bursts interacted with their environment and produced very bright signals, so called "afterglows." And those afterglows, the brightest, can be seen across the universe. In fact gamma-ray bursts, because of their brightness in the gamma ray, and perhaps because of their afterglows, may be the best, or one of the most unique probes, of the farthest reaches of the universe, at redshifts of maybe 10 or 15, if they exist. They may be the best probes of the first stars.

The other type of gamma-ray bursts, with which I'd like to close, may have a very different origin, but are always associated with this class of violent event that gives birth to the neutron stars and black holes. The best model has two neutron stars that are so close that by the gravitational radiation they spiral in together. But what happens when neutron stars collide? We don't really know, but it can't be good. What we think might happen, however, is the formation of relativistic jets.

People have done some simulations of these collisions, and what I am showing is similar to something that Kip Thorne showed earlier. These simulations can give us a sense of what's happening, but notice the timescale. That all happened in 10 milliseconds.

The neutron stars are completely destroyed. They merge into something that's rapidly rotating. That object, when it loses its rotation, is too massive to be a neutron star and collapses to a black hole. During this process, you have a huge amount of energy available. You can generate very large magnetic fields. And those magnetic fields may actually be instrumental in producing a jet.

Opposite is a storyboard of a simulation just like that, with two neutron stars, but now with magnetic fields. And those magnetic fields can be wound up and we see the makings of a jet. This next is my last cheesy movie. And I'm showing it for another reason. You see these neutron stars that are merging, getting faster and faster as they come together. Then a miracle happens and you get this burst. That burst lasted only maybe half a second to a second. It's a so-called "short hard" gamma-ray burst. At the same time this happens, gravitational waves are being emitted. They are characteristic of this phenomenon. If you see the gravitational waves at the same time you see the gamma-ray bursts, this will be a very important event. We will have been able to predict something, and then verify it, something that could only have been hinted at many years ago — we will have understood the character of such gamma-ray bursts.

So let me summarize with what I think are the most important and salient points. What we're dealing with are stars that do have a birth, a life and a death. They evolve. Stars of different types evolve differently. Sometimes when they die, they die quite violently, but in the process give birth to the next generation of stars, produce the elements of existence and enrich the galaxy with what we need to survive on Earth. We are starting to understand the mechanisms of supernovae and gamma-ray bursts. Such understanding requires the computational arts. We have a yardstick for the universe, we'll try to measure it, and we'll hear more about that in Joe Silk's talk.

The universe gives birth to some exotic objects. But to me, one of the most interesting things is that, over the decades, people have been able to figure out a complicated story, a scenario, a general set of ideas that may well be true, about the fundamental phenomena of the universe. And this is only possible in the modern era, because we're at the confluence of great progress in physics, chemistry, mathematics, and computation, that has given us the capability, in our minds, and with our computers, to relive and figure out the great dramas of the universe that involve not only violence, but regeneration.

Thank you very much for your patience.

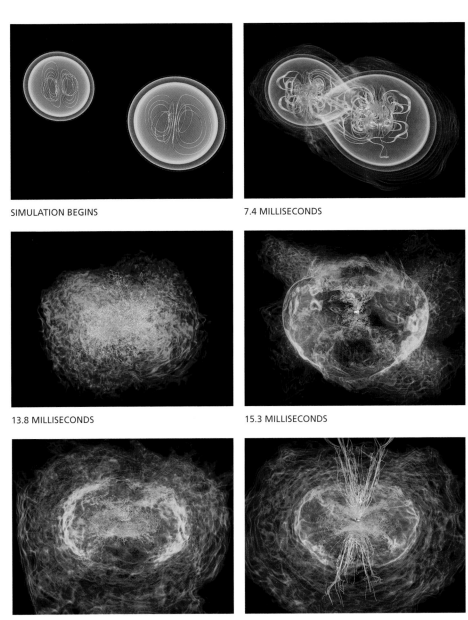

SIMULATION BEGINS

7.4 MILLISECONDS

13.8 MILLISECONDS

15.3 MILLISECONDS

21.2 MILLISECONDS

26.5 MILLISECONDS

SHORT HARD GRB MODEL: MERGER OF NEUTRON STARS - CRASHING NEUTRON STARS CAN MAKE GAMMA-RAY BURST JETS. STORYBOARD. WWW.ASTRO.PRINCETON.EDU/~BURROWS/

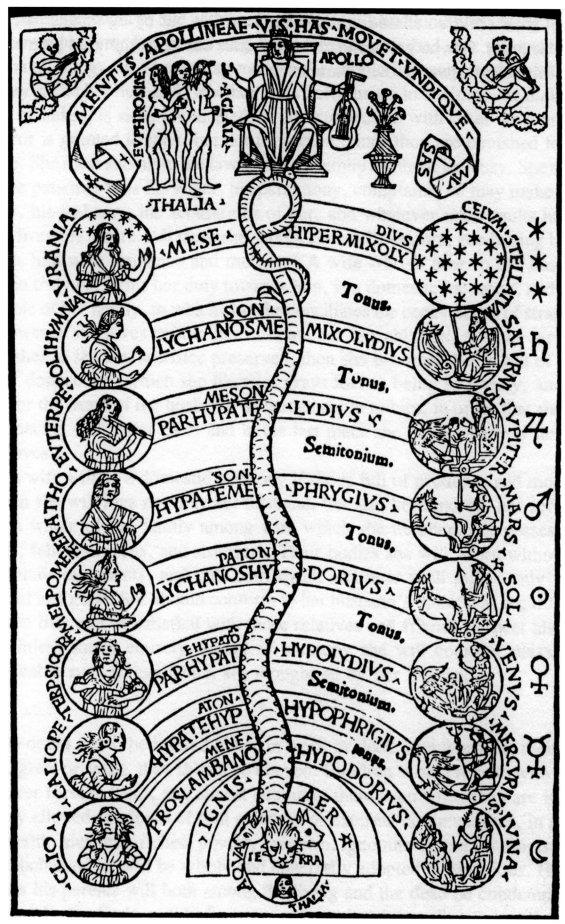

THE MUSIC OF THE SPHERES SEEN IN AN ENGRAVING FROM RENAISSANCE ITALY. CREDIT: PUBLIC DOMAIN.

GARIK ISRAELIAN

OUR ACOUSTIC UNIVERSE

Founder of the Starmus Festival, Garik Israelian was born in Armenia in 1963 and is an astronomer at the Institute of Astrophysics at Tenerife in the Canary Islands, Spain. He specializes in several areas of astrophysics, using spectroscopy as a primary tool. His main areas of research are the chemical evolution of the Milky Way, solar-type stars, stars with exoplanets, and massive stars. He has also done research on compact binaries, including x-ray binaries and systems with neutron stars and black holes. In 2010 along with collaborators Michel Mayor and Nuno Santos, he received the Viktor Ambartsumian International Prize, having been nominated by the Swiss Academy of Sciences. Israelian also brings us a new dimension on understanding the universe beyond our visual and spectroscopic means. His popular TED talk about spectroscopy has been voted as "Fascinating" by hundreds of thousands people. While studying at University he used to play guitars and keyboards in a rock band. Sound waves, acoustic waves, give us another measure of the cosmos around us, and tie us into the music we make on Earth.

GARIK ISRAELIAN AT STARMUS.

Until now, humans have always had to imagine the sounds that represent space, stars, and planets. We have always had an intuition that celestial sounds are mysterious and enigmatic. But do stars, galaxies, planets or other cosmic citizens make acoustic sounds or melodies? And if this is so, how can we hear them? Are these sounds as mysterious as the cosmic objects that produce them?

We know from college physics that sound waves (also called acoustic waves) are pressure waves in a gas or solid body. By contrast, all bodies, organic or inorganic, emit electromagnetic waves. Cosmic objects emit them too. In a clever analysis of the cosmos, some musicians, enthusiasts, and even science outreach officers have taken radio emissions from galaxies, planets or pulsars and translated or converted them into sounds that can be heard by us humans. However, these electromagnetic radio waves have nothing in common with real sound waves. Perhaps this explains why the cosmic "sounds" have been absolutely ignored by scientists. These electromagnetic low frequency radio waves can be produced by thermal or non-thermal motions of charged particles, so this phenomenon has nothing to do with acoustic sound waves.

For many millennia stars have been perceived as the silent confederates of humankind, mutely watching us perform our good and evil deeds, and go about our routine work, as we dream, grieve, and rejoice. To us, they have seemed eternally soundless; they have watched us at our most disgusting and our most beautiful. But no one has ever heard them utter a sound. We couldn't hear them, but they do have voices, and in reality they have not been silent all this time. Oh, yes, the stars make music, and this is not just a metaphor!

The idea of a harmonious order of the universe has been a source of inspiration for thousands of years. Music theory dates back to the 6th century B.C., when Greek philosopher Pythagoras of Samos discovered that consonant musical intervals can be expressed in simple ratios of small integers. His followers, Pythagoreans, believed that all matter emitted musical tones at such levels that we couldn't hear them. According to Pythagoras, earthly music was no more than a faint echo of a universal "harmony of the spheres." In ancient cosmology, the planetary spheres ascended from Earth to Heaven like the rungs of a ladder. Each sphere was said to correspond to a different note of a grand musical scale.

Having established that the intervals of the musical scale correspond to simple numerical ratios, Pythagoras thought that the particular tones emitted by the

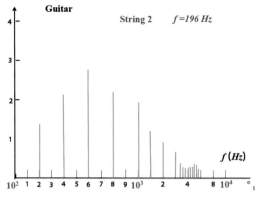

POWER SPECTRUM OF THE GUITAR STRING.
CREDIT: GARIK ISRAELIAN.

planets should depend on the ratios of their respective orbits, just as the tone of a lyre-string depended on its length. Another putative celestial scale related planetary tones to their apparent rates of rotation around Earth. The music of the spheres was never a fixed system of correspondences. Yet many philosophers and astronomers agreed that the motions of planets and stars created sounds in the universe that could not be heard on Earth.

In the early 1600s, German astronomer Johannes Kepler related the orbits of celestial bodies to simple ratios. He also believed that the planets were arranged in orbital positions like a musical progression. Rather than the fixed-tone planetary scales of earlier schemes, Kepler's measurements revealed ever-changing polyphonic chords and harmonies as the planets move between perihelion and aphelion (closer to or farther from the Sun). Furthermore, he had shifted the focus of celestial harmony from Earth to the Sun: "Henceforth it is no longer a harmony made for the benefit of our planet," he wrote, "but the song which the cosmos sings to its lord and center, the Solar Logos." The science and the philosophy of the time were heliocentric, and Kepler naturally ascribed the utmost importance to the Sun.

The Keplerian scholar Francis Warrain extended Kepler's researches and found that the angular velocities of Uranus, Neptune and Pluto, which were unknown during Kepler's lifetime, also correspond to harmonic ratios. The music of the spheres was more than a beautiful poetic intuition. The dynamics of the solar system, first laid bare by Kepler's mathematical genius, are directly analogous with the laws of musical harmony. One of the great astronomers of 20th century, Fred Hoyle, commented that the correspondence between musical ratios and planetary velocities as described by Kepler is "frighteningly good."

Is this a pure coincidence? What has mathematics got to do with musical harmony? What have the stars got to do with all this?

Humanity had to wait thousands of years to build supercomputers, big telescopes, artificial satellites, and very advanced technology in order to detect, compute and finally hear the acoustic sound waves of the cosmos.

Twenty-five centuries have elapsed since Pythagoras's attempt to merge music and the universe and to determine the laws of celestial harmony. Modern astronomy has allowed us to reveal the missing link in great detail.

Current theories of the Big Bang suggest that the very first "bang," the first

PLANCK CMB MAP. CREDIT: ESA AND THE PLANCK COLLBORATION.

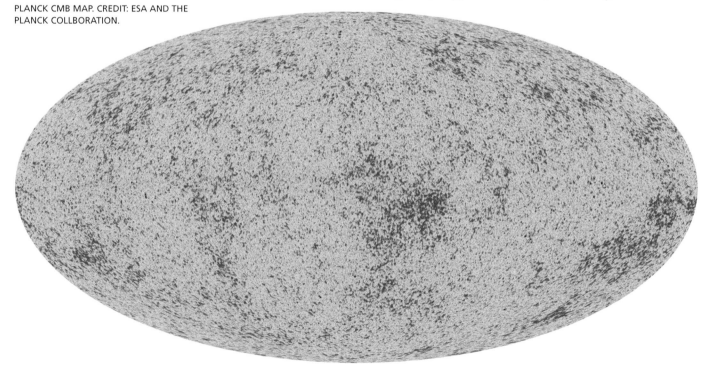

infinitely small moment, was never heard. It wasn't just that there was no one to hear it, but this uniquely explosive event happened in a peculiar soup of elementary particles. There was no ambience — no waves of any type, no sounds. The situation changed, however, a few hundred thousand years later. The early universe consisted of a hot and dense plasma of electrons, protons and neutrons. It was too hot for atoms to form. Photons travelling in this universe were essentially trapped, unable to travel for any considerable distance before interacting with particles. It means that the gas in the early universe was foggy. As the universe expanded, the plasma cooled to below 3000 K — a low enough energy such that the electrons and protons could combine to form atoms of hydrogen.

This process occurred when the universe was around 380,000 years old. With no free electrons, the fog cleared and the universe suddenly turned transparent. The mean free path of the photons changed to be on the order of the size of the universe. The cosmic microwave background (CMB) radiation, discovered by Arno Penzias and Robert Wilson in 1963, is nothing but a light emitted after recombination which is only now reaching our telescopes.

Therefore, when we look at CMB maps (such as Wilkinson Microwave Anisotropy Probe data), we are looking back in time to see an image of the universe when it was just 380,000 years old. NASA's COBE satellite, launched in 1992, has confirmed that the CMB came from hot gas. More surprisingly, however, it has also measured slight patchiness in the emission brightness — variations from place to place by a very small factor. The variations in brightness are caused by small differences in pressure, density, and temperature, from place to place. Apparently, this patchiness is caused by sound waves (acoustic pressure waves) moving back and forth in the 3000 K hot hydrogen gas. All the matter that is locked today in stars and galaxies was spread out uniformly in the 380,000-year-old universe. And how were these sound waves excited?

Let us imagine an overdense region of the primordial hydrogen gas. This over-density gravitationally attracted matter toward it while the heat of photons created an outward pressure. These counteracting forces of gravity and pressure produced sound waves analogous to those created in air. The overdense region contained photons, dark matter, and baryons (protons and neutrons). The pressure created a spherical sound wave of baryons and photons while the dark matter, which interacts only gravitationally, stayed at the center of the sound wave — the origin of the overdensity.

Is it possible now to capture those sounds from the CMB data and hear them? Let us consider three important parameters of sound: amplitude (loudness), frequency (pitch), and waveform (power spectrum, timbre or tone). The loudness of sound waves depends on the amplitude of the pressure waves — how much the pressure varies from peak-to-trough, compared to the mean pressure. From the CMB brightness variations we conclude that the strength of the pressure waves was between one ten-thousandth (10^{-4}) and one hundred-thousandth (10^{-5}), corresponding to around 110 decibels. Note that a loud rock concert produces about 115 decibels, a gunshot 140 decibels, and a whisper just 15 decibels. So our early universe was rocking!

The frequencies of these waves were very low, about 10^{-12} to 10^{-13} hertz. This means there was one sound wave every 20,000 to 200,000 years, moving with a velocity of about 50 to 60 percent of the speed of light. And this is roughly 48 to 52 octaves below a Concert A key, which resonates at 440 hertz. No human could hear this frequency. This is due to the enormous size (thousands of light-years) of the vibrating regions. But how do we measure the waveform (or timbre, tone, power spectrum) of these sounds? This is a most difficult task, and there are hundreds of research articles dealing with it. Analysis of the patchiness reveals the relative abundance of waves of different wavelengths. The most important property of the power spectrum is that it has a fundamental frequency with harmonics like any musical instrument. In this illustration, I show the CMB power spectrum and the

GARIK PLAYING BRIAN MAY'S COMPOSITION "39" AT THE MOSCOW INSTITUTE OF PHYSICS AND TECHNOLOGY IN 1983.

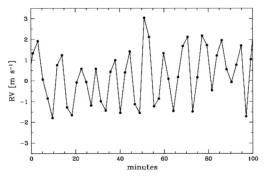

ZOOM OF RADIAL VELOCITY MEASUREMENTS SHOWING THE PRESENCE OF ACOUSTIC WAVES IN THE TIME SERIES WITH PERIODS OF AROUND 8 MIN IN THE ATMOSPHERE OF MU ARAE. CREDIT: F. BOUCHY ET AL. ASTRONOMY & ASTROPHYSICS, 440, 609-614 (2005).

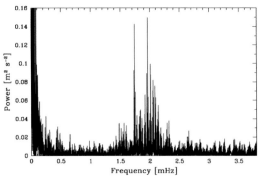

POWER SPECTRUM OF RADIAL VELOCITY MEASUREMENTS IN MU ARAE CAUSED BY ACOUSTIC WAVES IN THE SPECTRUM. CREDIT: F. BOUCHY ET AL. ASTRONOMY & ASTROPHYSICS, 440, 609-614 (2005).

power spectrum of a guitar.

The sound of the Big Bang appeared some 400,000 years after the Big Bang. This was a unique and peculiar moment in cosmic history. The sound was steady, rasping, rough, and not melodious. This is partly due to the fact that harmonics of the power spectrum are very wide, while the fundamental note itself contains almost two octaves! Nevertheless, this opening sound contains all the richness that is to come in the formation of galaxy clusters, galaxies, stars, and planets. In this sense, it was perhaps the most harmonic sound ever created in the universe.

Gas is a dominant state of matter in the observable universe. However, this does not mean that sound waves — pressure waves in gas — should be common, frequent and everywhere. There must be mechanisms to trigger these waves and provide sufficient energy for their propagation. Sound waves may last a very long time if certain physical conditions are satisfied. Even if all (or almost all) stars are made of gas, not all of them are able to create sound waves. And even if these waves are created, they may lose their energy very quickly and disappear. Things are not so obvious as they seem.

A star is a gaseous sphere, which may oscillate and form sound waves in different modes if suitable excitation mechanisms exist. Frequencies and amplitudes of the sound waves depend on the physical conditions (density, temperature, and so on) prevailing in the layers traversed by the waves. Observations of sound waves yield information about the age, internal rotation, composition and structure of a star. This important information cannot be obtained in any other way.

The discovery of sound waves in the Sun in 1962 opened a new area in astrophysics. Astronomers noticed in the spectrum of the Sun that some of the spectral lines were wiggling back and forth slightly, with periods of around five minutes. Because the frequency of spectral lines can be shifted if the source is moving toward or away from the observer (the Doppler effect), astronomers concluded that the surface of the Sun is vibrating back and forth. Apparently, some parts of the surface of the Sun were moving toward us and other parts were moving away from us. It was as if there were waves, rising and falling on the surface of the Sun. It became clear that the waves were in fact the surface manifestations of acoustic oscillations (sound waves) trapped beneath the surface of the Sun. After many years of hard work and with the advent of high-precision spectroscopy, positive detections of low frequency sound waves, infrasounds, in several solar-type stars, have been reported since 1999.

These oscillations are responsible for brightness variations frequently observed in many sunlike stars by such space telescopes as CoRoT and Kepler. However, one cannot convert light variation into a sound in a direct way because the amplitudes of sound waves (pressure) do not depend on light intensity in a linear way. This dependence is very complex and cannot be done without involving detailed model calculations.

Solar oscillations are thought to be excited by turbulent convection near the surface. Sunlike stars with temperatures below about 7000 K have a convective layer in their external envelopes, so one would expect that all these stars produce sound waves. But this is not the case. Even the acoustic spectrum of the Sun is variable on timescales of hours, days, or weeks. The amplitudes of individual modes can vary by a factor of two over timescales of a few days. The shape of the waveform is highly variable, and so far we were not able to identify a physical mechanism responsible for those variations.

Astronomers know very little about the formation and evolution of sound waves in sunlike stars. The field called asteroseismology is very young and we cannot yet understand everything about how it works. Nevertheless, theoretical models have made considerable progress in explaining and predicting a complex frequency distribution of sound waves in these stars. The most important problem with interpreting the observations is our poor knowledge of the amplitude of the expected oscillations. We can predict the frequencies of oscillations, but not their amplitudes. About 10 years ago, my colleague Patrick Eggenberger from Geneva Observatory in Switzerland and I calculated the waveforms (power spectra) of a large number of sunlike stars using theoretical models. We assumed that the distribution of amplitudes (the so-called envelope, or amplitude as a function of oscillation frequency) is similar to the one observed in the Sun. We also assumed that the velocity amplitude scales directly with the luminosity-to-mass ratio of the star.

Our goal was simple: compare the soundwaves of sunlike stars that have different temperatures, masses, and chemical compositions. Then, given that those sounds have very low frequencies, we had to transform them into the audio domain without changing their "waveforms" (e.g. timbre), as we heard them. We wondered if we could distinguish, for example, the sounds of stars that have similar temperatures, masses, and ages, but very different chemical compositions. We also compared the sounds of stars of similar masses and chemical compositions but different temperatures.

Moreover, we were able to follow the evolution of sound waves during stellar evolution. Apparently, we can distinguish different sounds when the star evolves for more than a billion years. The sound of a star suffers no significant change over a period of a few hundred million years. However, the way a star sounds changes considerably after a billion years. Given that the ages of these stars vary between 0.1 and 12 billion years, we could enjoy their "songs". Different stars would produce different songs! Obviously, our experiments had no scientific goals. I was simply having some fun with those sounds.

While playing some games with these star-sounds, I was in contact with the legendary science fiction writer Sir Arthur Clarke, the author of scifi "bible" 2001: A Space Odyssey. Somehow, I emailed him about my "experiments" and the game with these sounds.

Sir Arthur came up with an idea of "talking stars." Indeed, the acoustic spectrum of a star in a binary system will be affected by its neighbor. The star will have a different "sound" if it's alone. I was shocked to receive this email from a person who was not familiar with asteroseismology (although Sir Arthur had a background in astronomy). In fact, I called him to discuss this subject. I will never forget my long conversation with Sir Arthur, his voice, his heavy breath. I was thrilled to speak with one of the heroes of my childhood: Arthur C. Clarke!

He expressed an idea that stars may change their sounds if they have company (e.g. in a binary system). I responded to his email and received his amazing reply: "Looking back on the year which has gone wherever it is years go to, I am happy to report that it has been a fairly quiet and productive one. Best of all, peace does appear to have returned to Sri Lanka as have half a million tourists during the year! And the world has emerged from the long shadow of 9/11: I am still spooked by the fact that, more than 30 years ago, I chose the very date of the World Trade Center atrocity for the disaster which opens RENDEZVOUS WITH RAMA."

The laws of nature that govern the structure and the evolution of stars assign a unique spectrum of sound waves to each star. Just like every human being has his or her own voice, many stars have their own typical soundwave pattern which changes as the star evolves. The everlasting star songs cannot reach us because they cannot propagate in the interstellar space: they are locked inside the stars, but a careful researcher can reveal them.

For example, supernovae are very powerful stellar explosions that suddenly outshine entire galaxies and emit more energy than the Sun will in its entire lifetime. Only a star that is at least eight times more massive than our Sun can become a supernova. After the massive star has burned for at least eight to 10 million years, the star runs out of fuel and forms a dense iron core about the size of Earth. The iron core grows until its density becomes so great that it collapses under its own weight. The core contracts, but then, almost immediately, expands back again. This sudden expansion generates a shock wave that speeds outward and triggers the supernova explosion.

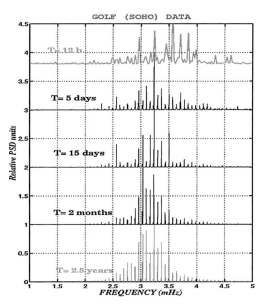

GOLF / SOHO: THE AMPLITUDES OF INDIVIDUAL MODES CAN SUFFER LARGE VARIATIONS OVER TIMESCALES OF HOURS, DAYS AND MONTHS.

FROM: SIR ARTHUR C CLARKE
<BLENHEIM@SRI-LANKA.NET>

SUBJECT:
RE:TALKING STARS, VERY IMPORTANT

DATE: MARCH 2, 2004 10:32:56 AM GMT
TO:GARIK ISRAELIAN <GIL@LL.IAC.ES>

DEAR GARIK,

THANKS FOR YOUR EMAIL OF 1ST MARCH
I AM FLATTERED! NOT SURE I CAN CLAIM
THE IDEA OF TALKING STARS! STILL I AM
PREPARED TO TAKE THE CREDIT AND RUN. . . .
I FEEL THERE IS A POSSIBLE TITLE COMBINING
SERENADE AND SERENDIP — THINK IT OVER!

I EXPECT YOU'VE SEEN MY LETTER IN THE
MARCH SKY AND TELESCOPE. ALSO, SENDING
YOU MY NOTE ON 'LUCY.'

ALL BEST,

ARTHUR,

2ND MARCH 2004

FRIENDS, EARTHLINGS, E.T.S LEND ME YOUR
SENSORY ORGANS!

There is a long standing problem related to the energy available to drive the supernova shock. In many simulations, the shock wave isn't powerful enough on its own to break through the dense layers of superhot gas that surround the core. Many theorists have focused their work on what might revive the shock wave into becoming a supernova explosion. It was proposed in the mid-1980s that ghost particles — neutrinos — may provide the extra energy needed to complete the explosion event. Nevertheless, it turned out that even this energy may not be enough.

Apparently, the old models of supernova explosions were not taking into account the presence of the proto-neutron star core in their simulations. The behavior of the core was considered unimportant. The effect of the neutron star core was taken into account in the most recent simulations done by the group of Adam Burrows (see his chapter in this book). With their simulation, Burrows's group found that another mechanism takes over and completes the explosive event. The Burrows simulation shows that rising hot matter and falling cold matter cause the star's core to oscillate and generate sound waves within hundreds of milliseconds. The core converts the gravitational energy of infalling material into acoustic waves that propagate outward on the opposite side of the star. The sound waves ram into one another and merge into a powerful shock wave that has sufficient energy to expel most of the stellar mass. Typical sound frequencies are about 200 to 400 hertz, in the audible range bracketing Middle C. Nevertheless, 3D simulations are required to confirm these results obtained from 2D models.

Acoustic sound waves exist in many different environments. The process of accretion onto a compact object in neutron star and black hole binaries can lead to the formation of sound waves. Some part of accreting matter with large angular momentum forms a disk, while another part (participating in a sub-Keplerian rotation) undergoes practically a free fall accretion until the centrifugal barrier becomes sufficient to halt the flow. Thus, one may expect that two distinct zones, a disk and a barrier, can be formed in the vicinity of a compact object. The acoustic waves standing in the hot area surrounding a neutron star have been proposed as an interesting possibility for the interpretation of the quasiperiodic oscillations detected by x-ray satellites. X-ray observations reveal a wealth of high-frequency x-ray variables which are believed to be due to the processes occurring on, or in the very vicinity, of an accreting neutron star or black hole.

Numerical simulations show that after passing a shock, the accreting gas becomes involved in the complex, predominantly tangential vortex motions. The resulting picture is quite distinct from a simple, spherical accretion: it allows for the existence of a hot coronal postshock region around a neutron star perfectly suitable for sound wave propagation. The standing acoustic waves may oscillate between two surfaces, the stellar surface and the outer boundary. These surfaces can reflect, absorb, and even emit sound waves. The acoustic oscillations of such a region can manifest themselves as high frequency (from a few hertz to 1 kilohertz) quasiperiodic oscillations.

Large scale sound waves carrying enormous amounts of energy may exist in galaxy clusters. Astronomers discovered in the 1970s that the vast reservoirs of gas located in galaxy clusters — large groups of hundreds or thousands of galaxies — glow brightly in x-rays. This suggested that the gas should be cooling and contracting as it radiates its energy away. For years, astronomers have tried to understand why there is so much hot gas in galaxy clusters and so little cool gas. Hot gas glowing with x-rays should cool because x-rays carry away some of the gas's energy. Dense gas near the cluster's center where x-ray emission is brightest should cool the fastest. As the gas cools, the pressure should decrease, causing gas to sink toward the center. Billions of stars could have been formed in these gaseous flows.

However, little evidence (if any) has been found for flows of cool gas or for star formation. This has forced astronomers to propose several physical mechanisms to explain how gas contained in clusters remains hot. One possible explanation for the heating appeared in 2003, when the Chandra X-ray Observatory observed enormous

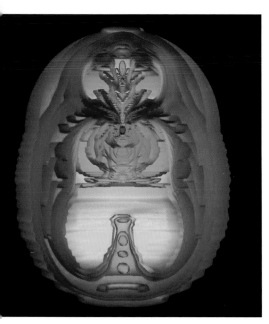

SUPERNOVA SIMULATIONS OF ACOUSTIC SOUND WAVES. CREDIT: ADAM BURROWS.

ripples — spanning thousands of light-years across — in the gas inside the Perseus Galaxy Cluster. Astronomers have proposed that the sound waves are generated by an active galaxy at the core of the cluster. This galaxy was spreading jets of radiation and matter into its surroundings due to the supermassive black hole at its center. Such sound waves could be responsible for heating up the gas in clusters.

Observations of the Perseus Cluster reveal two bubble-shaped cavities extending away from the central black hole. These cavities have been formed by jets of material pushing back the cluster gas. The jets, which are a counterintuitive side effect of the black hole gobbling matter in its vicinity, have long been suspected of heating the surrounding gas. However, the exact mechanism was unknown. The sound waves, seen spreading out from the cavities in the Chandra observation, could provide this heating mechanism. Interestingly, these waves have a frequency of millions of years.

Acoustic sound waves are everywhere: in stars, gaseous disks, and supernovae. They always require some medium to move through and require certain conditions to be formed. This medium could be stellar or planetary atmospheres, liquid water, or even the solid crusts of planets or superdense stars. Most of the time, the sound waves are detected indirectly because they produce certain observational effects (gas heating, Doppler shifts of spectral lines, etc.). It is a very serious observational and theoretical challenge to detect and study them in different cosmic environments.

The optical universe has been with us for thousands of years and only recently have we became aware of another "type" of the universe — the acoustic one! The acoustic universe is as enigmatic as the electromagnetic. Amazingly, we can "hear" the sounds of the acoustic universe if we continue the magnificent battle of understanding the physical world that surrounds us.

BLACK HOLE CYNGUS X-1. CREDIT: NASA/ CXC/M. WEISS.

A BLACK HOLE LIES IN THE HEART OF THE
MILKY WAY GALAXY, IN THE BRIGHT OBJECT
SGR A*, SEEN BY THE CHANDRA X-RAY
OBSERVATORY. CREDIT: NASA/CXC/MIT/F.
BAGANOFF, R. SHCHERBAKOV ET AL.

KIP THORNE

BLACK HOLES: THE MOST LUMINOUS OBJECTS IN THE UNIVERSE — BUT NO LIGHT!

Born in Logan, Utah, on June 1, 1940, Kip Stephen Thorne has made a career of groundbreaking contributions in astrophysics and theoretical physics. One of the world's preeminent experts on black holes and on general relativity, Thorne graduated from the California Institute of Technology in 1962 and earned his Ph.D. at Princeton University in 1965.

Joining Caltech as an associate professor in 1967, he progressed to become the Richard Feynman Professor of Theoretical Physics, eventually retiring with an emeritus addition. He is now involved in film and writing projects. His first film project, Interstellar, teams him with Steven Spielberg.

In 1984, he cofounded the LIGO Project (short for Laser Interferometer Gravitational-Wave Observatory) to open the gravitational-wave window onto the universe. LIGO is the largest project ever funded by the National Science Foundation. In 1988, Thorne triggered modern research on whether the laws of physics allow backward time travel. In 1973, he coauthored the classic textbook Gravitation with Charles Misner and John Wheeler, from which most of the present generation of scientists have learned general relativity theory.

KIP THORNE AT STARMUS.

When a massive star exhausts the nuclear fuel whose burning keeps it hot, the star's internal pressure plunges. Gravity overwhelms the pressure and pulls the star inward upon itself. The star implodes, shrinking smaller and smaller, and the gravity on its shrinking surface becomes stronger and stronger (because of Newton's Inverse-Square Law). Ultimately, when the star has shrunk to a few tens of kilometers in size, its gravity grows so enormous that nothing, not even light, can escape its grip. The star creates a black hole around itself. The star itself, inside the black hole, continues to shrink and is destroyed by a singularity of infinite, chaotic gravity that resides at the hole's center. This story is an unequivocal prediction of Albert Einstein's general relativity theory.

There are millions of black holes in our Milky Way Galaxy, and trillions in the universe; and they can wreak havoc on their environments.

If the imploding star had a companion star orbiting it, the black hole will inherit the companion. The hole's gravity can then pull gas off the companion, and the gas will spiral inward toward the hole, producing a gaseous disk so hot that it emits x-rays rather than light. Astronomers see many such disks, encircling heavy, dark objects that must be black holes.

In the centers of galaxies, such as our Milky Way, supermassive black holes have somehow formed — perhaps from the implosion of supermassive stars, perhaps from the collision and merger of many smaller black holes. These giant holes, a million to 10 billion times heavier than the Sun, and with sizes as large as our solar system, can tear stars apart and spread the stellar debris around themselves as hot, gaseous disks. Magnetic fields, embedded in such a disk, interact with a vortex of twisting space that sticks out of the black hole (and that I shall discuss later), to produce gigantic jets of outflowing energy. These jets sweep out into intergalactic space, sometimes carrying as much luminosity as all the stars in the galaxy put together! Astronomers have seen and studied hundreds of these jets and their surrounding disks, but have never seen the central black holes because they are black. They emit no light.

What is a black hole made from? Not from matter like you and me, but from warped space and time.

As an analogy to explain this, imagine a child's trampoline, a large sheet of rubber attached to tall stilts. A heavy rock bends the rubber downward as shown in

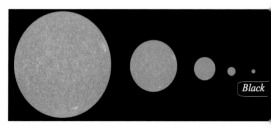

THE IMPLOSION OF A STAR TO FORM A BLACK HOLE.

A BLACK HOLE ENCIRCLED BY A HOT, GASEOUS ACCRETION DISK, AND TWO JETS EMERGING FROM THE HOLE'S VICINITY. CREDIT: K.S. THORNE, BLACK HOLES AND TIME WARPS (NORTON, 1995).

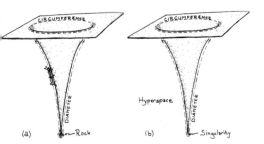

(A) A TRAMPOLINE WITH A ROCK AT ITS CENTER AND AN ANT EXPLORING ITS SHAPE.

(B) SPACE AROUND A BLACK HOLE, AS VIEWED FROM A HIGHER DIMENSIONAL HYPERSPACE THAT IS NOT PART OF OUR UNIVERSE.

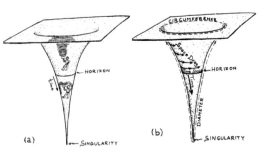

(A) I FALL INTO A BLACK HOLE, TRANSMITTING MICROWAVE SIGNALS TO YOU AS I FALL.

(B) THE WARPING OF TIME AND DRAGGING OF SPACE INTO MOTION AROUND A BLACK HOLE.

this illustration. Now, imagine you are an ant; a blind ant. The rubber sheet is your entire universe, and you explore it by measuring its shape. You measure the circumference of a circle surrounding the central rock by walking around it, and you then measure the circle's diameter. You walk and walk and walk along the diameter. It is a great distance, you discover; the diameter, in fact, is far larger than the circumference. Being an intelligent ant, you conclude that the space of your universe is warped. It does not have the flat geometry described by Euclid; rather, it has the geometry of a warped rubber sheet.

If we, in our universe, could take a two-dimensional slice through the equator of a black hole and measure its shape, we would find a shape identical to that of the ant's rubber sheet: a diameter far larger than circumference, as suggested in this illustration. The hole's space is bent downward in some higher-dimensional "hyperspace" that is not part of our universe. And at the center, in place of a heavy rock, there is a so-called singularity where space is infinitely sharply warped— a vicious singularity that destroys any matter that strays into its vicinity.

Suppose I fall into a black hole, transmitting microwave signals to you on the outside as I fall, as suggested in this illustration (a). When I reach the black hole's edge, which we call its horizon, gravity becomes so strong that my signals can no longer escape. Inside the horizon, the signals get pulled downward into the singularity along with me. I pay the ultimate price that I can't publish the results of my explorations. I also die, and my results die with me.

The horizon and its overwhelming gravity are actually produced by an extreme time warp: near the horizon, time's rate of flow slows to a crawl, as shown in this illustration (b). If you were to fly down near a black hole's horizon and hover there for a few days and then return home to Earth, you would discover that millions of years have elapsed on Earth. You have aged only a few days, but your friends are long since dead.

Now, Einstein's Law of Time Warps says that, "Things like to live where they age the most slowly, and gravity pulls them there." On Earth, time flows more slowly than in outer space by 4 parts in 10 billion, and that (according to Einstein) is enough to account for the gravity that holds us on Earth's surface. Because the slowing of time becomes enormous as one nears a black hole's horizon, the pull of gravity becomes enormous there; and precisely at the horizon, time slows to a complete halt, so the pull of gravity is infinite.

Inside the horizon, time still flows. But, strangely, it flows in a direction that you would have thought is spatial: toward the singularity at the hole's center. This is why nothing can get out of a black hole; to get out, things would have to travel upward, which means backward in time, and nothing can do that. This explanation of a black hole's blackness is equivalent to the "infinite gravitational pull" explanation. The two explanations are related by Einstein's Law of Time Warps.

This next figure is a precise map of warped spacetime around a fast-spinning black hole, as predicted by Einstein's relativity. The shape of the 2-dimensional surface is precisely that of the hole's space, in its equatorial "plane", as seen from hyperspace.

The colors indicate the slowing of time near the horizon. The horizon is the black circle at the bottom (it becomes a sphere if we examine the hole's full three-dimensional space rather than just its two-dimensional equatorial "plane." The white arrows indicate the speed of whirl of space caused by the hole's rotation.

If two massive stars orbit around each other in a binary system, and both stars implode to form black holes, the result is two black holes orbiting each other: a black-hole binary. As these holes travel around each other, they produce ripples in the fabric of space that travel outward, like water waves from your finger if you stir it in a quiet pond. Those ripples are called gravitational waves. They travel into the universe at the speed of light, carrying a detailed, but encoded, picture of their source, the orbiting black holes. The waves also carry energy.

As the orbiting black holes lose energy to the waves, they gradually spiral together, then collide and merge to form a single, larger black hole, as depicted in this illustration. When they collide, the holes emit gigantically strong gravitational waves. The waves' luminosity (the power emitted per unit time) is 10,000 times greater than the luminosity of all the stars in the universe put together. Ten thousand universe luminosities, and no light! Only gravitational waves.

If the holes have small masses, say 10 times as great as the Sun, then the collision and humongous waves are brief: a few milliseconds. If the holes are supermassive — the denizens of the cores of two galaxies that themselves have collided and merged — the collision and waves last longer: a few days or even a year. The waves carry a detailed, encoded picture of the collision, a picture we would like to extract and study. To this I shall return.

The tornados of whirling space, attached to each black hole in a binary, behave wondrously when the holes collide. To explain this, I must first describe the tornados more carefully.

Imagine two people hanging above a black hole's poles, as in this illustration. The top person's feet are closer to the hole than her head, so they get dragged by the hole's whirling space (purple arrows) faster than her head. As a result, her head sees her feet dragged counterclockwise (lower red arrow), and — remarkably — her feet see her head dragged counterclockwise (upper red arrow). It's like wringing water out of a wet towel; your left hand sees your right turn counterclockwise, and your right hand, looking at your left, sees it turn counterclockwise. In this sense, the whirling space at the hole's north pole has a counterclockwise twist.

This twist was recently discovered in Einstein's equations, by a team of young physicists working with me. And we discovered that the twist is guided by, in other words carried by and controlled by, things we call vortex lines, a name we have borrowed from the theory of fluids. There are counterclockwise vortex lines, collected into a single vortex, sticking out of the north pole of the black hole (colored red in this illustration) and a vortex of clockwise vortex lines sticking out of the south pole (colored blue).These are similar to magnetic field lines that stick out of Earth, but instead of guiding compass needles like a magnetic field lines do, they control the twist of space, and they twist everything they encounter. We have painted the hole's horizon the color of the vortex lines that stick out of it.

My team has simulated the spiraling in and collision of two spinning black holes using a large cluster of computers. Our simulations revealed that, when the holes collide and merge, their four vortexes of twisting space get deposited on the merged hole's horizon. As the merged hole itself spins, it splays the four vortexes outward and backward, like four streams of water splaying out from a whirling sprinkler head, as in part (a) of the illustration (overleaf, top). As these vortexes spiral outward into the universe, they become gravitational waves.

If, instead of spiraling together from a binary orbit, the two black holes collide head on, then the four vortexes attached to the merged black hole do not acquire an outward spiral. Instead, each vortex sloshes back and forth between clockwise twist and counterclockwise, and with each slosh, the hole throws off a toroidal vortex ring that resembles a smoke ring, shown in part (b). As these rings travel outward, they become gravitational waves.

The power of a black hole's vortexes is illustrated next (overleaf, bottom), showing snapshots from a computer simulation of a spinning black hole ripping apart a companion neutron star. The star is 1.5 times as massive as the Sun and has a diameter of 25 kilometers. The black hole is 4.5 times as massive as the Sun and spins around the axis marked by a red line. The star and black hole initially orbit each other in a horizontal plane in part (a) of the figure. As they orbit, they lose energy to gravitational waves and, consequently, spiral inward. As they near each other, the hole's gravity begins to tear the star apart in part (b), and the hole's vortexes then throw the disrupting star upward, into the hole's equatorial plane (perpendicular to the red line; see parts (c) and (d). Imagine the power required to throw 1.5 solar masses of nuclear material upward from the horizontal plane and

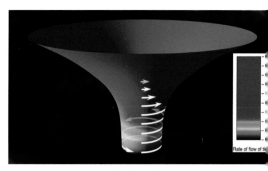

A MAP OF THE WARPED SPACETIME AROUND A FAST-SPINNING BLACK HOLE.

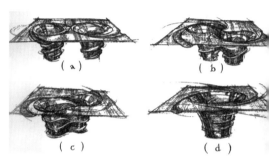

AN ARTIST'S CONCEPTION OF TWO BLACK HOLES IN A BINARY, SPIRALING INWARD, COLLIDING AND MERGING TO FORM A SINGLE BLACK HOLE.

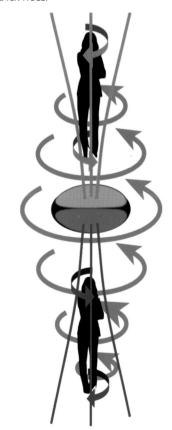

TWO PEOPLE HANGING ABOVE A BLACK HOLE'S POLES.

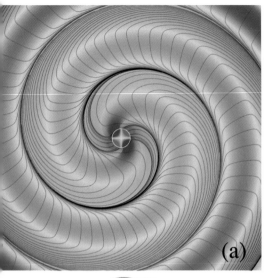

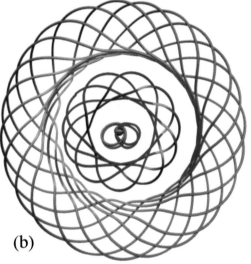

(A) FOUR VORTEXES OF TWISTING SPACE, STICKING OUT OF A MERGED, SPINNING BLACK HOLE. (B) VORTEX RINGS EJECTED BY A MERGED, NONSPINNING BLACK HOLE.

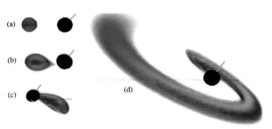

A SPINNING BLACK HOLE TEARS APART A NEUTRON STAR, ONE MADE FROM NUCLEAR MATTER.

into the hole's equatorial plane! The hole's vortexes are impressive.

About 70 percent of the disrupted star's matter is quickly swallowed by the hole, according to this simulation by Matt Duez and his colleagues at Cornell University. The remaining 30 percent gets strung out into a disk of very hot gas, which emits a short burst of neutrinos and gamma rays and then shines brightly with light.

Coordinated observations of the gravitational waves, neutrinos, gamma rays and light will reveal much about the black hole and its vortexes, the neutron star and its nuclear matter, and their behaviors in this cataclysmic event. Comparison with computer simulations will be crucial for understanding the observations. This is called Multimessenger Astronomy and will be an exciting enterprise when it begins, around 2017.

How can we detect and monitor the gravitational waves? Each wave contains space-twisting vortexes; but after traveling across the great stretches of intergalactic space, the vortexes have become exceedingly weak. Their twist is far too small for detection with modern technology.

Fortunately, the waves also stretch space and squeeze it. This stretch and squeeze are also weak, but they are ideally suited for detection and monitoring by a technique called laser interferometry. Accordingly, in 1983 my colleagues Rai Weiss at MIT and Ron Drever at Caltech and I conceived the Laser Interferometer Gravitational Wave Observatory — LIGO for short.

The concept for LIGO's gravitational wave detectors is depicted in this illustration. Four mirrors (each weighing 40 kilograms) hang from overhead supports. Two mirrors are oriented along one direction (say, east-west); the other two, along the perpendicular direction (say, north-south); and the mirrors on each "arm" are separated by 4 kilometers (denoted L in the figure).When a gravitational wave arrives, it pushes the east-west mirrors apart and the north-south mirrors together, by a tiny amount: $DL = 10^{-17}$ centimeters (approximately). As the wave moves on from crest to trough, the directions of the stretch and squeeze reverse, and then reverse again; and the time pattern of those reversals (called the wave's waveform) carries, encoded, the picture of the wave's source.

In LIGO, these motions are monitored using a laser beam — ultrahigh precision laser metrology, and pictures of the source are extracted from the observed waveform by comparing with computer simulations.

Weiss, who invented this idea, is brilliant. For several years, I was extremely skeptical that it could ever succeed, but I was wrong. To understand my skepticism, consider just how small are the mirror's motions: the thickness of a human hair is about 10^{-2} centimeters. Divide that by 100 and you get the wavelength of the light used in LIGO, one micron. Divide by 10,000 and you get the diameter of an atom, the smallest thing ever imaged by any kind of microscope. Divide by 100,000 and you get the diameter of the nucleus of an atom. Divide by another factor 1,000 and you get the motions that LIGO must monitor: 10^{-17} centimeters!

This distance is so small, that at this level of precision, LIGO's moving mirrors are governed not by the laws of classical physics, but rather by the laws of quantum physics. For example, the Heisenberg uncertainty principle dictates that the very act of measuring the location of a 40-kilogram mirror with this precision will inevitably perturb the mirror's velocity by an amount that is discernable in LIGO. Humans have never before seen a human-sized object behave quantum mechanically. In LIGO we will do so within the next several years, and to deal with this we have had to incorporate principles from a new, 21st century technology, called quantum information theory. My students and I spent much of our time in the early 1980s exploring the needed technology theoretically, and again in the early 2000s developing concrete designs for it.

LIGO is now nearing maturity. In the 1990s, my experimental colleagues (under the leadership of Caltech's Barry Barish) built facilities to house our gravitational wave detectors, and from 2000 to 2005, they installed a first generation of detectors and debugged them meticulously until they reached their design sensitivity. From 2005 to 2010 we carried out an initial set of searches for cosmic gravitational waves, not just from colliding black holes but also from many other sources. We saw nothing; but that was expected.

When my colleagues and I proposed LIGO, we warned that this first generation of detectors might not be good enough to see waves. However, the experimenters had to build them and get experience with them as a precursor to building a second generation of detectors, called Advanced LIGO, which are far more complex technically and will be far more sensitive — sensitive enough to see a rich variety of waves. Our experimental team began installing Advanced LIGO into the LIGO facilities in October 2010, and the installation is going well. By 2017, and perhaps sooner, these detectors should be seeing many waves, and together with similar detectors in Europe (the French-Italian-Dutch Virgo Project and the German-British Geo Project), and other types of astronomical instruments, they should be ushering in the era of Multimessenger Astronomy.

LIGO and its partners can only observe black holes less massive than about 1,000 suns. Heavier black holes — the supermassive ones in the cores of galaxies like our Milky Way — produce waves with far longer wavelengths (of the order of the distance between Earth and the Moon, or Earth and the Sun) and far lower frequency (one cycle per minute or hours or longer).These waves will be detected and monitored by a LIGO-like detector that flies in space: three spacecraft that track each other with laser beams. The European Space Agency is planning a space mission of this sort, called LISA, the Laser Interferometer Space Antenna, and will fly a precursor space mission to test its technology in 2014. (The U.S. space agency NASA used to be a partner in LISA, but was forced to pull out of this and other astrophysics missions by huge cost overruns on the James Webb Space Telescope.)

For even heavier black holes, those weighing billions rather than millions of suns, a third type of detector is needed. These holes waves have wavelengths far larger than the solar system and wave periods of months to years. They are being sought using LIGO-like detectors in which one of the "mirrors" (really just a moving mass) is Earth, and the other is a pulsar far out in interstellar space. Radio telescopes on Earth monitor the radio pulses from a network of dozens of these pulsars, looking for tiny oscillations in the pulses' arrival times, caused by gravitational waves. This International Pulsar Timing Array, as it is called, is likely to detect its first gravitational waves in the coming 10 years; maybe five.

Black holes are made from warped space and time — and that warping exhibits a remarkable richness. I have only exposed you to one piece of that richness: the vortexes of twisting space that black holes transfer to each other when they collide, and that generate rings or spirals of gravitational waves that fly outward. There are also objects called tendexes that stick out of black holes. They stretch and squeeze space in interesting ways and participate in the gravitational waves that black holes generate.

Numerical simulations are a powerful tool for probing these vortexes and tendexes theoretically. Gravitational wave observations will reveal them in nature and show us their richness and influence in the real universe. These tools — numerical simulations and gravitational wave detectors — are ushering in a golden era of research on black holes.

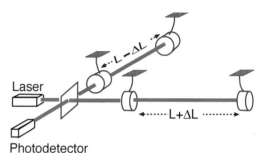

A LASER INTERFEROMETER GRAVITATIONAL-WAVE DETECTOR.

LIGO'S TWO GRAVITATIONAL-WAVE OBSERVATORIES. TOP: HANFORD, WASHINGTON. BOTTOM: LIVINGSTON, LOUISIANA.

ROBERT WILLIAMS

GEORGE SMOOT

SECTION 5

BEGINNINGS AND ENDINGS

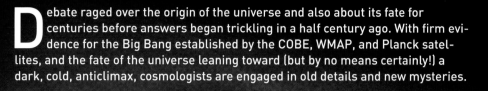

Debate raged over the origin of the universe and also about its fate for centuries before answers began trickling in a half century ago. With firm evidence for the Big Bang established by the COBE, WMAP, and Planck satellites, and the fate of the universe leaning toward (but by no means certainly!) a dark, cold, anticlimax, cosmologists are engaged in old details and new mysteries.

Oxford University astrophysicist Joe Silk paints a vivid overall picture of the history of things in his discussion of the creation of the universe.

George Smoot of the University of California at Berkeley talks about a message from the beginning of the universe, which allows walking through the cosmic distance scale. Time and space are interwoven in this grand cosmic journey through the history of eternity.

As a slight look back to the past, Robert Williams of the Space Telescope Science Institute looks at five breakthrough discoveries — the cosmic microwave background radiation, dark matter, exoplanets, dark energy, and compact objects like pulsars and black holes.

JOE SILK

WOODCUT REPRESENTING THE MEDIEVAL UNIVERSE; UNCERTAIN ORGIN.

JOE SILK

THE CREATION OF THE UNIVERSE

English astronomer and cosmologist Joseph Ivor Silk was born in London on December 3, 1942. He is one of the world's great authorities on dark matter, galaxy formation, and cosmology, and was until 2011 holder of the Savilian Chair of Astronomy at the University of Oxford and director of the Beecroft Institute for Particle Physics and Cosmology.

Silk studied mathematics at the University of Cambridge and earned his Ph.D. from Harvard in 1968. In 2011 he received the Balzan Prize for his work on the early universe. Collisionless damping of the structure of the cosmic microwave background anisotropies, called "Silk damping," is named after him.

JOE SILK AT STARMUS.

How did we get to where we are, and to where are we going? There are surprises out there, and one can ask finally, how much have we really learned about the universe?

The person who was behind most of this was Einstein. He saw that something was wrong with astronomy. There was a great puzzle, it was a very, very specific observational result confirmed over many years of observation, and it motivated him to build a whole new theory of gravity, the theory of general relativity. From this framework there emerged a radical new vision of the universe, a consequence of the theory of gravitation he had just invented. Einstein began with the idea that the geometry of space is curved, so that Euclid's laws of geometry no longer applied, and this led to a new way of describing gravity. He viewed the source of gravity as the curvature of space, and the curvature of space in turn as the manifestation of gravity, with matter as the ultimate culprit for doing all of this. He had a famous equation that tells us how matter curves space, and matter moves in response to the curvature of space. That's gravity. So I'm doing something bad here. I'm describing equations, and now I'm going to put the equations aside.

What ultimately came out of Einstein's theory was the theory of the expanding universe. This was not due to Einstein in any way, because he tried to understand the universe and he realized that, with gravity and mass, it would collapse. He invented something that seemed very ugly to him, called the cosmological constant, which opposed gravity. It was a sort of anti-gravity. That was how he stabilized the universe. And then everything was turned on its side, in large part by a Russian.

Here we are in meetings where Russians have had a great influence on space exploration, and, really, we should also celebrate their contribution to cosmology. The Russian scientist who revolutionized cosmology was a great theorist who died at a relatively young age. His name was Alexander Friedman, and he found an error in Einstein's calculations that had led Einstein to overlook a much simpler explanation of the universe. The universe really could be expanding, and then there would be no need to have this somewhat arbitrary addition of anti-gravity.

Friedman originally published his work around 1924 in Russian, but apparently no one in the West was aware of his results. At the same time, in Pasadena, California, Edwin Hubble, an observer who had little respect for theory, was busy measuring the distances to galaxies. He realized, with other data and eventually with some of his own, that the galaxies were moving away very fast indeed. And the further you looked, the faster they seemed to go. Hubble's major contribution was to establish the distances to the nearby galaxies that possessed significant redshifts. Hubble plotted distances against galaxy velocities, inferred from the redshifts, and discovered what we now call the "Hubble Law of the Expansion of the Universe." This relation proved that, if you interpret redshifts as velocities, we have emerged from a very dense and compact phase. The further you look, rather like an explosion, objects are apparently moving faster away from you just like on the surface of an expanding balloon. This was much later called the Big Bang.

Not everyone accepted that the universe was expanding. The delay in the interpretation was in large part because Hubble, and a number of his colleagues, were not convinced that redshift is equivalent to velocity. The water had been muddied by another cosmologist, the Dutch astrophysicist Willem de Sitter, who found a solution of Einstein's equation in which a completely empty universe was expanding according to a Hubble-like law. Clearly here it was space that was expanding. In fact our modern view of the universe is indeed that it is space that is expanding, with the galaxies carried along for the ride.

But let us return to 1929 when Hubble published his discovery. What is perhaps not so widely known is that another person, Georges Lemaître, independently of Friedman, had also discovered the expanding universe. Moreover, Lemaître went one step further than Friedmann, and did this at least two years before Hubble announced his new law. What Lemaître did was to examine the data on galaxy distances and redshifts, published in part by Hubble, and plot, just as Hubble later did, redshift against distance.

This illustration is a graph that was never published in the 1920s, but certainly could have been. It is data that Lemaître compiled and fitted with an expansion law in 1927. His paper was written in French, and was not known in the West at all until after Hubble's work was published. With the encouragement of Sir Arthur Eddington, it was translated into English and published in 1930. The remarkable part of the story is that the data with Lemaître's fit to what we now call the Hubble constant was omitted from the paper.

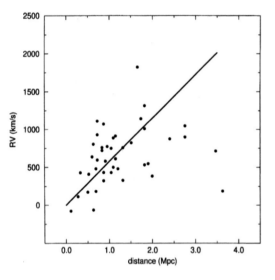

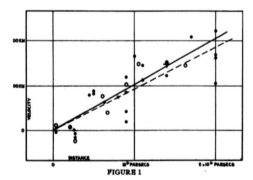

DATA AS FIT BY LEMAÎTRE IN 1928 (TOP) AND
BY HUBBLE IN 1929 (BOTTOM).

Some recent research shows that this omission of Lemaître's fit to the data was not censored, but was cut due to Lemaître's modesty. In recently discovered correspondence, he told the editor of the Monthly Notices of the Royal Astronomical Society that in the English version of his 1927 paper, which he himself translated, he decided to omit his derivation of the expansion rate of the universe because Hubble had subsequently obtained a similar result.

You can see, if you look at Hubble's data, compared to Lemaître's data, that Hubble and Lemaitre had basically the same slope, and indeed the same data. That's how things were, until Hubble went on of course to achieve worldwide fame as the discoverer of the expanding universe. So what we should be calling the Hubble-Lemaître Law of the universe is called the Hubble Law. We should be waiting, in my opinion, for the future Lemaître Space Telescope. But we'll see if that occurs.

One year after Hubble's discovery, Einstein came to visit Hubble in Pasadena. A famous photograph, presumably staged for the press, shows Einstein peering through the 100-inch Mt. Wilson reflector alongside Hubble to presumably confirm the discovery of the expansion of the universe. Einstein later regretted very much introducing the cosmological constant, as a mechanism for implementing anti-gravity. Cosmology was to go on relatively smoothly for several decades with an expanding universe that required no weird additions to simple physics. In fact, Einstein had opened a Pandora's Box, and the cosmological constant was to return with a vengeance half a century later.

Astronomy in the first half of the twentieth century was a fairly classical field. Astronomers were trained to measure the brightnesses of stars and measure their distances with spectrographs and so forth, and the whole field of cosmology just went on gathering more and more data. This is what astronomers love to do, to accumulate more and more data. It was only when another group of scientists got involved in the 1940s that things changed.

Before then, just to put things into perspective, we can compare the region where Hubble and Lemaître had data, in the plot of expansion versus distance, to where all the modern data is situated. This takes us out from a fraction of the speed of light to almost the speed of light, and just continued relentlessly as telescope power increased. Of course Lemaître and Hubble did not get the slope quite right. But that's a detail due to errors in distance measurements. Now the expansion law of the universe is well confirmed out to distances of gigaparsecs.

The astronomers worked long hours, but it was not their work that led to the next revolution in cosmology. What was it that changed? Well, the nuclear physicists also had a long hard look at the expanding universe. They realized that the early universe was very dense, and therefore it could, in principle, if it were hot as well, replicate the interior of a star. And it would then be an ideal place to study nuclear reactions.

Now, this wasn't obvious to all of the nuclear physicists, but there was one particular genius, Russian émigré to the United States George Gamow, along with his graduate student Ralph Alpher, who calculated what might happen in the first minutes of the expanding universe. They realized that one could make, by nuclear fusion reactions, some of the chemical elements. In the first seconds, the universe consisted of a hot bath of electrons, protons and neutrons, along with radiation. Neutrons are very reactive and provided the essential ingredient for building up the chemical elements.

The first elements to be synthesized were the light elements. Helium, for example, as well as deuterium and lithium. Now, Gamow hoped that they could make all of the chemical elements in the first minutes of what soon came to be called the Big Bang. However, he turned out to be wrong because elements of mass 8 are unstable so one cannot go from helium at mass 4 up to carbon at mass 12. But he and his collaborators did make most of the light elements, and this has turned out to be one of the great predictions of physics. We have since measured those abundances, and the results are a wonderful testimony to the fact that the universe once was a very perfect furnace. And one of the outcomes of what Gamow did was to realize there would be a fossil glow left over from this early heat in the universe.

We will come to what that means in a second, but before I do let me tell you briefly how the elements out of which we are made formed, and that is from exploding stars, which you heard about in the previous talk. One of the results of the theory of exploding stars is that as the star uses up its hydrogen, it then makes heavier elements. As it burns nuclear fuel, a massive star gets hotter and hotter in the center. It eventually becomes unstable and explodes. The debris is scattered into clouds that form more stars, and lo and behold, here we are!

The researchers who first put this into context, quantitatively, of understanding the origin of the ashes of which we are made, and what fraction of them came from stars, were Margaret and Geoffrey Burbidge, Fred Hoyle, and Willy Fowler, in the 1950s. Fowler, in particular, brought nuclear physics into mainstream astronomy, along with his more astronomical collaborators, to reach these conclusions. One of the interesting sociological factors in physics and astrophysics, is that of these four researchers, only one of them received the Nobel Prize for this work. That's the way it often happens in physics.

The next step in the story arises from the fossil glow from the first minutes of the universe about which Gamow and Alpher had speculated. It had to be there in the sky. They never thought too carefully about how the relic heat might actually be measured. Decades later, the glow from the Big Bang was finally discovered. It was detected by two researchers who were allocated a telescope, the Echo telescope that was originally used for early satellite telecommunications at Bell Laboratories in New Jersey. The telescope was discarded by the engineers and put at the disposal of two radio astronomers, Arno Penzias and Robert Wilson, to map the Milky Way Galaxy.

The telescope's novel asset was sensitivity over a large beam, and Penzias and Wilson soon realized that not all of the microwave glow they measured could possibly be coming from our galaxy. A component of the glow was completely uniform over the sky, not associated with the Milky Way or indeed with any other feature on the sky. They had of course discovered the relic radiation from the Big Bang, the cosmic microwave background. This was in 1964. And this radiation has since been realized to be another of the principal pillars of the Big Bang.

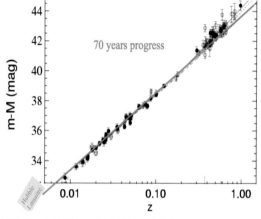

THE HUBBLE LAW, CIRCA 2000, WTH THE REGION SURVEYED BY HUBBLE IN YELLOW.

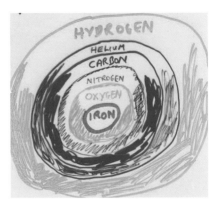

A MASSIVE STAR AT THE END OF ITS LIFE.

Over the subsequent decades, astronomers made improved maps of the microwave background. One of the few modern scientific discoveries that has made major headlines around the world occurred one day in February 1991 when George Smoot, designer of an experiment on board the COBE satellite, announced the first all-sky maps of the background radiation for which Penzias and Wilson had just measured one or two frequencies some two decades earlier. Here was real progress. A discovery like this really captured the attention of the world. The COBE satellite, in 1991, produced some remarkable maps of the microwave sky. We are looking at tiny deviations at a few parts in a hundred thousand, hundred thousandth of the average temperature in the sky, which is itself just three degrees Kelvin above absolute zero in temperature. This made headlines in the United States, and an even bigger splash in the U.K., with banner headlines on newspaper front pages of "How the Universe Began." Even in France, it was on page 3 of Le Monde," Les grumeaux de la soupe cosmique."

Of course this discovery eventually received confirmation by much better data. This illustration shows another satellite image, results from the WMAP satellite that was launched a decade ago and is still taking data after some 11 years in orbit. You see a map of the sky in microwaves, with the average radiation intensity of 3 degrees Kelvin subtracted out. The contaminating foreground of the Milky Way has been subtracted. The resulting tiny fluctuations in temperature are the seeds of structure from which all galaxies emerged. We are looking at a snapshot of the universe as it was when it was hot and dense. The microwave photons travel directly to us, carrying information about the first 300,000 years of the Big Bang. From these tiny fluctuations, the universe took on its present form.

This discovery of fluctuations also merited a Nobel Prize for the pioneering results from the COBE satellite led by George Smoot and his colleague John Mather. The second dramatic experiment on the satellite was designed by Mather to measure the spectrum of the radiation. In the sky, we find a perfect blackbody spectrum, testimony to the ideal furnace of the first few minutes of the Big Bang, that Gamow and his colleagues had conjectured about many years before. The next illustration shows the blackbody spectrum in microwaves, and for those of you who care about error bars, these are 400 standard deviation error bars. It is the best blackbody that we have ever seen in any terrestrial laboratory, yet it is up there in the sky pervading the universe. If you turn your TV set in between stations, out of tune, and see the fuzz on the screen, one percent of that fuzz is this universal signal from the distant universe.

There was one more "revolution" in astronomy when another group of physicists entered the field. It is interesting sociologically in science to see how something new often is brought in from some external community and succeeds in having a big impact. That seems to be what has happened in physics, in astrophysics, and certainly in cosmology, and this time it was the turn of particle physics. Just as Gamow had realized, decades earlier, that the first minutes of the universe were fertile territory for nuclear reactions at high density and high temperature, particle physicists noted that by going to even earlier instants in the conjectured Big Bang, one would get to such extreme densities and energies that one could do better than any conceivable particle accelerator. You would have to build a linear collider all the way from Earth to the Moon to replicate the energies in the first fraction of a second of the Big Bang. This is impossible in the best of times, with any conceivable budget.

So the early universe was paradise for particle physics, and this was how cosmology took off as a branch of physics. It was realized that the fundamental interactions — there are four of them — become unified as you go to very high energy. So here we are today in a universe with extraordinarily diverse forces. We live in a universe dominated by electromagnetic forces, on the very smallest scales there are the nuclear forces but so bound up that it is hard to see them directly, and gravity is incredibly weak compared to these forces. But as you go to larger scales, the nuclear and electromagnetic forces are shielded. And as you move to higher

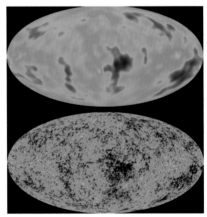

A COMPARISON OF COBE (TOP) AND WMAP (BOTTOM).

energies, the forces get unified. We measure the trend toward this unity already in current day colliders, but if you extrapolate with particle theory you reach a point where the nuclear and the electromagnetic forces are unified together.

Continuing this journey to higher energies, we reach an ultimate point about which we only conjecture, and for which we don't have the theory yet. This is where gravity and quantum physics were unified together. Finally, we have arrived at the end of a long climb to higher and higher energies, which means smaller and smaller scales. This is truly what we think of as the beginning of the Big Bang. It is some incredibly high energy, at some incredibly small time, that we call the Planck scale, named after Max Planck, the founder of the quantum theory of atoms. This is the point where we think things began but we do not yet have the quantum gravity theory in hand to describe it properly. I will tell you in a moment about some of the consequences of the quantum theory of gravity.

We are now in a low temperature universe. Looking back in time, to where does this lead us? Well, some new cosmology came out of this conjecture about the beginning of the universe. Pioneering particle physicists Andrei Linde and Alan Guth realized that as the universe went through these transitions, from unification to the breakup and separation of the fundamental forces, there was an inevitable phase transition. It was a bit like ice melting; you released a lot of latent heat. In this case, this extra energy from this changing phase gave a boost to the expansion that dramatically accelerated for a brief moment. This rapidly became known as the Theory of Inflation. And it had one remarkable effect.

The universe became very, very large. The universe, initially, could have been completely chaotic and arbitrary. Imagine a wrinkled balloon. You blow this balloon up enormously, it becomes very flat, very smooth, and we live, in this analogy. in some small part of this two-dimensional surface where space is apparently more or less flat, more or less Euclidean. Nearly everything that was not flat inflated away. This means you can tolerate more or less anything in the beginning. It explains why the universe is so big and why it is so apparently regular and homogeneous. And there is a bonus: infinitesimal density fluctuations on all scales are generated. These are destined to be the seeds of large-scale structure.

There is a bit of hand waving in here perhaps, but where has this taken us to at the moment? Well, the old Big Bang, prior to 1980, was a bit of a coincidence. We could not understand why the universe is 14 billion light-years or so across: it is enormous compared to the tiny scales you expect naturally from quantum gravity. Just a coincidence, but in the new version of the universe, in some sense you can think of it as even worse, because here we are now, the universe is incredibly big, and finite, we can understand why it is so infinitely big, but why we live in a non-generic, non-random small patch is another question.

It may be this is just a question of time because eventually, if we wait long enough, we will see more and more of the universe and be able to better assess how special our patch is. Unless it continues to accelerate, in which case we might see less and less. But that's another story.

Just before inflation occurred, the universe was completely chaotic and irregular. This is the beauty of inflation: it gives an understanding of why the universe is relatively simple and relatively big. That's all I want to say for the moment about cosmology in general. Now let me turn to one of the most important issues in cosmology, namely how did we get here, and let me be more specific, and ask why and how did structure form in the universe? Why is this universe, which should in a two-dimensional analogy resemble the surface of a balloon, and which should be incredibly smooth, full of lumps called galaxies and stars and planets?

Again, the answer goes back a long way, to the two pioneers of the subject: Isaac Newton and James Jeans. What Newton realized when he wrote down his wonderful theory of gravity, back in the seventeenth century, was that gravity would destabilize the distribution of matter. Imagine, he said, that you had a uniform distribution of matter. It would naturally be unstable because there would be tiny fluctuations, and

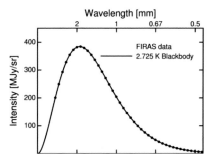

THE SPECTRUM OF COSMIC MICROWAVE BACKGROUND, A PERFECT BLACKBODY AS MEASURED BY FIRAS, THE SPECTROMETER ON COBE.

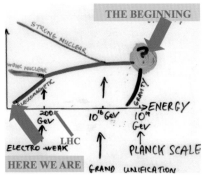

HOW PHASE TRANSITIONS CONTROL THE EVOLUTION OF THE STATE OF MATTER IN THE UNIVERSE.

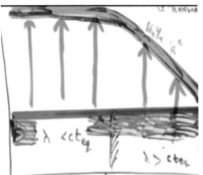

THE WRINKLED BALLOON INFLATES AND FLATTENS (TOP). DENSITY FLUCTUATIONS ARE GENERATED ON ALL SCALES FROM INITIAL SCALE-INVARIANT FLUCTUATIONS, WITH LARGER FLUCTUATIONS DOMINATING ON SMALL SCALES (BOTTOM).

these would grow because of the extra bits of self-gravity associated with them. In more modern parlance, it is a little bit like capitalism: the rich get richer, the poor get poorer, so the tiny, excess areas of slight over-density grow, and the tiny under-dense bits get less dense. And this is the way, he said, the universe would make structures, and would make the stars and planets.

Now Newton had a slight problem. He could not understand why it is that some stars were shining and other objects were opaque, like planets. At this point, Newton gave up, and he said, "I appeal to some other explanation." He was a religious man, so he left any further enlightenment to a higher authority.

However, it took a little while longer, a couple of hundred years in fact, before James Jeans, the great English physicist and mathematician, realized that there was a very natural way to understand Newton's dilemma, by what he called gravitational instability. Jeans argued that these fluctuations would naturally form clouds, and then from these clouds there would be fragmentation and eventually, according to Jeans, stars would form. This is the basis for our modern understanding of star formation.

Two pioneering researchers have really put all of this into the current context of the large-scale structure of the universe. One is Russian, and one is Canadian, based in the United States, Yakov Zel'dovich and James Peebles. These are the two modern cosmologists who may be said to have founded physical cosmology. Over the last three decades of the twentieth century they were almost singlehandedly responsible for most of what we know about how structure forms.

So, what have we learned about structure? There are beautiful numerical simulations of fluctuations growing in the expanding universe, by the theory that Jeans pioneered, forming what is going to be the Milky Way and many other galaxies. So the idea is that we start off with fluctuations, laid down by inflation and they grow.

This illustration shows a schematic of density fluctuations. The amazing thing is that the simplest prediction of the inflation theory, that's the cyan line, fits all the data that we can lay our hands on, and this includes data from the microwave background, data from galaxies, intergalactic clouds and clusters of galaxies. All of

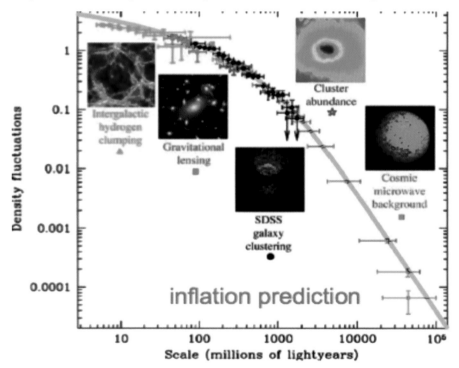

DENSITY FLUCTUATIONS VERSUS SCALE, COMPARED TO THE INFLATION PREDICTION (FROM TEGMARK, 2004). THE CYAN CURVE IS A MORE ACCURATE RENDERING OF THE GREEN CURVE IN THE FIGURE ABOVE THAT SHOWS INFLATION-GENERATED DENSITY FLUCTUATIONS.

the data lie on this same curve.

The plot tells you that density fluctuations are larger, the smaller the scale you measure them, which means that the small objects become structures, become stars or galaxies, before the bigger objects. The universe builds up hierarchically, from the bottom up. That's what we expect from inflation, that's what the simulations show, and the data more or less agree with theory.

This illustration shows one of the results from the numerical simulations. It shows you a virtual universe compared to a real universe. The remarkable thing is that you have to stare at this for a while to tell the difference because here we have data from all the surveys that you saw in George Smoot's talk: galaxy redshift surveys, with us in the center, yield maps as we position galaxies farther away, using the Hubble law as a distance measure, to get a three-dimensional map. You can see big clusters of galaxies and even the Great Wall that you saw previously. And here are computer simulations of the expanding universe, they're filtered the same way as the data, and they look indistinguishable. So this tells us that we are pretty much on the right track. We now have an understanding of how gravity works, and of how structure forms.

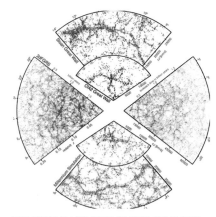

THE VIRTUAL UNIVERSE (IN RED) COMPARED TO THE REAL UNIVERSE (IN BLUE), AS VIEWED BY DIFFERENT GALAXY SURVEYS IN REDSHIFT SPACE. CREDIT: SPRINGER, FRENK AND WHITE, 2006.

Now there are two very big questions that are really driving us crazy in cosmology. And it is all to do with the dark side of the universe. Let me start off with dark matter, because this is something substantial. It turns out that 90 percent of what you cannot see here, of the matter, is dark, in this simulation. And in some sense the great success of the comparison of data with simulations is the realization that there is a lot of dark matter in the universe.

So who found the dark matter? A number of people contributed. One of the key players was Vera Rubin who, in the 1950s when it was very unusual for there to be women astronomers on mountaintops, would go up to observe galaxies, take photographic plates, develop them, and then have to come down the mountain at dawn, because there were no facilities for women at the mountaintop. Those were primitive times. Anyway, she persevered over many years and by studying galaxies like the Andromeda Galaxy she was able to measure the rotation of stars and of gas clouds and of galaxies. She produced what we call a rotation curve. What she's learned is that the galaxy is spinning around, and that if all the mass were where the light is, as you move farther away there's less light, so the stars should be slowing down. But they don't. The stars are moving in their orbits just as fast the farther out you go.

This was very strong evidence for dark matter on the scales of hundreds of thousands of light-years. This was not such a surprise. It was for galaxies perhaps, but the idea of dark matter had been floated decades earlier by a Swiss-American astrophysicist called Fritz Zwicky, who studied clusters of galaxies. He noted that galaxies would all fly apart were it not for something that you couldn't see. And that, he said, was dark matter. We now have modern versions of measuring this. These galaxies, the ones behind the cluster, the very faint ones, have tiny distortions in their images. And these distortions are due, as simulations show, to a gravitational lens first predicted by Einstein, the same idea that led to deflection of light, the first test of Einstein's theory. These tiny deflections enable you to make maps of dark matter.

Zwicky was a strange person who had strong views about his colleagues at Caltech. He is also famous for being the first person to really develop catalogs of galaxies, which are at the basis of modern astronomy.

So what have we learned from all this? Well, there is the disturbing conclusion to some that most of what is out there in the universe is invisible — it's dark. This is tough to get one's head around. And we know for sure that this dark matter is not ordinary matter; it's not made of the same stuff we are, that's for sure. It's not even made of neutrinos, which are also predicted and have a tiny mass. It's made of some elementary particle that's very weakly interacting.

Physicists and astronomers are looking very hard for evidence of this dark matter because one of the best theories that we have for what this dark matter might be says that these particles were created in the early universe, when temperatures were very high, and we're just left with relic numbers of them. Most annihilated with each other into pure energy, and as the universe expanded and cooled down, there are a few particles left behind. These are the dark matter particles. And it so happens that a theory, called supersymmetry, predicts there should indeed be such particles. It postulates a new particle for every known particle, and the lightest one of these is expected to be stable. Supersymmetry is a beautiful theory of symmetry, it applies to particle physics, and it applies at very, very high energy. We are not living in a supersymmetric universe now; otherwise, we would be bombarded by antimatter, but we may have been in the first nanoseconds. One of the major goals of the Large Hadron Collider at CERN is to test the theory of supersymmetry and thereby find a possible candidate for dark matter.

The lightest stable supersymmetric particle is one of many candidates for dark matter, but why do we think we are on the right track? Well, it turns out that if this particle that the theory conjectures had a certain interaction with itself, and it interacted too strongly, then there would be none left over today. If it interacted too weakly there would be too many left over today; so we know precisely how it should interact. It's a bit like Goldilocks and the three bears. And this precise interaction rate is exactly what the theory predicts. It's called the Weak Interaction Rate. This tells us that we are indeed probably on the right track. This has motivated lots of astronomers around the world to look for signals from this elusive particle. You may say if it is dark, how do we see it? Well when one of these particles meets another particle it will annihilate with itself, just as it did in the early universe when they almost all went away leaving radiation behind, but this happens rarely today, very rarely. However, because space is vast, you have a chance of seeing annihilation events, especially as they are highly energetic.

These dark matter particles fill our galactic halo and they actually are passing through us. There are millions per second going through our bodies. With the right kind of detector these particles will recoil off a detector and give some small energy, which we can then look for. There are experiments with some very unconventional telescopes. Some are in tunnels under mountains and some are in mines, deep underground in order to avoid cosmic rays, and look for tiny amounts of heat or ionization induced by the recoils in sensitive detectors from these elusive particles. Other telescopes are crude reflectors of very large area, situated in dark sky sites in Tenerife, Arizona, or Namibia, and designed to look for the nanosecond light flashes that particles induce when they pass through the atmosphere and generate what are called Cherenkov light flashes associated with showers of cosmic rays.

You can also look deep under ice, or deep in water, because these particles, or rather their annihilation products when they collect in the Sun, pass through Earth and generate high energy muons that yield tiny light flashes. One can monitor a huge transparent medium, such as Ice Cube at the South Pole or ANTARES in the Mediterranean Sea, with detectors that look at the Sun, where the particles collect as the Sun orbits the galaxy. Yet another telescope in space, the Fermi Gamma-ray Space Telescope, searches for gamma rays produced by dark matter annihilations. All of these experiments are currently working, but we haven't yet detected any dark matter signals.

Let me now move on to the other big mystery with all of this, which in some sense is even greater than dark matter. With dark matter we know what to look for, according to our different models, we know where to look, we have many experiments underway or planned to look for it, and we are going to find it or not find it. Dark energy is a more profound mystery. What is dark energy? Of course we can blame Einstein, when he wrote down his field equations, for an ad hoc addition that motivated anti-gravity to balance gravity and stop the universe from collapsing. He came to completely regret this, but the damage was done. The cosmological constant would not disappear.

There has been a huge wave of fancy mathematics to analyze what this means but there is a very simple version of this mathematics. You simply rearrange the cosmological constant term which Einstein introduced as a balancing force to curve space in the opposite way that mass curves space. You take it from the left-hand side of his famous gravitational field equations and put it on the right-hand side of the equations. The right-hand side contains the mass and energy that sources gravity. What this means is that what was anti-gravity a moment ago is now treated like a negative pressure, and is part of what we call the energy momentum distribution, the source of gravity. Negative pressure is repulsive. So what we said previously was anti-gravity is now a source of repulsive energy that we call dark energy. It has never been detected except, as we shall now see, in relatively recent studies of the very distant universe.

The question is, have we really seen dark energy or not? The news is that many, many years after Einstein abandoned the cosmological constant (in 1930), which in modern parlance is dark energy, we have found evidence that has come back to haunt us. The evidence is the following: supernovae, or exploding stars, are wonderful explosions, and in particular a certain type are calibrated in a very precise way by their release of a particular amount of radioactive nickel. They are perfect bombs, and this leads us to think that they should be, if we know their distances, really good measuring rods for measuring the expansion of the universe. When you find one far away, you can infer its distance. And you have Hubble's Law to tell you, for a given redshift, what its distance should be. The surprising result discovered, when astronomers looked far away, was that the supernovae were too faint, and they were too faint by a significant amount, by as much as 25 percent of their light. That's a quarter of a magnitude, something that you can measure very precisely with big telescopes for the distant supernovae.

This excess of faintness can most simply be understood if the universe is accelerating. In this case, the supernovae are further away than they otherwise would be in a uniformly expanding universe. This is the best evidence that we have for the presence of something new: acceleration. What you measure with supernovae is the competition between gravity and dark energy; that is, anti-gravity and gravity, in some sense. We measure the difference between the two.

Think of this as an equation; A minus B equals something that we know. Obviously, with only two numbers in the equation, you can't solve it. Too much is unknown. Because someone who says "Aha! There's dark energy!" could then mess about with gravity, and the matter that causes gravity, to balance it out. So how do you get around this problem? Well, there's a beautiful way to do that, because we now have a way of measuring the density of all the energy and matter in the universe, and this has come from the cosmic microwave background.

The idea is the following: there are these very tiny ripples in the microwave background, or waves in the plasma of matter and radiation, which are imprinted because there were primordial density fluctuations. These came from very early epochs, and behaved like sound waves, or like pressure waves in the early universe. As the universe cooled, they turned into structures, and made the galaxies. That in essence is our theory. In measuring the tiny fluctuations in the radiation field, we can transform these into what we call a power spectrum, a way of representing the distribution of the strengths of the fluctuation over densities with increasing size. We measure the fluctuation strengths, precisely, really precisely. This illustration shows the peak of one of these sound waves, followed by the corresponding minimum, and the maximum of the next wave, and so on. You see a whole bunch of these sound waves gradually fading away.

Here are results from two different experiments. One is the satellite experiment, WMAP, and one, with the blue points, is an experiment based at the South Pole, again measuring recently released data to even smaller angles on the sky. You can see an incredible trend in these sound waves: they match up precisely. Now what is this telling us? It is telling us about the propagation of light in the early universe.

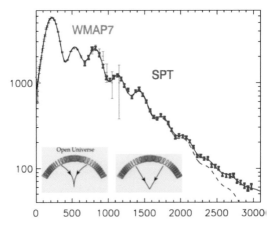

TEMPERATURE FLUCTUATIONS IN THE COSMIC MICROWAVE BACKGROUND. THE POWER SPECTRUM INCLUDES DATA FROM WMAP AND THE SOUTH POLE TELESCOPE.

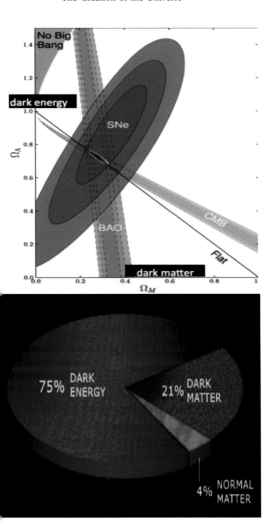

THE DARK ENERGY VERSUS DARK MATTER
CONSTRAINTS (TOP) AND THE MASS BUDGET
OF THE UNIVERSE (BOTTOM). CREDIT:
AMANULLAH ET AL.

Imagine a sound wave, in two different universes. One of them is a universe in which space is curved, that is, it is not Euclidean geometry. Recall that what makes the curvature of the universe is the total energy, kinetic plus potential. So the sum is different from zero.

Now it is a certain value of the total energy that makes space flat. It is actually zero, so negative gravitational energy just balances kinetic energy. There is no net curvature of space in this case. The light rays, which come to us, are curved in one space, and they're straight in the other. This means that all these peaks that you see would be shifted. You'd see them shifted if space is curved as in an open universe, to larger angles. The fluctuation peak is not shifted. This tells us that we can measure, with very little ambiguity, the total energy in the universe, all the energy plus all the matter. And space is flat.

This is progress. Now we have two equations for two unknowns. And it gets even better, because we also can measure the dark matter directly, from experiments using gravitational effects, such as gravitational lensing. Now we have three distinct observational techniques to measure what amounts to two dark unknowns: dark matter and dark energy. We think we have the matter contents of the universe pinned down, but it's a bit discouraging at first because most of the universe is dark.

This illustration that astronomers are fond of showing compares dark energy and dark matter. What I want you to take home from this is that we're zeroing in on both, with our independent experimental constraints. These take us through different combinations for dark matter and dark energy, toward a very tiny region of uncertainty. That means that we have measured both precisely, and our conclusion, now that we have a model of the universe which begins very small, expanding, forms structure as it ages, and then accelerates, is that above all, it is dominated by the dark side. And what does this dark side amount to?

Here is a summary of the dark side. You have 75 percent of the universe as dark energy; 21 percent as dark matter; and the rest, the stuff that we're made of, the stars, the galaxies, the clouds of gas and dust between the stars, that's just 4 percent. This is the universe. And this led to what is called the greatest problem in physics today, and so let me explain what this is, and I'll tell you about a possible solution to finish my talk.

What is the greatest problem in physics today? It is this: that we measure, and never mind what the units are, this dark energy, which is sometimes called the energy of the vacuum, because there's actually nothing there but it's just energy, uniform, and quantified by a certain number, which is very small. Now we can go to theory, the beautiful theory brought in by particle physics, and this gives us a very, very simple prediction of the energy of the vacuum at the onset of inflation. And the prediction is that it should be a very large number. The difference between these two numbers, measurement and prediction, is 120 factors of 10. It's the biggest possible discrepancy you can imagine in physics, and it is causing many physicists sleepless nights.

So what can we do about this? Well, we have a theory that purports to give you an explanation. It comes from inflation, and the idea is that there are varieties of inflation theory that never cease to inflate. Inflation is due to quantum fluctuations suddenly taking off and growing enormously for a brief fraction of a second, but in principle this can happen anywhere at any time. If you're unlucky, the atoms under your chairs could separate and you would fall through the floor. It would take many, many years; many, many billions and billions of years; but quantum physics says there is a finite chance.

And, equally, there is a finite chance for new universes to spawn off. And in certain versions of the inflation theory, this cannot only happen, but did happen. Again and again and again. There is the universe that we can see, but there are other bubbles, other universes that we can never see. This leads to a whole network of what has been called the multiverse, containing all of these parallel universes, and there are countless numbers of them. There are probably not infinite numbers of them, because in some versions of the theory at least, we have only a finite time, but still, there are vast numbers.

This leads us, then, to a possible understanding of the smallness of dark energy and this cosmological constant. It goes like this: we live in one universe, which has a certain highly unlikely value of the fundamental constants in the form of the vacuum energy, as well as vast numbers of others all with different values. But in all these others, with all these different values, we could not be here. Conditions would not be susceptible to forming stars and planets and galaxies and, perhaps, life. So there's something special about our environment. This has been advocated by quite a large number of physicists.

But there's a very strong counter view, by at least an equally large number of physicists. These say that it's all very well to postulate other universes, which have all these hostile places where we couldn't possibly exist, but how can you possibly prove this? There is no way we can observe or communicate with these other universes. It's not a theory of physics in the standard sense. It's a theory that doesn't make predictions. It can explain anything.

So here we are, what other hope is there? Well, one thing you should remember about cosmologists is this dictum of Lev Landau's: they're often in error but never in doubt. So what do I think is the most likely resolution of this? I believe that we're just waiting for the next Einstein to emerge with some new theory that will put all of these things together and lead us to understand why there is some more natural explanation of dark energy. That's one possible approach.

There is another view, and that is that the acceleration may be fooling us, that it is after all only slightly indirect; we're not even sure how to explode nearby supernovae, let alone fully understand how they work in the early universe where conditions certainly were very different. So maybe there are more astrophysical, more complex explanations of this apparent acceleration. Maybe gravitation is different from Einstein's theory, and a new theory might someday account both for dark matter and for dark energy. Again, we need better data and better theory to really sort this out.

Where the data will come from is the future in our field. There are many grand projects. One of them, the Planck Satellite launched by ESA, is taking data now in space, and will release its data within the next two years or so, with far more precise measurements of the background radiation fluctuations. Next in line, we have projects for vast telescopes: the U.S.-led 20- and 30-meter telescopes, the European 39-meter telescope; an 8-meter survey telescope to give unprecedentedly large surveys of galaxies; a square kilometer radio telescope, and a new space telescope designed to measure dark energy with unprecedented precision.

Let me just end, then, with this dictum that deserves to be engraved into the consciousness of scientists: extraordinary claims require extraordinary evidence. I think we still have a long way to go in order to understand some of these mysteries that pervade cosmology today.

GEORGE SMOOT

SIGNALS FROM THE BEGINNING

Born in Yukon, Florida, on February 20, 1945, George Fitzgerald Smoot III is a widely recognized astrophysicist and cosmologist. He graduated from the Massachusetts Institute of Technology with degrees in mathematics and physics in 1966 and then earned a Ph.D. in 1970. Smoot began his research at the University of California at Berkeley and the Lawrence Berkeley National Laboratory, where he studied antimatter with particle physics experiments.

Smoot has focused strongly on the cosmic microwave background radiation, which had been discovered in 1964. Eventually, Smoot proposed the Cosmic Microwave Background Explorer (COBE) satellite, which was launched in 1989 and by 1992 detected fluctuations in the microwave background, the cosmic afterglow of the Big Bang.

In 2006 Smoot was awarded the Nobel Prize for Physics for his work on the cosmic microwave background radiation, sharing the prize with his colleague John C. Mather. Smoot is a professor at the University of California at Berkeley and the Paris Diderot University in France.

GEORGE SMOOT AT STARMUS.

Today I'm going to talk about a message from the beginning of the universe. This is the kind of thing that usually gets me into religious trouble. It's like seeing the face of God or something like that. However, what I'm going to talk about is how we've learned at lot about the way the universe is. And we've learned it from light, light that comes to us from the beginning of time, from a little later in time, and from closer to us. It tells us a lot about the nature of the universe and about the effect on Earth. It's no surprise that you'll see that the Spanish are involved in this, because you'll see we're in a phase of exploration the way the great navigators were, from Portugal and Spain, in the 1500s, in exploring Earth. But now we're exploring the whole universe.

So just to let you know that I'm paying attention, this is a cosmic scene investigation. We've happened upon the universe and we're trying to figure out what happened. So it's like coming to the crime scene and investigating to figure out what has happened. There are hidden fingerprints in there. If you can unravel it, you will be able to understand exactly what happened. You all know from watching the TV show that just by analyzing a few things and doing some computer simulations you can recreate the entire crime and figure out who did what. Well, that's what we're trying to do. And let me remind you when I say we're trying to recreate the scene, it's not just this room, all the materials that are in this room, but it's the whole universe that we're trying to recreate.

One of the great things that you heard a little bit of discussion about is the Hubble Ultra Deep Field, pictured here. When I was young we had individual galaxies or a couple of clusters; now we have clusters like this, in which you can see more than 2,000 galaxies. Essentially everything you can see in this image, apart from four objects that are stars, are galaxies. You can see the galaxies have different colors and some are bigger than others. Some are different; they're smaller and differently shaped. You see ellipticals, you see spirals. Just from this picture alone you can realize that somebody made a universe that has a lot of galaxies in it! You've heard there are 100 billion — why do you need 100 billion galaxies when it was obviously enough just to have a solar system?

A solar system is enough for life, so why do you need 400 billion stars and 100 billion galaxies? That's one of the things you have to explain.

If you do a little interpretation, you can see that there's some evolution going on here. The galaxies that are smaller and therefore farther away have more irregular

THE ANDROMEDA GALAXY SEEN BY THE SPITZER SPACE TELESCOPE. CREDIT: NASA.

shapes, and the surprising thing is, we know the universe is expanding — they're actually whiter and bluer — which means they're hotter. And they're much hotter, because they should be shifting to the red but their temperature is actually hotter than the nearby galaxies, the yellow ones we're seeing here.

So just from this picture we realize it's not going to be a simple tale, but it turns out that it's a lot simpler than trying to understand life, so we have a break. We have one simple tool. I'm not going to spend this talk describing what our other tools are in order to do this. Our primary tool is that light, though it travels very fast, but the universe is very big, and the speed of light is finite. When we look out to a great distance, say if we look out to the Sun, the light from the Sun takes eight minutes to get here. So if I make an image of the Sun right now it's what happened eight minutes ago; or if I go to Jupiter it's 40 minutes ago.

If you look at a typical set of stars around us they're more than 10 years old. If you look to the galactic center you're talking many thousands of years. The Andromeda Galaxy, two million years. If you have a picture of Earth two million years ago it doesn't look quite like Earth today in the sense there's no Great Wall, no cities, no anything else, There's no sign of mankind, we don't think men even showed up until then.

But the issue here is if you're looking at light that comes to you as an observer you can think of yourself as at the center of a set of nested spheres, each one of which is a given distance away, but also a given distance back in time. So that if you are able to reconstruct what's going on in every sphere you can reconstruct the time history of the universe from the very beginning to the end.

Let's imagine the beginning of the universe as a sphere, it's the greatest distance away from us. The present's the sphere that's closest to us, the stuff that's between us and the Moon, anything within a light-second. We're in a spiral galaxy, we're part way out on one of the spiral arms, and we have this set of concentric spheres around us. If you look nearby, you see what we recognize as fairly developed and modern galaxies. So you see these spiral galaxies and elliptical galaxies and so forth.

If you look farther out you start seeing irregular galaxies. These are galaxies that haven't had time to evolve, haven't merged with other galaxies, haven't gotten either into the elliptical or spherical shape in any full way. So let's imagine the universe; this whole concept of the cosmic spheres of time, where the beginning of time is way over here on one side and the present is here where we are right at the moment in Tenerife; and around us are billions of galaxies. We can't draw them all so imagine there are 100 billion, and the ones that are near to us are the evolved galaxies like the one we live in, and the ones that are farther away, they're what used to be thought of as irregular galaxies but we know they're the forming galaxies.

By studying this we can map out this whole volume, we can have a map not only so you know where to go in your lunar rover, but you can see the whole history of the universe stretching out in front of us. That's our goal.

I want to talk for a second to describe two movies. I will mention one because Jill Tarter is here. Some of you know a movie that debuted in 1997. This movie was Contact, and Jodie Foster is making her trip out to meet the aliens. Jill Tarter was the inspiration for the character that Jodie Foster plays. If you watch Contact, you'll see that white light represents Jodie Foster, not the Sun. You can watch one part in which the sound is terrible, but what it's representing is the sound of radio waves coming out. So we're going by Mars and the asteroids. If you listen carefully you hear the Moon landing; then you hear Kennedy's assassination and so forth.

An important part of the movie shows you passing all the planets. This is really cool, as astronauts know all the planets line up perfectly for your trip out. So you get to go by Saturn. Why do they do that? This is something of high production value, they wanted to impress people, and what did we have data for in 1997? It seems like ancient times. We'd been to the planets and we had great pictures. We'd sent our probes out to the planets; we had great pictures of planets. Now we're out in the Kuiper belt and the Oort cloud, you start seeing other stars, and they have to make most of this up from now on out, until Jodie gets to meet the aliens. But there are a few pictures, because the Hubble Space Telescope was up. So you get to go through a dust cloud, a famous dust cloud (in the Eagle Nebula, M16), this is called the Pillars of Creation. It's a place in our galaxy where a lot of star formation is going on. When the stars became hot they evaporated the material around them and forced them into these pillars.

My research group has also made some movies that simulate the composition of the universe. One shows our galaxy, and Andromeda. There are a whole lot of galaxies out there. You know when the astronauts tell you Earth looks tiny, here, if you hold out the tip of a pen, you can cover our galaxy, never mind a planet!

Another movie that we finished last summer features a different kind of music, very much more inspiring, although still not perfect. This movie starts on Earth, showing real images of Earth; nothing's simulated. We started by showing Tibet because that's an impressive place and also because there weren't any clouds there. To make a Google Earth you have to take lots of pictures and take them at a time when there aren't many clouds. There's one new feature added, which I appreciate. We're here, on Earth, and we've put our stuff in space. It's not a question of the door to space being closed; humans have a presence in space, not as people but as machines.

As our group's movie continues, it shows some orbits. I'm getting to know some of the Russian orbits because I'm having to pay attention now. It shows these very extreme orbits, the Russian orbits. It also depicts the famous Clarke belt, the geosynchronous orbit belt. It's very highly utilized. Finally, it shows the Moon, just a whole light-second away, and when you see the Moon's orbit you can hardly see Earth. That's where you can cover it with your thumb. There are the inner planets. If you were in a space capsule going out there you'd really feel quite alone.

The movie also moves out to show constellations, at least those are familiar. When you get far enough away they're going to get distorted. It shows how the nearby stars are moving due to parallax. That's how, in Contact, the signal should have been there. The movie now reveals the Milky Way Galaxy, and shows a couple of galactic friends around us. This is a funny shape because we haven't mapped it yet. It's not that there are no galaxies; it's just that we haven't looked there. Let me remind you, all these things are real things. Every little dot in our movie is an actual galaxy.

You reach a point where the movie shows space as far as we can see; this is the cosmic microwave background, the relic radiation from the Big Bang, in fact from the beginning of time. And then our movie takes you back home, so you won't feel so insignificant.

I'll explain to you how we did some of these things. It's the putting together of the work of many, many people with reasonable production values. This is still not nearly as complicated as the simple mapping of a DNA molecule, that's the incredible thing. Even though you'll see the numbers of equivalent atoms, the galaxies here, are more than a million in our set of pictures. So we have to do a kind of impressionist drawing of the galaxy. I'll show you a little later in less high quality — we actually know the positions of half a billion stars. We're making progress. It may turn out to, according to my calculations, I do a slightly different calculation to other people, that roughly one percent of the stars in the galaxy probably have a rocky planet of a reasonable size inside their habitable zone. That's roughly 2 to 4 billion planets. That's one for every family on Earth just in our galaxy alone.

As our movie continues, it reveals one of your favorite planets. The incredible thing is we still violated the speed of light, because we made it to the edge of the universe and back in three and a half minutes! It's a little fast. Then we're eventually going to come back to the plateau. It's interesting to see Earth, it's just interesting to see these large plains. The movie shows the maria on the Moon, and you don't think

THE ICONIC HUBBLE SPACE TELESCOPE IMAGE "PILLARS OF CREATION". CREDIT: NASA.

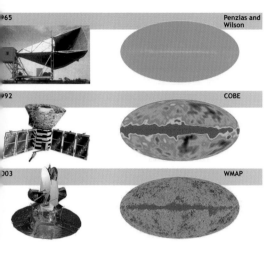

50 YEARS SINCE THE DISCOVERY OF THE CMB.
CREDIT: NASA.

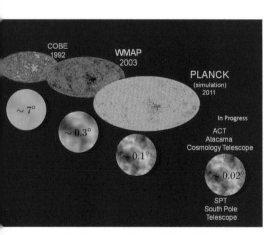

OUR EVER-SHARPENING VIEW OF THE
EMBRYO UNIVERSE.

that we have very similar things like the Deccan Flats in India and so forth.

The movie also features some pretty nice music. One thing that Brian May will tell you, as beautiful as pictures are, is that somehow music brings the emotion out so much better. That's why the sound is so much better. It's funny; you'd think that in Contact they would have known that better than we did.

So when you see our group's map, you're seeing not only a map of the universe, you're seeing a map in space and time along a special thing that we call a light cone, which is really a light sphere.

How do we do this? I've spent a lot of my life trying to make a map of that earlier surface and we've been incredibly lucky and incredibly more powerful in what we're doing. It started with the COBE satellite, where we saw the original fluctuations. It's been followed by WMAP and now, in May 2009, we launched the Planck satellite. Some of the people here in Tenerife and the rest of Spain are involved in this project. And we're making better maps that show these small structures, not only the seeds of the galaxies and the structures, clusters of galaxies, galaxies and other things that we see, but also give us a lot of information about what the universe is made of, what it's structure is. I'll give you a slight interpretation a little later on that tells you something about how space and time themselves were created. You'll be able to see that with your own eyes.

We're coming up on the 50th anniversary of the discovery of the cosmic microwave background, in 2015, so we have a little wait, marking 50 years after Penzias and Wilson made their great discovery. If they could have scanned the whole sky, they would have made a map that looked like that. You'd really only be able to see the galaxy; everything else you see is just uniform diffuse background glow from the universe itself. It's only because they're at such a long wavelength that the galaxy shows up.

Then with COBE, we went to a factor of 10,000 more in sensitivity and resolution. We see the galaxy saturating across the field of view. We see these large scale structures, cool regions together, warm regions together, that are structures we were able to show came from the very beginning of the universe, from the time when the universe was the equivalent of 12 hours after your conception to your lifespan.

We follow that with WMAP, which has much higher angular resolution, then we are able to study these and we still see these cool regions grouped together and warm regions grouped together. But now we have much more detail, and that allows us to say how much matter there is, how much ordinary matter, like what we're made out of, what kind of other structures there are. We're able to learn the content of the universe as well as the DNA for what's going to happen in the future. Soon we're going to be publishing a higher resolution map from Planck. And we have what I would call our ever-sharpening view of the embryo universe, even though it's the largest sphere that we can see — it's truly the embryo universe, it's the way things were before the birth of the universe, in terms of a human thing.

So in 1992 we had a very coarse map; in 2003 we had a better one; some time later this year or early next year we'll publish a better one from Planck. And we have two other big telescopes working on the ground, one in the high Andes in Atacama, the Cosmology Telescope, and one at the South Pole telescope, that are making very high-resolution maps of Earth.

Why are we doing this? The answer is it's very, very rich in information and very, very detailed. We're able to map what's going on in the universe in a really ancient time with very high precision, and we're even getting so good now that we're seeing not only the first order effects but the second order effects. That allows us to split things and really understand what we think is going on in the early universe with high precision. And then we have to see if it links all together and if everything in between fits with the pattern that we think we have uncovered.

So we have a brief story. Instead of concentric spheres I give you the "waste can" version. If I'm going to show time I have to suppress one of the space dimensions.

The sphere that exists in the present time is this sphere here, and if you follow this sphere back in time, we think there was a time when we can see the universe was in a region that's smaller than an atom and quantum mechanics is extremely impor-

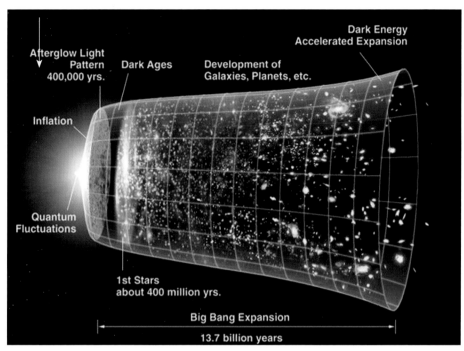

BRIEF HISTORY OF THE UNIVERSE. CREDIT: NASA/WMAP SCIENCE TEAM.

tant. Those quantum mechanical fluctuations eventually get to be galaxies and clusters of galaxies and everything else. So it's a really cool story, you make a small area at the beginning and it turns into a beautiful galaxy.

We go through this period when the universe becomes transparent and the radiation is free to come — we mapped that very precisely. Then we go through a dark age and we get the first set of stars and galaxies forming, and they evolve over time until eventually you get to the point where we can make our solar system.

But we also find that some strange things happen. We think the universe was accelerating its rate of expansion early on, then it had to slow down for structure to form, and then around 5 million years ago the universe began to accelerate its rate of expansion again. So we have all these extra ingredients, but they're still a lot less than the ingredients in one cell, so we count ourselves lucky.

That's why we've spent a substantial amount of time and effort and a huge amount of money on studying this. We're talking three satellites over 30 years, not a trivial amount of money, to map the beginning of the universe with incredibly high precision. And 400,000 years, or 380,000 years to be more precise, seems like a long time. But remember we're talking close to 14 billion years for the age of the cosmos.

What else have we done? We started a project to map the galaxies. And the first one of those was the Sloan Digital Sky Survey. This illustration shows a map of a million galaxies, and it's this funny fan shape. Our own galaxy blocks out some of the measurements, but at the other end you just point your telescope at the sky and take a picture, Earth rotates, you take another picture, you get this fan across the sky and then you plot where the galaxies are, and their angle. And you have to estimate their distance, and then you do that for another plane, and you get another fan.

On the Internet you can see a rotating version so you can realize where we've looked. By watching a version like that, you'll see something amazing. Every little spot on there is a galaxy. But the galaxies are not distributed randomly — they have

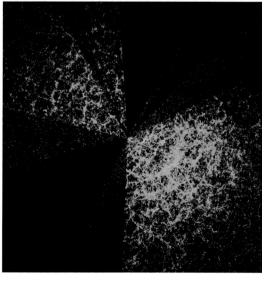

SLOAN DIGITAL SKY SURVEY. CREDIT: M. BLANTON AND THE SLOAN DIGITAL SKY SURVEY.

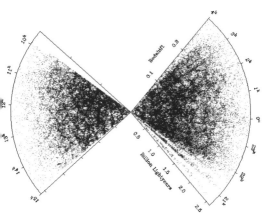

THE TWO DEGREE FIELD (2DF) GALAXY
REDSHIFT SURVEY. CREDIT: MATTHEW COLLESS
(ANU) ET AL., 2DF GALAXY REDSHIFT SURVEY.

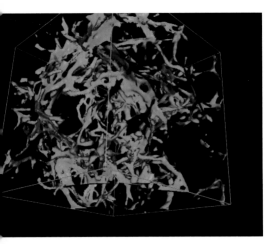

LYMAN-ALPHA FOREST. CREDIT: J. SHALF, Y.
ZHANG (UIUC) ET AL., GCCC.

a very complicated pattern, and there is one thing that everybody is always intrigued with. This thing, this structure, it's got the name of the Great Wall, it looks like a big string of a galaxy, maybe a million galaxies, because in fact we know with samples of other places that it actually extends over a larger region than just the string. It's a Great Wall.

So now the question is, who'd build a Great Wall of galaxies? That's an engineering job. That would take a lot of people to accomplish. The answer is, we think the universe was all set to do that right from the beginning.

Here's the two-degree field of view look at these galaxies, which was a competing one, a European one. Here we get to fly through roughly a million galaxies, and you will notice that sometimes there are colors, shapes, because we're making a catalog and this catalog's got a million galaxies, and it's got pictures of each of these galaxies. We know a galaxy's spectral type, we know all that kind of stuff. Now we're going to go outside so we can look back on what we see. But you'll notice that you've got more information, you've got this hypercube of information. And as part of this project we have Galaxy Zoo, a project wherein people can download images of galaxies onto their personal computers and then scan and write their comments back. The creators of Galaxy Zoo did a big survey to see if galaxies are rotating left than right more so than right to left, and the answer is they are, because people have biases. Even if you give them mirror images of the galaxy they still find the same thing.

The illustrations I'm showing you now have come from surveys. But in fact, we're doing more, so one of the projects I'm collaborating with is a thing called BigBOSS, which is the big version of the Baryon Oscillation Survey, a sky survey with all the spectrographs. We just received approval to use a 4-meter telescope to do this, but why would we? Well, by approximately 2015 we should have 5 million galaxies surveyed. Five million galaxies is pretty good, but it's 5 million out of 100 billion, so I've been pushing my colleagues to keep going. We're only arguing about how many. I want 50 million galaxies. They say let's do 20, and let's do a million quasars too.

Now check out the next illustration. You'll see that all these little fingers sticking out here each have a quasar at the end. You take a good image of a quasar, you do spectroscopy of it, and you see the light being absorbed by things that are forming in the galaxies. So this is called Lyman-alpha forest, and it's a way of studying what's happening then and going to happen in the future.

These first guys that turn on at a very large redshift, they light up the guys that are getting ready to turn on later; there's still this evolution going on. If you think for a moment about the problem of measuring 5 million galaxies, you realize you can do a million a year if you're really efficient. The way we do it is by trying to measure the spectra of a thousand galaxies at a time. And that's done by making this big plate and having a machine drill holes in all the right places where the galaxies are. So before doing the construction, you have to figure out where the galaxies are, and then there's a guy who comes and plugs a fiber optic into each one of these holes in the plate. Then you assemble it, and the fiber goes down to the spectrograph, and you line them up in a row, and you get the spectra of all the galaxies at once.

It's an international collaboration between my group and groups in France and Spain. So that's why I said we're like the great navigators; we're trying to map the universe. If we can just stay on Moore's Law, it's only going to take us 50 years to map the whole universe. The hard problem is how do you go from 5,000 galaxies in one picture to 50,000, then 500,000. But we're getting ready for the next one, and we have to be ready by 2015 to start.

So why is it called BOSS? Well, it turns out these fluctuations you see in the cosmic microwave background end up reflected in galaxies. That is, if you have a big clump, it's going to become a cluster of galaxies. The light pressure is so great, it blows the ordinary matter out to a great distance, roughly 450 megaparsecs, but the dark matter remains behind and then the dark matter attracts the stuff back in but a little bit of that stuff that's on the outside is left behind and forms future galaxies.

So you see these big bumps that are roughly the size of one degree on the sky. They're going to show up here, at 450 megaparsecs. And you look at the data we have from the Sloan survey we have now and you see this little bump. There's a few percent extra galaxies around this thing, caused by what we call baryon acoustic oscillations, the photons blowing the baryons out, and we want to measure that very precisely because that's a ruler — it's a fixed size that we know is a function of the universe and all we need to know is how much has the universe expanded since it got blown out there.

We have a ruler that's laid out there in place so we can measure the growth of the universe over time. And so we can measure both how the universe is changing over time, how quickly it's growing; and we can also measure how quickly galaxies and clusters of galaxies are forming. And those two allow us to distinguish between what we call the dark energy and some kind of modified gravity and so on. So there's extra science to be done, and that's why it's got the name BOSS, it's not that we sold out to Hugo, it's something else.

The BOSS team has also created some simulations. They show fluctuations; we let gravity take effect. You saw this before, but without rotation. You take these tiny fluctuations you see in the microwave background and you let gravity work for some number of billions of years, and you start forming structures that look very strange. They don't just suddenly appear at random, they're long filaments. First you see little hotspots, and then you see the hotspots link up. It's not that the links weren't already there, it just takes a while for them to develop and for them to collapse and to form this kind of a web. This is a kind of cosmic web, and this is simple gravity. So this is what dark matter does.

You can do bigger simulations too. Another we produced shows what this distribution of matter versus dark matter looks like over time. Dark matter is going to be white and the ordinary matter appears to be yellow like stars, like the Sun. Most stars are slightly yellow in color and slightly smaller than the Sun.

Our simulations allow us to zoom in on what we think the universe looks like today. In the large scale it looks very uniform, but when you zoom in it's going to look like a biological system. There are going to be filaments, and where they intersect you get a cluster of galaxies, or even a large cluster of galaxies. We have produced a 10 billion-particle simulation. The width represents 3 billion light-years. And it's uniform on the average, but there's a lot of structure in here and Jack Szostak will tell you this looks like a biological system, it looks like a brain or something. But you see the voids, and you see the filaments.

What's happened is that gravity has sharpened up what was otherwise a pretty uniform distribution. Gravity has made a lot of sharp edges. But when you have a lot of filaments come together, you get a large cluster of galaxies. So not only are we not in the center of the solar system, or the center of the galaxy, we're not even in a big cluster of galaxies — we're in a little dinky cluster of galaxies. If we lived in a big one, we'd see galaxies everywhere in the sky. And as our simulation moves a little closer it shows two little things that are pretty close together like these two; that's about how far we and the Andromeda Galaxy are apart.

But if we lived in the center, it would be like living downtown. It's just a different kind of thing. I like to zoom way out on our simulation. It's good to be a simulator, or a physicist, or God, because you can see the big picture. On the other hand, if you were inside — Volker Springel at Max Planck did one of these — now you see just white from the dark matter halos and in their centers, stars. Or the ordinary matter that will have dissipated energy and collapsed to form stars, which creates these halos of white with clusters of stars in the center. The entity we think of as the visible galaxy is just a part of a much bigger structure. When you're inside, it's hard to figure out where you are. You need to actually make the maps and look at it in the grand perspective.

Now we can do big-time simulations. We have produced one that shows the same cosmic web in which you're looking out in space and you're looking back in time

BIG BOSS SUPERIMPOSED ON WMAP. NEW INSTRUMENTATION IN THE HISTORIC 4 -METER MAYALL TELESCOPE ON KITT PEAK.

— back billions of years. In the early universe it was quite warm, quite uniform, and all kinds of stuff was going on. But, slowly, structure began to form and our simulation shows that structure gets to be more and more spectacular. There's a little trick here, because the universe is expanding. As the universe ages, you get sharper and sharper edges. That's the non-linear gravity causing the tiny structures to eventually link together and all add together in phase.

Here's a picture from the COBE satellite, smoothed a little bit, after subtracting a model of the galaxy. It's smoothed so you can see the big features. But now look at what we're getting with WMAP and Planck. You're seeing a map with the same resolution.

Now look at a map of Earth. There's no question those two are different. You see these long linear features — the edges of continents, the Atlantic Ridge, various features in the Pacific, South Pacific, and South Indian Oceans. Earth has features that are long and linear. That tells you there's a mixing of the modes; that is, phases are lined up in different ways. The formation of the surface of Earth, the formation of continents, was a non-linear process.

Looking at the cosmic microwave data again, you will see hot and cold spots. But the correlation of the cold and the hot spots is, as far as we can tell, substantially insignificant. That means the structure, the mechanism that made space and time, is linear to extremely high level, to as high a level as we're able to see. And that's a great feat.

So we're really seeing that the processes that make space and time are the simplest ones. That really gives us hope; we can calculate it. It's the exact opposite of life — the closer we get, the simpler the system is. So when we're looking for these signals from time we're seeing through the light but now we're seeing actual things that happened in a tiny fraction of a second at the beginning of the universe, when we were going through inflation, or whatever made the large stage that the universe is today.

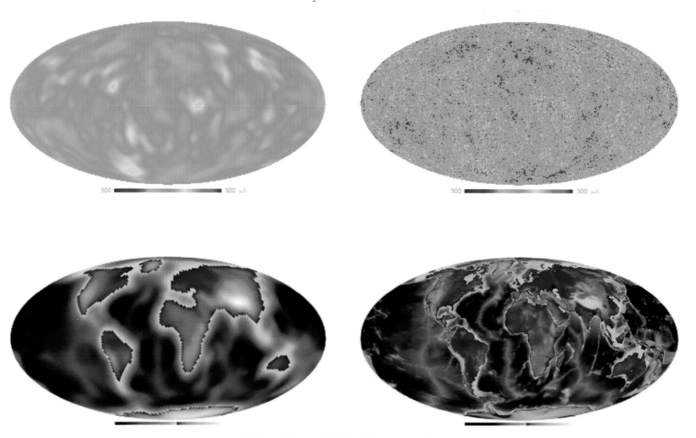

(LEFT) COBE DMR, (RIGHT) WMAP AND PLANCK.

We have also produced pictures without the high production values, images based primarily on the data from the Hipparcos satellite. One shows the location of the nearest half-billion stars. We can zoom away. These require a lot of computer power. But then you realize you've got a French impressionist painting, because there are about 400 billion stars in each of the galaxies. So you're only at a tenth of a percent of all the stars in the galaxies. We've got more mapping to do.

We've also produced simulations representing our Local Group of galaxies. If you zoom out in one of these simulations you can actually see where our nearest neighbor is. We're pretty much alone. Our galaxy? You can cover it with your thumb.

Now imagine travelling down one of those wedges and we're going a little faster. Remember, it takes light two million years to get between nearest neighbors. Now you can start to see some red ones — those are large, red, luminous galaxies. You can see them over great distances. And quasars, they're so bright you can see them. You can't see normal galaxies at this great distance.

We want to go up a factor of detail by 10 to 50 in our mapping, and we will have actually begun to map out a significant fraction of the volume. First you have to talk about what kind of scale you use from the beginning — is it distance, is it time, is it what?

This is our program in cosmology, to map out the whole thing and see if we understand it and then work it out so we can do simulations to make sure we have the whole picture. Then we can calculate every step along the way and compare it to what we've got and see if we have a detailed understanding of the universe.

ALEX CHERNEY WITH GEORGE SMOOT AT STARMUS. ALEX WON THE
PRESTIGIOUS STARMUS 2011 ASTROPHOTOGRAPHY PRIZE.

THE ANTENNAS OF THE LARGE MILLIMETER/
SUBMILLIMETER ARRAY (ALMA) UNDER THE
CLEAR SKY OVER THE CHAJNANTOR PLATEAU,
IN THE CHILEAN ANDES. CREDIT: ALMA, AUI
INC., ESO/B.TAFRESHI.

ROBERT WILLIAMS

FIVE BREAKTHROUGH DISCOVERIES OF THE PAST 50 YEARS

Robert Williams is Distinguished Research Scholar and former Director of the Space Telescope Science Institute in Baltimore, Maryland. Together with NASA's Goddard Space Flight Center, the Institute operates the Hubble Space Telescope.

Williams graduated from the University of California at Berkeley in 1962, and earned a Ph.D. from the University of Wisconsin in 1965. He was professor at University College London in the early 1970s, and spent many years as a professor of astronomy at the University of Arizona in Tucson. He was also director of Cerro Tololo Inter-American Observatory, the greatest collection of U.S. telescopes in the Southern Hemisphere.

Focused on residents of the Milky Way Galaxy, Williams has studied nebulae, novae, and projects involving emission-line spectroscopy. He is a past president of the International Astronomical Union.

ROBERT WILLIAMS AT STARMUS.

The development of astronomy flows from its discoveries. Key findings change the course of the way we think about the universe and they drive current research. So how does one seriously go about identifying those discoveries that have had great impact on astronomy and human perception of the universe? I looked at a wide range of current observational and theoretical programs being carried out on a number of large facilities in astronomy and then identified the major discoveries that motivated them. On that basis I have selected five influential discoveries from the past half century. Mine is an admittedly subjective judgment, but the point is not so much to emphasize these particular discoveries as to understand the process by which discovery motivates research and how that research has influenced our understanding of the universe and the role of humans in it.

One cannot separate key discoveries from the technological developments that make them possible. Occasionally a novel discovery comes about by sheer persistence and good luck, using old equipment in a new way or simply catching a new phenomenon by chance. The first optical discovery of a pulsar occurred this way in 1968 using an old telescope of small aperture. More normally, however, new capabilities that reveal the workings of objects in space are those most likely to succeed in finding things not seen nor understood before.

Discoveries are made by people, and people use tools to study the sky. In recent decades the explosion of technology has transformed what and how astronomers see through our telescopes. In particular, there are three technological developments that have had a huge impact on some of the most notable of recent astronomical discoveries and they have created the culture that now envelops all astronomy.

The human eye has many excellent capabilities, such as the ability to discern patterns. As a device that can detect faint light and store it, however, it has severe limitations. For this reason, the photographic plate was the best detector for astronomers for more than a century. A faint, distant galaxy imaged on a photographic plate in a 10-hour exposure can produce an image hundreds of thousands of times fainter than the eye can see. And one can easily archive a photo, which the eye cannot. Despite these qualities, however, the photographic plate has limitations in converting information stored on the plate into quantitative information. Complex machines and algorithms were developed over the years that extracted quantitative information, but in the 1970s, photographs were severe limitations to the new large telescopes.

Fortunately, the demands of industry and the military, which were looking for

CCD DETECTOR. CREDIT: BALL BROS. RESEARCH CORP.

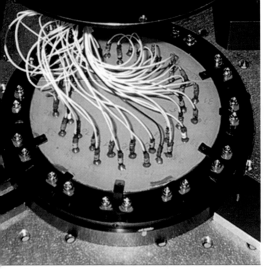

DEFORMABLE MIRROR. CREDIT: ESO.

STAR CLUSTER SEEN WITH ADAPTIVE OPTICS TURNED OFF (LEFT) AND ON (RIGHT). CREDIT: KECK OBSERVATORY.

better, more sensitive light detectors, drove research that utilized a physical process called the photoelectric effect. Initially described mathematically by Einstein, this effect resulted in electronic devices covered with a substratum of silicon, producing sensitive detectors. These devices, called charge coupled devices, or CCDs, are extremely efficient light detectors. They can detect light in a way that makes it easy to store and to study using electronics, so an explosion of imaging information can be obtained and stored electronically in a trivial manner. The CCD is the primary detector for modern television cameras and your normal pocket camera. They are safe, durable, and accurate, and they represent a revolution in astronomical detection.

This illustration shows a CCD detector. Currently their sizes are relatively small compared to large photo plates, so in order to capture a large field of view one must make a mosaic of many CCDs that are placed next to each other, as seen here. The CCD mosaic is the heart of the camera for the important NASA Kepler spacecraft, for example, that has discovered so many exoplanets around stars other than the Sun.

Earth's atmosphere is essential for life; it provides humans and animals with oxygen. This life giving resource does present limitations for astronomers, however, in that the atmosphere distorts and blocks out the radiation from astronomical objects. It produces a severe limitation on the quality of images from telescopes. This is one of the main reasons astronomers go to such efforts to place new telescopes into orbit around Earth, above the atmosphere.

Recently, scientists have developed a novel way to correct for atmospheric distortion, using lasers and a deformable mirror inserted in the optical train of telescopes. This enables telescopes to form images virtually as well as if they were above the atmosphere. This technique is called "adaptive optics" because it requires the deformable mirror to continually change its shape in times less than one-tenth of a second to counteract the air distortions. The key to the process is the deformable mirror, one of which is shown in this illustration, and which is made of a very thin sheet of reflective material. The changing shape is formed by actuators that respond to electrical signals generated by a beam of reflected light from dust in the atmosphere that scatters a beam of laser light back into the telescope.

Adaptive optics requires fancy electronic equipment, powerful lasers, and complicated optical elements but it has been shown to work wonders in producing excellent astronomical images. This illustration shows two identical images of a star cluster, one that was taken without adaptive optics engaged and the other with it turned on. The difference in the clarity of the image with adaptive optics is remarkable. This technique is now widely used on the largest telescopes and it has enabled astronomers to detect fine detail and resolution of stellar objects that were previously impossible to attain.

There are many interesting practical aspects to operating adaptive optics on telescopes. In particular, the light from the intense laser beam piercing the sky in the direction the telescope is observing is a potential hazard to aircraft. So, all such systems require notification of civil and military aviation authorities beforehand, and they require that several observers be stationed outside the telescope dome to search the sky for passing aircraft. If an aircraft is spotted that has a path carrying it near the observatory, the adaptive optics system must be immediately shut down. Discovery does not come easily!

Science requires precise measurements to be made of many quantities and it also requires sophisticated calculations to model various phenomena. In the case of astronomy, where one deals with billions of stars clustered together in a galaxy, the number of objects that can interact with each other gravitationally and whose motions and physical states need to be described can be mind boggling. Imagine the difficulty of trying to follow the orbits of billions of stars that are all interacting with each other.

It was impossible, in fact, until recently. The new breed of fast, large supercomputers is capable of treating millions of interacting objects in a meaningful way. One postulates how the objects interact with each other according to known natural laws, such as gravity and magnetic fields, and then programs the supercomputer to apply these laws to all objects. The result can be a complex picture of the behavior of what we call "many body systems" that would otherwise be impossible to predict. Simulations of the evolution of star clusters and galaxies have resulted in beautiful movies that show how stars and gas clouds evolve over long periods of time. An example of just one frame of a very large computation is shown in this illustration, depicting two galaxies containing many millions of stars that collided with each other due to their large mutual gravitational attraction.

A crucial role of large computers and their distributed networks is the archiving of valuable astronomical data. The CCDs now used on all telescopes produce many gigabytes of data each night. These data are now routinely stored for future analysis and also for access for educational purposes. Some of the most accessed websites in the world are those that contain astronomical images for all generations. The hubblesite.org website that contains many of the processed images from the Hubble Space Telescope receives among the most hits of any website in the world. And the U.S. news magazine Time only last year rated the very popular World Wide Telescope website developed in cooperation with Microsoft Research Corporation as one of its 50 best websites in the world.

Large computers are an essential part of science, and astronomy would be an obscure field were it not for the beauty revealed by telescopes and their CCD detectors, and the stored images on large computers. With this background we can now more intelligently understand what I believe are arguably the most important astronomical discoveries of the past half century.

1. Big Bang Relic Radiation

The notion that our current universe originated in a huge outburst of creation was initially not universally accepted. Famed cosmologist Fred Hoyle derisively referred to the hypothesis as the "Big Bang." In fact, we now know beyond doubt that the space of the universe and the galaxies in it are all expanding away from each other and that this expansion began in an unimaginably dense, hot phase about 14 billion years ago. What preceded that event? Science can only address questions about which we have facts and data, and none exist about the state of things before the Big Bang. Thus, "what existed before the Big Bang?" is a question for philosophy and religion that hard science does not yet have facts on. This situation may change in the future if and when we devise ways to capture data from an epoch that may have preceded the Big Bang.

One of the early predictions of the Big Bang that emerged in the middle of the 20th century was that if one looked out far enough in space, which means looking back in time because of the time required for light to travel across space from its origin to the point where it reaches our telescopes, astronomers should be able to see relic radiation of the hot Big Bang. This radiation was predicted to be very faint and difficult to detect.

It is one of the fascinating stories of science that Big Bang radiation was first detected in 1963 by accident in an experiment at Bell Laboratories in New Jersey that was using a very sensitive radio receiver to search for sources of noise that could hinder telecommunications on Earth. Robert Wilson and Arno Penzias, two Bell Labs engineers, had been assigned the task of building a novel radio receiver, shown with them in this illustration, to look for sources of radio noise originating from every conceivable source.

They did detect a strange source of radiation "noise" whose source they could not identify. They realized that it seemed to come from the sky and with some detective work involving astrophysicists from nearby Princeton University they realized that the explanation was that they were detecting the relic radiation from the Big Bang, confirming its very existence. The announcement of their discovery and its implica-

SUPERCOMPUTERS AND DISTRIBUTED NETWORKS. CREDIT: MIT LABS.

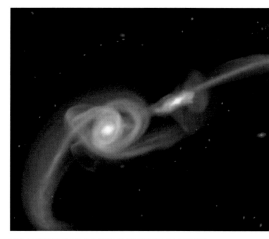

STILL FROM A SIMULATION OF TWO GALAXIES COLLIDING.

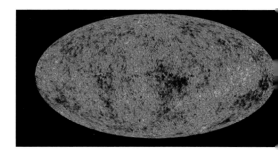

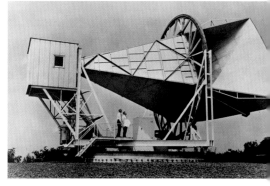

DISCOVERY OF BIG BANG RELIC RADIATION (1963). CREDIT: BELL LABS, WMAP/NASA.

tions were a scientific sensation, making the front pages of newspapers around the world. Penzias and Wilson were awarded the Nobel Prize in Physics in 1978 for their important discovery.

2. Dark Matter

It's hard to imagine that matter can exist in the universe that scientists are not able to detect through its own radiation, because all normal matter in the universe, whether humans or things, interacts with radiation by emitting, absorbing, or (in the case of black holes) gravitationally distorting it. This is how astronomers study all objects in the universe. Yet, it has become clear in the past decades that certain large amounts of matter in the universe do not appear to be emitting or absorbing radiation; they only interact with it through their own gravity, serving as a lens that distorts the light of more distant objects that pass near concentrations of the dark matter. This matter is truly strange stuff and we have no idea what it really is. We can't see it in any way, so we call it "dark matter."

Is dark matter made up of some sort of strange fundamental particle? Probably so, because it does exhibit gravity, a force that characterizes all matter in the universe. Thus, it might be simply one more exotic tiny fundamental particle of nature that we have not yet managed to produce in our most energetic atom smashers. The CERN Large Hadron Collider in Geneva is conducting experiments that could detect a particle or field that would indicate more clearly just what dark matter is.

This illustration shows a schematic of how astronomers have been able to map out the distribution of dark matter and determine the amount that exists in space, even though we don't know what the material is. The image was taken by Hubble Space Telescope and shows a prominent cluster of galaxies. The beautiful arcs surrounding the bright galaxies are distorted images of more distant galaxies whose light has been "lensed" by dark matter associated with the bright galaxies. So we know from these arcs that the patch of sky being imaged by the telescope is domi-

HUBBLE IMAGE SHOWING LIGHT BEING LENSED BY DARK MATTER. CREDIT: HST/NASA.

nated by matter that we cannot see.

Astronomers have observed other arcs of material that are caused by the gravitational lensing of matter and this has enabled us to determine that dark matter associates itself in space with normal matter. That is, it seems to be concentrated around normal galaxies and to be more massive than normal matter by huge amounts. In other words, most of our universe consists of this strange material, which is far more common than normal matter. Like some of the normal fundamental particles of nature, the dark matter could be passing through Earth and our bodies at all times, as do cosmic rays and neutrinos.

3. Extrasolar Planets

One of the fundamental lessons taught by the history of science is that whenever one appeals to a situation as being unique in the universe, it is usually demonstrated to be incorrect. It was once thought that Earth was unique in the universe and that it was the center of the solar system. Not so, we now understand. Astronomers have studied the formation of planets in the solar system and have concluded long ago that they formed together with the Sun as part of a process that is associated with the formation of stars from gravitational collapse of large gas clouds. Because many stars inhabit our Milky Way Galaxy, the scientific community has long assumed that many planets must exist around other stars. We believe the universe is brimming with planets.

The detection of planets around other stars is not a trivial exercise because planets are much smaller than stars and they do not shine very brightly by their own radiation. Rather, they primarily reflect the light from the stars that they are associated with and therefore are far fainter than their host star. Even the closest stars to the Sun are so distant that it is difficult to distinguish the presence of planets, which are lost in the humongous glare of their host star. The situation is like trying to detect a mosquito flying in front of the bright Sun.

Over the past 20 years astronomers have developed several techniques to overcome this hurdle so we can determine without question whether or not a star has planets. The first technique has been to forget about detecting the planet itself, and instead infer its existence due to the weak gravity the planet exerts on the more massive star around which it revolves. Newton's Law of Gravity tells us that in the same way that a planet such as Earth orbits the Sun, it also exerts a very small gravitational attraction on the Sun that causes the Sun to move in its own tiny orbit around the center of gravity of the Sun-planet system. The tiny wobble of the star is a clear signal that it must be accompanied by its own planet or planets.

The equipment required to detect the small orbital motion of stars is very delicate. It is easier to observe the changing velocity of the star than its actual change in position. It is one of the interesting facts of astronomy that an object's speed is frequently easier to determine than its absolute position. Large surveys were undertaken by several international groups in the early 1990s to try to detect miniscule changes in the velocity of stars that would signal the presence of a planet. The first detection was made by Michel Mayor of the Geneva Observatory in 1995. Breaking the light from stars into a spectrum, Mayor's team was successful in observing over time a miniscule change in the velocity of the star 51 Pegasi that indicated a periodic wobble caused by a planet very close to the star and having a mass greater than that of the planet Jupiter. A holy grail of astronomy had been achieved. We are not alone. At least in terms of the existence of other planets. We still cannot say that about life elsewhere. That even holier grail remains to be revealed.

Soon after this discovery, Mayor and other teams intensified their searches for planets and now, 17 years after that initial discovery, there is solid evidence for the existence of more than 450 planets around other stars. Some of the stars show evidence for complicated wobbles that signal the presence of multiple planets. One star has been determined to have at least five separate planets and in that sense

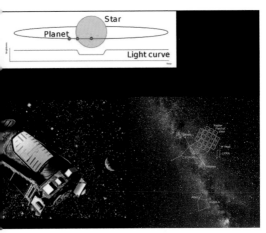

THE KEPLER SPACECRAFT IMAGES 100,000 STARS DAILY LOOKING FOR PERIODIC LIGHT DIPS INDICATING THE PRESENCE OF A PLANET. CREDIT: NASA.

may be analogous to the system of planets around the Sun.

Given the sample of stars around which we have found planets, we can infer what the likelihood is that the vast majority of stars in the Milky Way Galaxy possess in terms of planets. The conclusion is: the majority of stars are likely to have at least one planet, and perhaps many more. Thus, there are almost certainly more planets in our galaxy than stars, of which there are as many as 400 billion. Most of these planets, however, are less like Earth than they are the giant gaseous planets such as Jupiter, Saturn, and Uranus.

Planets with solid surfaces that happen to occur at a distance from their host star that causes them to have surface temperatures such that any water would be in liquid form — at temperatures between 0 and 100 degrees Centigrade — are called "habitable," or "in the Goldilocks zone." Life as we know it requires liquid water and so any life forms like our own would need to develop on such planets that are habitable. There is no guarantee that life has existed or evolved on such a planet, but exploring that possibility is one of the fundamental driving forces of our time.

The actual detection and study of planets has now gone on for almost two decades. In several cases, the Hubble Space Telescope has been used to observe light passing from the host star through the atmosphere of its planet, even though the planet is not directly seen, and we were able to determine that the atmosphere contained gaseous sodium. This fact alone does not tell us much about the planet or its atmosphere, but the fact that we are even able to obtain data about such a faint, distant object is mind boggling when compared to our complete lack of knowledge of other planetary systems just a generation ago.

There are methods other than the detection of a star's wobble that demonstrate the existence of planets. Small periodic brightness dips caused by the transit of an orbiting planet across the disk of its host star can signal the presence of a planet. Regular hourly and nightly monitoring of areas of sky where there are many stars, looking for tiny regular brightness dips, is an excellent way to discover planetary systems around other stars. NASA recently launched a mission called Kepler in an orbit around the Sun with a small telescope that continuously monitors each night the exact brightness of tens of thousands of stars with its sensitive equipment. Kepler is shown in this illustration together with the area of the Milky Way Galaxy where it takes imaging exposures every few hours. Kepler has been remarkably successful in identifying hundreds of stars that have planets. Astronomers are now busy training our large ground-based telescopes to study these stars in order to try to characterize the physical nature of the planets.

Finally, as difficult as it is to directly detect a dim planet seen near its bright host star, it is possible for a few of the stars closest to the Sun that the technique of coronagraphy might enable us to actually see a planet if it happens to be situated in a large orbit far from the star. Coronagraphy consists of placing a small disk at the focal point of the telescope to block as much light as possible from the star, allowing the light from a faint planet to be detected. This procedure has been tried with large telescopes for a number of relatively nearby stars and one star in particular has yielded fascinating results.

The image of the environment of this star, called HR 8799, is shown in this illustration. It shows a dark central hole where the starlight was blocked, surrounded by a bright ring which represents starlight scattered within the telescope. Surrounding the central star is material that appears to be in orbit around the star and which is believed to be material associated with a planetary system. There are three bright spots that are believed to be planets that have formed out of the dusty material. If so, the planets should be orbiting the star, in which case in the coming years the motion of the spots should confirm that they are indeed planets. This image could represent one of the first photos of a planetary system around another star than the Sun.

4. Dark Energy: The Accelerating Expansion of the Universe

The recent discovery by two independent international teams that the expansion of the universe is speeding up, accelerating, is one of the most unexpected scientific results of the past century. This conclusion follows from more than 15 years of exacting observations of distant supernovae. Astronomers have used these super-novae as yardsticks to determine how fast the universe was expanding in the past, when the light from these very distant exploding stars first began its long journey toward us. At first treated with some skepticism within the scientific community, this result has finally gained acceptance such that the leaders of the two teams that reported the result of the accelerating universe, Saul Perlmutter, Brian Schmidt, and Adam Riess, were awarded the 2011 Nobel Prize in Physics for their work.

The irony of the discovery of the accelerating universe is that the only known force that should affect the basic interaction of stars and galaxies has been thought to be gravity, which is always an attractive force. Thus, scientists have believed for the past century that the expansion of the universe must be slowing down, decelerating, under the influence of mutual gravitational attraction. It was the attempt to determine exactly how much deceleration there was that produced results that showed that in fact the universe's expansion is now greater than it was in the past.

What conceivable force could produce the accelerating expansion that counter-acts the attractive decelerating force of gravity? We do not know. Lacking solid information on the nature of whatever is producing the acceleration, astronomers have called it "dark energy." Numerous hypotheses exist, and they need to be clarified by experiment and subjected to scrutiny and consistency with those natural forces that we know and understand. In Einstein's formulation of general relativity in 1915, the concept of a so-called cosmological constant was introduced as a result of the mathematical formulation of general relativity. The cosmological constant is a mathematical representation of a repulsive force or positive energy that would serve to produce the universal acceleration observed.

The physical basis for this constant needs to be understood and whether it may be the cause of the accelerating expansion. Whatever is producing the increasing expansion of the universe, it represents a gigantic energy that dwarfs all other known sources of energy that we are aware of in the cosmos.

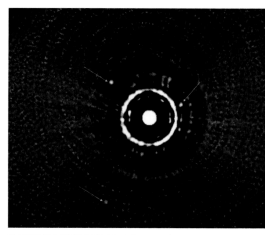

THE ENVIRONMENT OF HR 8799.
CREDIT: D. APAI, ESO.

5. Detection of Compact Objects: Pulsars and Black Holes

As is true for many phenomena in the universe, the existence of very compact objects of incredibly dense matter was predicted from our knowledge of physical laws before these objects were really known to exist. The study of the evolution of stars in the early years of computers led to the result that the inner regions of stars should contract due to their exhaustion of nuclear fuel, and therefore their inability to resist the huge pressure of the gravitational forces of the overlying material should produce an overwhelming force leading to the collapse of the star toward the center. Indian-American astrophysicist Subrahmanyan Chandrasekhar applied physical laws to this situation and predicted that the collapse of a star should result in a very small, highly compact object where the matter was unlike any in existence on Earth. The state of this compact mass was called "degenerate electrons."

Famous scientists refused to believe Chandrasekhar's conclusions and argued against the existence of degenerate stars until such objects, called white dwarf stars, were confirmed to have the characteristics deduced theoretically by Chandrasekhar. It is not uncommon in science for creative, unexpected ideas suggested on a theoretical basis to be eventually confirmed by observation and experimentation. In Chandrasekhar's case, he was awarded the 1983 Nobel Prize in Physics for novel conclusions from his detailed calculations.

It turns out that extremely compact objects such as electron degenerate white dwarf stars, and more compact neutron stars — and even more compact black holes — represent among the most bizarre environments in the universe. These strange objects manifest themselves in unusual ways. Pulsars, novae, supernovae, low-mass X-ray binaries, gamma ray bursters, Seyfert galaxies, and quasars are all examples of, or are associated with, such compact objects and are powered by them in some way. It is not too much of an exaggeration to claim that if you are trying to explain some weird phenomenon in the universe, invoke a compact object to do so!

In the 1960s, Anthony Hewish and Jocelyn Bell developed a new radio antenna and receivers that could detect rapid changes in radio emission. They conducted a survey of large areas of the sky looking for unusual radio radiation, especially that which exhibited sudden peaks in brightness. Over a period of months they discovered a number of sources that emitted radio emission in bursts, like the light of a terrestrial lighthouse. In this illustration Bell (now Jocelyn Bell-Burnell) is shown with this instrument together with a paper recording of one of the signals that she and Hewish detected. The radio radiation was highly periodic and repeatable over intervals of less than one second, unlike radiation ever seen from any astronomical object. Baffled, they quixotically labeled the radio sources LGM, for "Little Green Men," because of the regularity of the radiative pulses, as if they were signals from

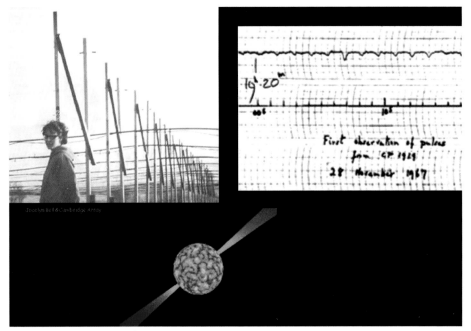

DISCOVERY OF COMPACT MATTER: PULSARS 1969. CREDIT: J. BELL-BURNELL, UNIVERSITY OF CAMBRIDGE.

an extraterrestrial civilization.

The astronomical world immediately began studying these unusual sources and came to realize that they represented extremely rapidly spinning compact stars with sizes on the order of 10 kilometers and immensely strong magnetic fields that consisted of atomic neutrons. The stars, named pulsars because of their pulsed radiation, were explained as the rapidly spinning collapsed remnants of massive stars that had expended their nuclear fuel. The strong magnetic field causes the radio emission to be beamed by the spinning star, explaining the pulsed radio waves.

The ultimate compact object is one that is so dense that light cannot escape it, hence its name of a black hole. As with many other astronomical objects, the existence of black holes was predicted from known physical principles. Because one cannot directly see any object that does not emit radiation or light, the only way to demonstrate its existence is from gravitational effects on nearby objects. The situation is similar to that of detecting planets around stars, which are difficult to see. Just as planets cause their host stars to exhibit very miniscule orbital wobbles, the strong gravity of a black hole is capable of causing any star near it to wobble. This has led to astronomers inferring the existence of black holes in double star systems and also in the form of huge concentrations of dark mass in the centers of galaxies. Although black holes cannot be seen directly, astronomers are agreed that they have been detected without doubt in a variety of different places.

The impacts of technological innovation and these discoveries on the development of astronomy in the last half century have been dramatic. Looking back in time in a historical perspective almost always elicits amazement at progress that could not have been foreseen. I believe these five discoveries have had a huge effect on our current understanding of the universe and our current plans for new projects that are being formulated to advance our understanding of the universe.

I found it difficult to confine myself to just the above five discoveries. Others could easily have found their place in the list. I consider Maarten Schmidt's 1963 discovery that the spectra of quasars required their interpretation in terms of cosmological redshift, and therefore very distant objects in the universe, to be one of those creative realizations that had an inordinate influence in opening up astronomers' commitment to study the distant universe. I debated whether to put it in my top five discoveries, especially since Maarten's work had such a strong influence on the trajectory of my career. But in the end I rated it as #6 on my list. There were other strong candidates for inclusion in a list of the most significant astronomical discoveries of the past half century.

What lies ahead for astronomy and how can it most effectively utilize its discoveries and understanding of the universe to influence human beliefs and activity on Earth? The first part of this question is difficult to predict because the diversity of natural phenomena extends beyond the imagination. As evolutionary biologist J. B. S. Haldane once observed, "The universe is not only queerer than we think, it is queerer than we can think." Whatever strange phenomena emerge from astronomical study are almost guaranteed to stimulate interest in the public.

The real challenge for astronomy is to communicate an understanding of the universe to society. Astronomy is one of the few pure sciences whose primary reason is to satisfy curiosity rather than an applied science that produces concrete things that directly affect daily life. As with music, one could live one's life without having any knowledge or interest in astronomy. Yet, like music, astronomy enriches one's life through the global perspective it brings to one's thinking. Unlike music, which people are intrinsically attracted to as an expression of life and which binds people together, astronomy does not necessarily have an obvious universal attraction.

Therein lies astronomy's biggest challenge for the future. The United Nations and UNESCO proclaimed the year 2009 as the International Year of Astronomy (IYA). Astronomers around the world created programs in every country of the world to bring the fascination of outer space to all people and the result was an amazing success. UN personnel agree that the IYA was by far the most successful of all international years. At all levels, from exhibits to special lectures to websites to school programs the IYA elicited an enthusiastic response from the public.

Astronomy needs to continue placing emphasis on the communication and sharing of its discoveries to everyone. This is perhaps the biggest challenge that confronts our science in the coming decades. If we are successful, it is assured that it will foster an understanding of ourselves and our global and universal environment that will enhance our ability to evolve together in greater harmony with ourselves and with our environment.

RICH GOLDMAN

LESLIE SAGE

SECTION 6

BEYOND ASTRONOMY

Astronomy affects our lives more than most people think. Beyond the study of our Sun and planets, the Milky Way Galaxy, and galaxies beyond, astronomy goes hand in hand with technological developments that push society on Earth. And our Sun, as it gives us power and life, also one day will kill life in the solar system. Is the Sun's variability to blame in some part for the current global warming? No matter, an awareness of the universe and our place in it definitely changes us in significant and in subtle ways.

Technology executive Rich Goldman surveys the ways in which technology has lunged forward in its sophistication, and how the exploration of space is linked to that powerful growth.

Astrophysicist Sami Solanki, director of the Max Planck Institute for Solar System Research, examines the possible involvement of the Sun in the current clear trend of global warming on Earth, an effect that is rapidly changing our planet and its habitats for life.

And finally, what does astronomy do to our sense of being human? Astronomer and editor Leslie Sage reflects on the historical awakening of our place in the universe and how it has changed mankind's innate sense of itself.

SAMI SOLANKI

NASA REPLICA OF SPUTINIK 1. CREDIT: NASA.

RICH GOLDMAN

Tech and Space: A Symbiotic Relationship

Rich Goldman is Vice President of Corporate Marketing and Strategic Alliances for Synopsys in Mountain View, California, a CEO of Synopsys Armenia, and a finalist for the 2010 U.S. Secretary of State's ACE Award. He is Chairman of the Board of the Synopsys Outreach Foundation and of the Synopsys Charitable Foundation for Armenia. Goldman is a Guest Professor of the Chinese Academy of Science and a Commissioner of the Advanced SOC Design Joint Lab Academic Committee. He is also an honorary Professor at the Moscow Institute of Electronic Technologies and currently serves on the Board of Directors of the Silicon Valley Technical Institute and the board of editors of Economics magazine.

RICH GOLDMAN AT STARMUS.

No two industries have revolutionized the world more than space exploration and technology. Looking back over the past 60 years, these two industries are deeply intertwined, each driving the other to achieve new heights. The resulting successes of both have paved the way for astounding new advances that have changed the way we inhabit our own world and travel beyond it and will continue to change our world in ways we cannot even fathom today. To understand the close linkage of space and technology, it is critical to look at historic touch points between these two industries. Our journey starts over six decades ago in the 1950s.

Both the space and technology industries were in their infancy in the 1950s. During this decade, the effort and creativity of engineers and astronauts led to foundational advancements that would spark the immense growth and success of space travel and technology industries.

Russian engineer Sergei Korolev was key in jumpstarting space travel. Despite years in the gulag where he sustained many injuries, his intelligence and drive were never deterred. His immense effort culminated in his role as the chief designer of Sputnik 1. He and his team persevered through numerous setbacks and seemingly insurmountable obstacles. Sputnik 1 was a simple design, consisting of a polished metal sphere, a transmitter, thermal measuring instruments, and batteries. On October 4, 1957, the Soviet Union launched Sputnik 1, the first human-made object to orbit planet Earth. Compared to today's capabilities, the technology used to monitor Sputnik 1 was primitive — in fact, all three of the ground guidance computers combined had the computational power of only 0.00005% of an iPhone 4S! Just two years later, the Soviet Union put the first manmade object on the Moon, Luna 2, using similar computational power to Sputnik.

These achievements amazed and inspired the world to imagine just how far humans could travel. It also prompted the United States to start investing in space travel. In 1961, U.S. President John F. Kennedy famously said, "I believe this nation should commit itself to achieving the goal, before this decade is out, of landing a man on the Moon and returning him safely to the Earth." Of course, in order to accomplish this inspiring goal, the technology that would enable further space exploration would require a massive focused effort.

Advancements in space travel were the initial drivers for more advanced technology to support these lofty goals. In his paper, "The Economic Impacts of the U.S. Space Program," Jerome Schnee states, "The space and defense market accounted for over 60 percent of all computer sales during the industry's first decade, and the sales of commercial computers did not overtake space and defense hardware sales until 1962."

Between the Sputnik 1 and Luna 2 milestones, in 1958, was a critical technical milestone. It was then that Jack Kilby created the first integrated circuit (IC) while working at Texas Instruments (TI). Because Kilby was a new employee at TI, he had

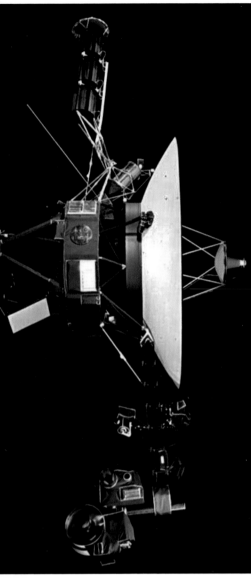

VOYAGER 1. CREDIT: NASA.

not yet accrued vacation days and, as a result, while everybody else at TI went home for summer vacation, he stayed and worked in the lab. Instead of relaxing, Kilby created the first IC, a feat for which he later won the Nobel Prize in Physics in 2000. Though Kilby may never have guessed at the time, his invention would have a dramatic impact on the success of the space industry, as well as the world, for decades to come.

The sixties was a decade of intense competition between the Soviet Union and the United States that really drove advancements in space. In 1961, Yuri Gagarin became the first man to orbit Earth. This was an incredible achievement for the Soviet Union at the time. During the launch of Vostok 1, Gagarin famously said "Let's go!," inviting the world into space. Around the same time, the first silicon IC chip was invented by Robert Noyce of Fairchild Camera in Silicon Valley. Just as Gagarin's achievement invited the world into the cosmos, Noyce's achievement opened the doors to an explosion of creativity and advances in technology that would ultimately fuel the space industry as well.

In the 1960s, we changed the way we thought about technological advancement. In 1965, Gordon Moore, a young Intel engineer, published a paper now known as "Moore's Law," which has defined our thinking model for technological progress for the past fifty years. Moore predicted that the numbers of transistors we can manufacture on a silicon IC will double every 18 months. This was later modified to every two years, still an incredible pace of progress unprecedented in history. Moore's Law applies to the number of transistors on a chip, computing power on an IC, or halving the cost of computing power for the same IC function. These three measures remain core aspects of how the semiconductor industry is evaluated today.

In 1965, the Soviet Union claimed another victory in the space race when Alexei Leonov became the first man to walk in space.

But the United States wasn't far behind, and on July 20, 1969, Neil Armstrong and Buzz Aldrin became the first men to set foot on the Moon — a defining moment in human history. Armstrong's Apollo 11 was guided by the Apollo Guidance Computer (AGC) as were all other Apollo Moon missions. Designed by MIT Instrumentation Laboratories in the early 1960s, AGC was one of the first IC based computers, utilizing 4100 ICs, each a single 3 input NOR gate. It operated at 2.048 MHz frequency with a 16 bit word length, with 2,048 words of erasable magnetic core memory and 36 kilowords of read only core rope memory. The computer weighed 70 pounds.

That same year, George Smith and Willard Boyle at Bell Labs made a seminal invention for astronomy: the Charge Coupled Device (CCD). The CCD would prove critical in decades to come as the foundation of digital photography, which enabled satellites such as the Hubble Space Telescope and Kepler spacecraft to take pictures of the cosmos and send them back to Earth. Throughout this decade, the space and defense industries were absolutely critical in the development of the semiconductor industry. Many semiconductor startups relied on funding from the government in order to advance exploration in space.

The pace of advancement in both the space and technology industries was unsurpassed in the 1970s. In 1971, the first space station, Salyut, was launched into orbit, another Soviet achievement. The same year, Intel introduced the first microprocessor, invented by Ted Hoff, Federico Fagin, and Stanley Mazor. The 4004 was powered with an incredible 2,300 transistors on a single integrated circuit and became the basis for computing as we know it today.

In 1975, the first personal computers started to emerge. People like Steve Wozniak and Steve Jobs were working at the Home Brew Computer Club in Menlo Park, California, creating personal computers that could sit on their own desks, a phenomenal achievement at the time. By 1976, modern supercomputers were created, performing functions at speeds never heard of before.

In 1977, another major space milestone was achieved when Voyager 1 and 2 were launched with the goal of traveling to Jupiter and Saturn. The technology in these satellites was cutting-edge — in fact, Voyager 2 is still sending pictures back to

Earth today. But as advanced as they were, just five years later, Intel released the 80286 chip used in personal computers, which was 26 times more powerful than the onboard computers on Voyager 1 and 2.

The 1980s ushered in a new era of space travel, represented by Columbia, the first reusable spacecraft and first manned Space Shuttle, in 1981. This feat was made possible by the latest advances in technology. As impressive as this achievement was at the time, it is a testament to how far technology has come that the iPhone 4S has more than 8,000 times more computing capability than the onboard computers that flew on Columbia. Six hundred times more state-of-the-art technology than what was needed to power a spacecraft now fits in the palm of your hand.

In 1981, IBM introduced the personal computer, which became a turning point in the development of microelectronics and computers. The personal computer was much cheaper and smaller than the older mainframes, allowing engineers to work at their desks rather than sharing time on a mainframe.

Another major accomplishment was the creation of the Cray supercomputer in 1985, the world's fastest computer. This supercomputer had eight processors, was the size of a car, and cost $17 million. Only large government agencies like NASA and the U.S. Department of Defense, along with several major corporations, could afford this state-of-the-art technology. Today's iPad is even more powerful than the Cray, is the size of a notepad, costs only $499, and is owned by millions.

In 1986, tragically, the space shuttle Challenger exploded, causing the United States to rethink everything about its space program. It led the United States to question whether space exploration was worth the cost — but, ultimately, the country decided it was committed to advancing our knowledge of the universe. At the same time, the Soviet Union was launching the MIR Space Station, a research lab created with the goal of developing technologies that would allow people to permanently live in space.

Technology also took a leap forward in 1985 when Intel introduced its 80386 microprocessor, which held 275,000 transistors. At the time, it was nearly unthinkable that that many transistors could be held on a single integrated circuit. It was further proof that Moore's Law continued to hold true.

At this time, it was becoming increasingly difficult to design chips by hand. Even a team of engineers could not keep thousands of logic blocks in their heads at one time. As a result, electronic design automation (EDA) was developed to enable the creation of these complex chips. EDA drove larger and larger computer chip designs. That was the time when Synopsys, this author's company, commercialized logic synthesis, bringing technology to another level of abstraction and leading to much higher productivity in designing these complex chips.

By the 1990s, the space and technology industries were increasingly intertwined, each driving the continued success and advancement of the other. As mentioned previously, CCDs drove the digital imaging revolution, a critical component to enable the mission of the Hubble telescope in 1990. Digital photography also provided immediate feedback to astrophysicists from large shared, expensive telescopes. They could then make adjustments to the telescopes accordingly, providing much more useful telescope time, rather than spending that time waiting for photographs to develop. This resulted in more useful data and accelerated discoveries. It also allowed images to be sent back to Earth from space. Just one year later, that same technology came to market in the form of the first commercial digital camera.

In 1995, Russia completed the longest manned space flight, of over 400 days. By this time, an Intel Pentium Pro microprocessor held over five million transistors, providing immense computing capability.

In the latter half of the 1990s, additional countries began taking advantage of the leaps in technology to begin their own space explorations. Japan followed the success of its Hiten lunar probe by sending the Nozomi probe to Mars to become the first country other than the United States or the Soviet Union/Russia to launch a lunar probe into outer space. In 1999, China launched an unmanned test flight of its

SPACESHIP 1. CREDIT: CREATIVE COMMONS ATTRIBUTION-SHARE ALIKE 1.0 GENERIC LICENSE.

first space capsule. Space had truly become international, and cheaper, more advanced technology made it possible.

The space and technological achievements of this century have continued to take humankind to new heights. In 2000, just 12 years ago, the USB flash drive entered the market, enabling us to today routinely carry gigabytes of data in our pockets. This small device contains more memory storage than what was contained in almost any spacecraft in history.

The year 2004 ushered in a new era in space when the first private spacecraft, SpaceShipOne, left our atmosphere. Space was no longer the sole domain of government; commercial entities now had the ability to explore beyond the reaches of our planet. In 2009, the Kepler spacecraft was launched, which utilizes highly advanced technology including 42 CCDs to continue to explore space and delve into its secrets. Kepler provides high-quality data that allows us to detect extrasolar planets, similar to Earth, which may host intelligent life. Technology has been crucial in creating Kepler as well as analyzing the massive amounts of data that it sends back to us. Without the availability of massive amounts of cheap and powerful microprocessors, we wouldn't be able to decipher the massive amounts of data that we are receiving from Kepler. Today, about 700 people from nearly 40 countries have left this planet, thanks mostly to the International Space Station and NASA's space shuttle program.

Technology also continues to leap ahead. In 2010 we saw 2.3 billion transistors on a chip and introduced just one year later, the latest Intel microprocessor holds 2.6 billion transistors. Today chips of eight billion transistors are being built. A simple example of just how far technology has come is the cell phone. In the 1990s, the cell phone was simply a phone people used to make calls. Over the years, features were added to these phones, such as calendars and address books. Today, our smart-phones enable us to do everything from playing Angry Birds, to tweeting, to checking email, to using global positioning systems to find directions to anywhere we want to go. Cellphones have virtually become supercomputing devices that can be held in the palm of your hand. At this continued rate of progress, 20 years from now, we will look back at modern devices and marvel at how primitive we were, just as we look back 20 years ago from today and marvel at how primitive our technology was before the turn of the century. Who knows what advances will make today's technology look as old-fashioned as a black-and-white TV?

In his book The Age of Spiritual Machines, Ray Kurzweil puts all of this computing power in perspective by demonstrating what the exponential growth in computing power means. By his estimation, we have advanced microprocessor technology to a level that is approximately equal to the brainpower of an insect. In just 10 years, computers will have the brainpower of a mouse. By the middle of this century, according to Moore's law, a single IC will have the computing power of a single human brain. A few decades after that, a single chip will have the computing power of all human beings in the world. It begs the question — what will humans achieve with such an immense amount of processing power?

The incredible advancements in technology over the past 60 years didn't come easily – continuing to service Moore's Law requires a lot of hard work, money, and research. As chips become smaller, and more transistors are packed on an IC, the physical challenges increase exponentially. For example, to verify a billion transistors (making sure what was designed is actually what was intended), the number of state spaces needed to verify quickly expands well beyond the number of stars visible in the night sky. Another key technological challenge is power consumption. For example, we are asking today's cellphones to function as mini-computers without using any additional power than they did when they functioned as simple phones. After all, we need our cell phones to last all day — no one wants to carry a phone the size of a car battery around. There are many novel design techniques that are applied, for example, to provide the capability to turn off certain parts of a circuit that are not being used. Still, power remains a critical and difficult challenge that we will continue to face.

In manufacturing, a chip fabrication factory capable of building leading-edge technology costs approximately $6 billion. Very few companies in the world — or even countries for that matter — can afford this cost. As we drive down in geometries, the building of chips becomes very challenging. Some of the layers of today's chips are just five atoms thick. To be just one atom off is a 20 percent discrepancy. Furthermore, with such thin layers, the electrons can leak power very quickly and uncontrollably. As we move forward, shrinking the silicon is no longer enough. New ideas must emerge in order to continue to advance technology at its current trajectory.

Moore's Law may eventually come to an end with silicon, and transition to new technologies so that the rate of progress can continue. Engineers will work with new paradigms such as carbon nanotubes, graphene, or even light waves. But this isn't the first time engineers have had to find out-of-the-box solutions to their challenges. Years ago, Intel realized that processors couldn't continue on their current power and frequency trajectory, growing exponentially from 20 megahertz, to 100 megahertz, to 1 gigahertz and beyond. It was a race of frequency. But to continue down this path, the power density of the chip would increase so much that it would be beyond the power density of a nuclear reactor and eventually reach the power density of the Sun, and nobody wants something that hot sitting on their lap. So Intel realized that they needed to rework their designs, and thus created the multiprocessor. Instead of making one processor do more work by clocking faster and faster, we divide the world into two, four, eight, 16 or more cores, which enables bringing the frequency and power down.

Advances like multiprocessors are changing the way we live. For example, cars are becoming computers on wheels. Everything from safety systems to engine controls to infotainment systems are all computerized, which improves the efficiency and cost of our cars. Mobile communications are booming. According to the "Cisco Visual Networking Index: Global Mobile Data Traffic Forecast Update, 2010–2015," in 2010, global mobile data traffic grew 2.6-fold from 2009. Traffic in 2009 was three times more than 2008, which was three times more than 2007, much faster than Moore's Law would predict. In 2010, mobile data traffic was three times the size of the entire Internet in 2000. Our connecting speeds doubled in 2011 and our smartphone data usage doubled in this past year.

Where will we go next? Exciting possibilities with dark energy, extrasolar planets, and extraterrestrial contact are all being explored today. With the latest technology, discoveries are being made at a greater rate than ever before. Already, the brightest minds are working on cars of the future. Imagine you have a meeting across town. Your car knows when and where that meeting is. The morning of the appointment, your car sees that there is heavy traffic, so it sets your alarm to wake you up a little earlier. You hop in the car, and it drives you to the meeting without you ever having to touch the steering wheel. Your car detects an accident ahead, so it automatically navigates to a better route. Your car reschedules your meeting to later in the day and calls the person you are meeting with so you can talk to them about the new time. Add to all this that cars of the future might be powered by greenhouse gases, turning pollution into fuel, and can relieve congestion on roadways by being able to travel much closer to the car in front of it while still being much safer than any human driver.

Other projects in the works are virtual environments similar to the holodeck from Star Trek, zero emission buildings, and computers operated by strands of DNA. We need a future generation of semiconductor engineer specialists who are driven to continue technology's exponential growth and ensure that our explorations in space continue to push new boundaries.

The future is extremely bright. Just as they have for the past 60 years, space and technology will continue to be closely intertwined, each driving the success of the other and improving the lives of people all around the globe. Wherever the future takes us, one thing is certain — future successes will be possible because of advancements in microelectronics.

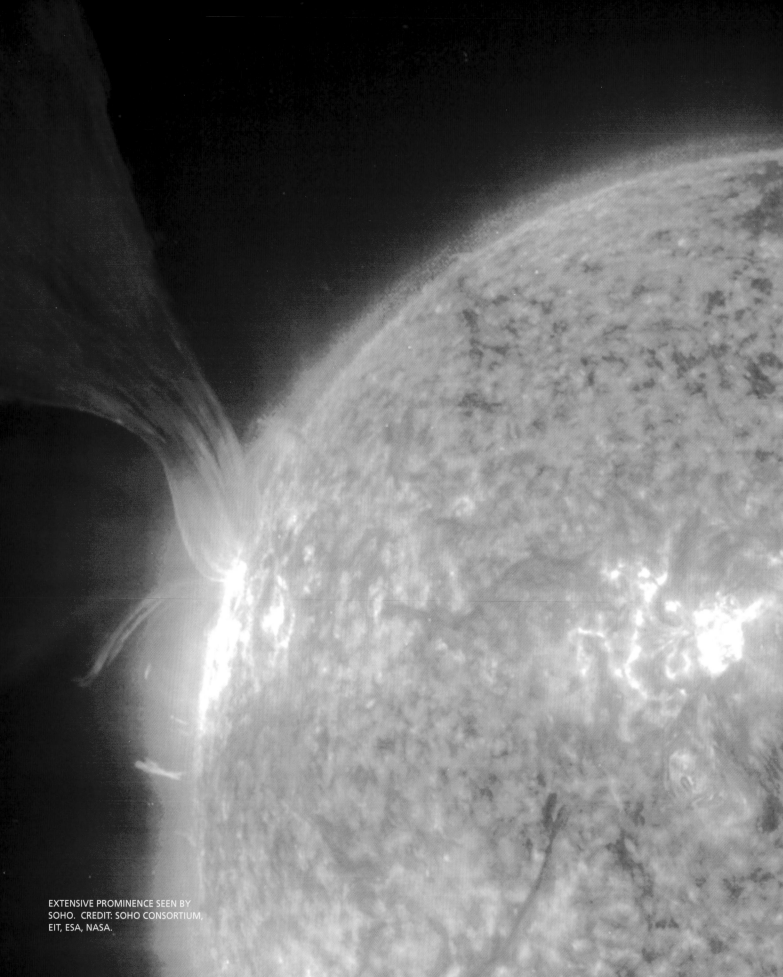

EXTENSIVE PROMINENCE SEEN BY
SOHO. CREDIT: SOHO CONSORTIUM,
EIT, ESA, NASA.

SAMI SOLANKI

IS THE SUN TO BLAME FOR GLOBAL WARMING?

S ami Khan Solanki, born October 2, 1958 in Karachi, Pakistan, is director of the Max Planck Institute for Solar System Research (MPS) in Lindau, Germany. He is a chair of the International Max Planck Research School on Physical Processes in the Solar System and Beyond, at the Universities of Braunschweig and Göttingen, Germany.

Solanki is also Honorary Professor of the Institute for Astronomy at the Swiss Federal Institute of Technology in Zurich, Distinguished Professor at the Kyung Hee University in Korea, and editor in chief of Living Reviews in Solar Physics.

His primary topics of research focus on solar and heliospheric physics, stellar astrophysics, astronomical tests of theories of gravitation, protoplanetary disks and exoplanets, and the radiative transfer of polarized light.

Solanki is principal investigator of the Sunrise project, which flew a large solar telescope on a stratospheric balloon, and of the PHI instrument on ESA's Solar Orbiter mission. He is also co-investigator for the Virgo instrument on the ESA/ NASA SOHO mission, the Secchi instrument on board NASA's STEREO mission, and HMI on NASA's SDO mission.

SAM SOLANKI AT STARMUS.

Today, global climate change, or more specifically global warming, is an indisputable fact. The scientific community also shows widespread, although not unanimous, agreement that mankind is responsible for a significant part of this. To what extent natural sources are involved in this process has been debated more controversially in the past decades. Alongside volcanoes, the Sun is the primary natural source of heat. Can the Sun be blamed for a relevant contribution to the current global warming?

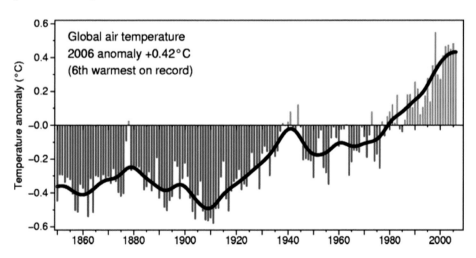

GLOBAL ANNUAL TEMPERATURE ANOMALIES FOR 1850 TO 2011 RELATIVE TO THE 1961 TO 1990 MEAN. THE SMOOTH BLACK CURVE SHOWS DECADAL VARIATIONS. CREDIT: CLIMATIC RESEARCH UNIT, UNIVERSITY OF EAST ANGLIA, NORWICH, UK.

Over the last century scientists have observed a clear rise in average global temperature. After a first step of about 0.3° in the first half of the century, the temperature remained almost flat for the next 30 years before it rose again, this time by roughly 0.5°, as shown in this illustration.

The consequences are already clearly noticeable. The vast majority of glaciers are retreating at an alarming pace, as shown in the illustration, sea levels are rising, and extreme weather events such as major storms are increasing. Projections from

Muir & Riggs Glaciers, Alaska

2004

1941

COMPARISON PHOTOS OF 1941 AND 2004
OF MUIR AND RIGGS GLACIERS IN GLACIER
BAY NATIONAL PARK AND PRESERVE,
ALASKA. CREDIT: ADAPTED FROM ROBERT A.
ROHDE / GLOBAL WARMING ART, BASED ON
PHOTOGRAPHS TAKEN ON AUGUST 13TH,
1941 BY WILLIAM O. FIELD, NATIONAL SNOW
AND ICE DATA CENTER, AND ON AUGUST 31,
2004 BY BRUCE F. MOLNIA, USGS.

the Intergovernmental Panel on Climate Change's Fourth Assessment Report of 2007, based on different scenarios for the further development of the emission of greenhouse gases, forecast a range of 1.5° to 3.5° for the global surface warming by 2100, threatening us with even more devastating consequences.

Temperature variations in general are common in Earth's history, as indicated by the numerous ice ages that have held Earth in their grip time and again over the last few million years. A huge increase in temperature occurred roughly 12,000 years ago, when the last ice age came to an end and the modern warm period began. Since then, the climate has been rather stable. This steady climate may well have played an important role in shaping the course of human development. It was in this period that agriculture started, as people gave up their nomadic existence to settle down in one place, both of which were prerequisites for the rise of human civilization. Although climate has shown some variability in this period of time, the rapid increase in the last 30 years seems to be exceptional. Various temperature reconstructions suggest that Earth is hotter now than it ever has been in the last 1,300 years, as shown in this illustration.

On longer timescales, current global warming does not appear to be unusual, but its occurrence in the past can usually be linked to natural changes. For the current global warming, scientists generally agree that it is largely driven by the release of greenhouse gases, foremost among them carbon dioxide, into Earth's atmosphere by the burning of fossil fuels.

However, determining the exact level of warming due to manmade greenhouse gases requires a good understanding of the natural causes of climate change and the magnitude of their influence. These natural causes are partly to be found in the climate system itself (which includes the oceans and the land surfaces, including vegetation, which undergo complicated interactions with the atmosphere and the climate). They are partly produced by the release of aerosols and dust from Earth's interior through volcanoes. And they partly lie outside Earth and are predominantly related to the Sun, which is the source of virtually all external energy input into the climate system. Does this special star, the originator of life on Earth, potentially constitute a risk in the near term for the current moderate climate? Let us now turn our attention to the Sun, resplendent in the very center of the solar system.

We all know that wonderful feeling of being warmed by the first rays of the rising Sun on a cold morning as they gently kiss the world awake and softly bring us back to life again after a night's deep slumber. The Sun's rays don't just give us fresh life in a figurative sense, but also keep Earth warm and cozy, because the Sun is basically Earth's only external source of energy. But what is this enigmatic object that has helped Earth to maintain life over billions of years? What is it made of?

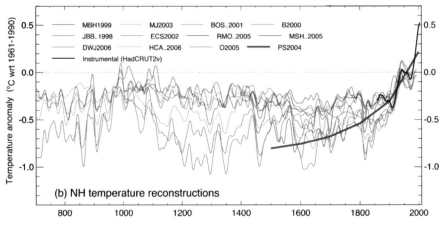

NORTHERN HEMISPHERE TEMPERATURE VARIATION DURING THE LAST 1300 YEARS. SHOWN ARE
DIFFERENT RECONSTRUCTIONS USING MULTIPLE CLIMATE PROXY RECORDS. THE INSTRUMENTAL
TEMPERATURE RECORD IS IN BLACK. CREDIT: IPCC (2007), FIG.6.1(B).

Where does it get its energy from — the energy that radiates so lavishly into space and only a tiny fraction of which reaches Earth? Does it change and evolve just like Earth and everything on it?

The Sun is a star, composed, like most stars, of hydrogen. It is a ball of gas, an immense ball of gas, stretching more than a million kilometers from side to side. The huge mass of this gas compresses it so that it is very dense at its core, where temperatures reach more than 10 million degrees. This is hot enough to force hydrogen nuclei to fuse into helium. This is the same process that makes hydrogen bombs explode with such force, but in the Sun it happens in a controlled manner, and has been happening safely for more than four and a half billion years.

The energy produced in this manner moves outward, initially in the form of radiation, but farther out the heated gas itself starts to move, so that on the surface of the Sun the gas starts to bubble and seethe, pretty much as boiling water in a pot. Incredibly, this chaotic and turbulent medium also produces a kind of music, by exciting the Sun to oscillate in millions of ways. The notes of the Sun's oscillations are much deeper than the human ear can hear, but they occur in well-defined intervals, pretty much like the notes of a piece of music — a piece of cosmic music — the long sought after music of the spheres (or at least of one particular sphere).

Although we would very likely not find such solar music to have an easy listening quality (if the tones were to be translated, as Garik Israelian has done), they are not a mere curiosity, but are of great scientific value. They allow us to literally look inside the Sun in much the same way as waves from an earthquake allow us to peek inside Earth. Just as the science of using waves inside Earth to determine its internal properties is called seismology, so the method by which we glean more about the Sun's interior is called helioseismology.

The seething convection at the surface of the Sun is interrupted by large dark spots, so-called sunspots, which appear apparently out of nowhere, live for a period of time that can range from a few hours to a few weeks, and then die again, leaving only a filigree of bright features, so called faculae, behind. These too fade away over time until nothing remains to remind us of the mighty spots, each the size of Earth, that once were there, as shown in this illustration.

If we leave the Sun's surface behind and travel farther out — if we dive into the Sun's ever-changing atmosphere — we find many more structures, such as the bright red chromosphere and the Sun's ethereal and beautiful crown, the million-degree corona. The corona is itself a source of further, often highly dynamic structure. It is constantly blowing a stream of charged particles in all directions, the solar wind, which is time and again intensified into a solar storm. At certain critical locations, the corona flares, brightens enormously, especially in the ultraviolet and in x-rays, while often throwing a huge bubble of gas into interplanetary space, as shown in this illustration.

These bubbles of gas become ever larger as they move away from the Sun until they dwarf the Sun itself, becoming the largest structures in the solar system. If such a bubble of gas, or coronal mass ejection (CME, as these structures are rather unromantically known) hits Earth, it influences the magnetosphere and ionosphere, leading to such beautiful phenomena as aurorae at high latitudes. If sufficiently strong, a CME may even reach right down to Earth's surface, inflicting damage to sensitive equipment, disturbing communication channels and navigation and, in exceptional cases, even causing the loss of satellites or blackouts over large areas.

This rich array of active phenomena has a common cause, the Sun's magnetic field. In contrast to that of Earth, the Sun's magnetic field is both changeable, complex and ordered on small scales — on such small scales that until recently we were not able to resolve the true magnetic features and only saw averages of many of them.

The direct impact of this reliable and trusted energy source on Earth's climate is mainly brought about by solar radiation. Basically, the solar influence on climate change can be threefold: through changes in Earth's orbital parameters, which

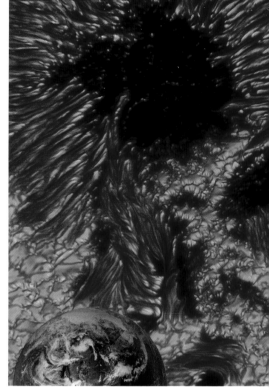

A SUNSPOT AS SEEN BY THE SWEDISH SOLAR TELESCOPE (SST) ON LA PALMA (CANARY ISLAND, SPAIN). THE INNER, DARK PART, CALLED UMBRA, IS SURROUNDED BY THE OUTER, FILAMENTED PENUMBRA. THE SUNSPOT IS EMBEDDED IN THE GRANULATION PATTERN RESULTING FROM CONVECTIVE ENERGY TRANSPORT. THE BRIGHT CORE OF A SINGLE CONVECTION CELL HARBORS HOT UPFLOWS, THE DARK BOUNDARIES (CALLED INTERGRANULAR LANES) ARE COMPOSED OF COOL DOWNFLOWING GAS. CREDIT: J. HIRZBERGER, MAX PLANCK INSTITUTE FOR SOLAR SYSTEM RESEARCH.

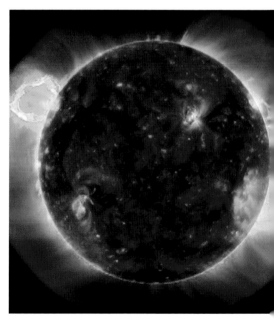

THE ATMOSPHERIC IMAGING ASSEMBLY (AIA) ONBOARD THE SOLAR DYNAMICS OBSERVATORY (SDO) RECORDED THIS ERUPTING PROMINENCE AND ASSOCIATED CORONAL MASS EJECTION (CME). CREDIT: NASA.

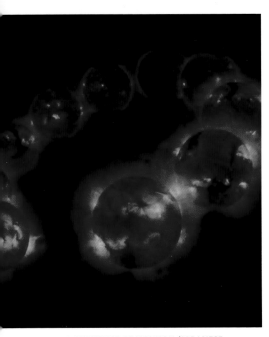

A SEQUENCE OF YOHKOH (JAPANESE SPACECRAFT LAUNCHED IN 1991) X-RAY IMAGES RECORDED BETWEEN 1991 AND 2001, SHOWS HOW THE CORONA CHANGES DURING THE SOLAR CYCLE. CREDIT: THE SOLAR X-RAY IMAGES ARE FROM THE YOHKOH MISSION OF ISAS, JAPAN. THE X-RAY TELESCOPE WAS PREPARED BY THE LOCKHEED-MARTIN SOLAR AND ASTROPHYSICS LABORATORY, THE NATIONAL ASTRONOMICAL OBSERVATORY OF JAPAN, AND THE UNIVERSITY OF TOKYO WITH THE SUPPORT OF NASA AND ISAS.

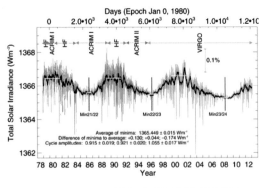

A SEQUENCE TOTAL SOLAR IRRADIANCE FOR ALMOST 3 CYCLES. DATA FROM 4 INSTRUMENTS HAVE BEEN USED TO CREATE THIS COMPOSITE PRODUCED AT THE PHYSIKALISCH-METEOROLOGISCHES OBSERVATORIUM DAVOS. CREDIT: C. FRÖHLICH, PMOD/WRC, DAVOS.

modulate the amount of solar energy reaching different parts of Earth, through changes in the Sun's radiative output itself, and through the influence of the Sun's activity on galactic cosmic rays.

Three parameters of Earth's orbit — eccentricity, precession, and tilt or obliquity of the rotational axis — vary at periods ranging from about 20,000 years to roughly 100,000 years, in the so-called Milankovitch cycles. These cycles mainly change the amount of solar radiation received at different latitudes in each season. Although the global annual mean of the solar energy input hardly changes, this localized redistribution can have an effect on climate due to the irregular distribution of land masses over latitude, which react differently to solar radiation then oceans. If such a redistribution crosses certain thresholds, it may trigger feedback loops and thus start (or terminate) glacial epochs.

These orbital changes are considered to be the prime cause of the pattern of ice ages and the interglacial warm periods that has dominated longer-term climate variations over the past few million years. Although the precession of Earth's rotational axis and the evolution of the obliquity and orbital eccentricity can cause large climate changes, all these processes run so slowly that they are unlikely to play a role on a timescale of centuries (although climate can react rather rapidly to a slowly changing trigger).

Variation of the solar radiation is generally considered to be the main cause of the contribution of the Sun to global climate change on relatively short timescales. These variations are closely related to sunspots, or, to be more precise, to the number of sunspots, which rises and falls over a solar cycle of roughly an 11-year duration. This correlation and its impact on the climate will be described in greater detail below.

The third possible line of impact refers to the fact that the flux of galactic cosmic rays varies roughly inversely with the level of solar magnetic activity. The fraction of the Sun's magnetic field spreading out to the edge of the solar system and the solar wind impede the propagation of the charged galactic cosmic ray particles into the inner solar system. The more active the Sun and the stronger its interplanetary magnetic field, the smaller is the cosmic ray flux that reaches Earth. Galactic cosmic rays have been proposed to provide a source of cloud condensation nuclei in the lower atmosphere and thus the modulation of their intensity may impact global cloud cover. To what extent this happens, and if it is in any way relevant to climate change, is still a subject of research. Variations in cloud cover will influence the share of solar radiation that is reflected into space as well as the amount of infrared cooling of Earth.

Ever since sunspots were discovered around late 1610 or early 1611, they have been a subject of intense study. One of the properties of particular fascination was the change in the number of sunspots with time according to an 11-year solar cycle. Along with sunspots, almost every observable feature on the Sun changes in relation to this cycle. For example, the x-ray brightness and structure of the corona change dramatically, as shown in this illustration, as does the frequency of flares and CMEs.

All these changes are driven by a single quantity, the Sun's magnetic field. The large-scale magnetic field of the Sun is produced by a dynamo mechanism acting deep within the solar convection zone. At the surface of the Sun, the magnetic field shows up as dark sunspots and bright faculae, composed of many small bright points. It is reasonable to suppose that these features of different brightness all affect the solar irradiance.

Since 1978, spacecraft carrying radiometers have recorded solar radiation almost without interruption. The measured variation of the total irradiance of the Sun — the total wavelength integrated solar radiative flux measured directly above Earth's atmosphere — is shown in this illustration.

This is a composite of measurements made by different radiometers on various spacecraft. Besides the strong short-term variability, there is also a clear solar cycle variation (best seen in the solid black line, which is a three-month running mean). The Sun is brightest at times of high solar activity (many dark sunspots, many bright faculae, a bright and complex corona), but the variation in the total irradiance over the solar cycle is only 0.1 percent. Hence, although the Sun is a variable star, it is changing only very slightly over the period of time for which direct measurements exist.

What causes the variations in solar radiation output? In the layers immediately below the solar surface, the outward energy flux is carried almost completely by convection. A strong vertical magnetic field hinders the development of overturning convection, and hence strongly impedes the convective energy transport. As a result, sunspots appear dark. Consequently, while a sunspot is present on the solar surface, the Sun should be slightly darker. This is indeed the case and the narrow dips in brightness seen in the figure (particularly marked at times of high activity) are due to the passage of sunspots over the solar disk.

For the smaller and numerous magnetic features forming faculae, the suppression of convection by the field is more than offset by the influx of radiative energy from the sides. Faculae are places where the solar surface level is depressed due to the pressure of the magnetic field, so that the solar surface area is increased. Hence, more radiation escapes through the normal "quiet" parts of the solar

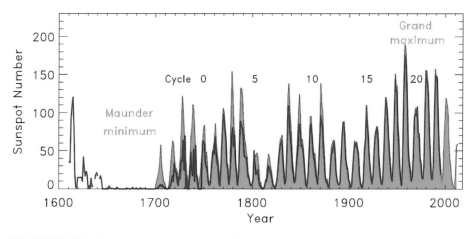

THE SUNSPOT NUMBER RECORD (YEARLY AVERAGES) SINCE THE BEGINNING OF TELESCOPIC OBSERVATIONS ABOUT 400 YEARS AGO. THE PERIOD IN THE SECOND HALF OF THE 17TH CENTURY THAT WAS PRACTICALLY FREE OF SUNSPOTS IS CALLED THE MAUNDER MINIMUM. CREDIT: H. WÖHL, KIEPENHEUER-INSTITUT FÜR SONNENPHYSIK.

surface.

In the sum, the irradiance change over the solar cycle should be explained by the energy blocked by sunspots and the excess energy released by faculae. Models based on this assumption have been very successful in reproducing the measured irradiance variations.

The solar rotation period of 27 to 30 days and the solar activity cycle period of roughly 11 years have dominated the temporal behavior of solar activity in recent decades. If we consider the 17th century, however, we find that the number of sunspots was extremely low for nearly 70 years and a cyclic behavior was far from clear, as shown in this illustration.

This so-called Maunder minimum period is the best-studied example of a "Grand Minimum" of solar activity, the only one detected in directly observed solar data. It is particularly intriguing because it falls together with the climax of the "little ice age," a time of bitter cold and suffering in Europe. This gives rise to the question whether other periods of low solar activity have occurred and what they mean for the Sun's irradiance.

This question can be addressed by using proxies of solar activity that allow us to reach further back in time than we can with sunspot observations. The most widely used such proxies are cosmogenic isotopes, in particular Carbon-14 (^{14}C) and

Beryllium-10 (^{10}Be). These isotopes are formed in Earth's atmosphere when high-energy galactic cosmic rays (mainly protons) interact with constituents of Earth's atmosphere, in particular with nitrogen atoms. After their formation, the isotopes are transported in Earth's atmosphere (and in the case of ^{14}C pass through the carbon cycle, which includes the oceans and the biosphere) until they are deposited in a natural archive (tree trunks in the case of ^{14}C and the Greenland or Antarctic ice sheets in the case of ^{10}Be).

With the help of physical models, scientists can reconstruct sunspot numbers from such data. The illustration below shows a reconstruction covering the last 7,000 years, based on a ^{14}C record obtained from (reliably dated) tree rings. Multiple grand minima and maxima — extended intervals of unusual low or high sunspot numbers — are visible in this period of time. Another striking feature is that in the last few decades we have been in a period of exceptionally high solar activity. Throughout the Holocene (over the past 11,400 years) the Sun spent less than 10 percent of the time in a state of similarly high activity to the one in the second half of the 20th century. But the prolonged minimum between solar cycles 23 and 24, and the relative weakness of cycle 24 indicate that the Sun is in the process of leaving its grand maximum of activity.

A critical quantity is the amount by which the Sun's irradiance changes between a grand minimum (such as the Maunder Minimum) and a Grand Maximum, a time of very strong cycles, such as the last 50 years. Recent estimates, based on simple physical models of the evolution of the magnetic field and the computation of the irradiance from it, suggest that the Sun has brightened by roughly 0.1 percent since the Maunder Minimum. Other recent estimates range between 0.06 percent to roughly 0.6 percent for the brightening since the Maunder Minimum. This large uncertainty highlights the need for additional work on this topic.

It is important to note that the solar irradiance variation is typically not homogeneous over the solar spectrum. It increases rapidly toward shorter wavelengths. Although the radiation in the ultraviolet range (shortward of 400 nm) contributes only about 8 percent to the magnitude of the total solar irradiance, it is responsible for at least 60 percent of the variation of the total irradiance. This is of some relevance due to the fact that different wavelength ranges are absorbed at different heights in the atmosphere and they may affect the atmosphere in differing ways.

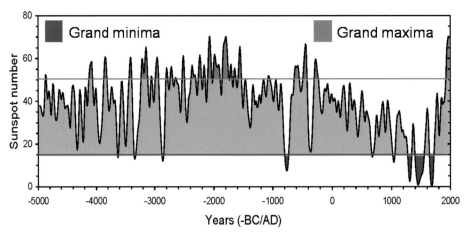

NUMBER OF SUNSPOTS (SMOOTHED DECADAL AVERAGES) OVER THE LAST 7,000 YEARS RECONSTRUCTED FROM ^{14}C IN TREE RINGS. THE SUN HAS BEEN UNUSUALLY ACTIVE DURING THE LAST 70 YEARS. CREDIT: USOSKIN ET AL. (2007).

When attempting to determine the impact of solar variability on climate, we need to first compare the trends in solar irradiance with trends in the global temperature on Earth. On long timescales where no direct temperature records are available, proxies for the temperature have to be used. Thus, ocean sediments have been employed to reconstruct temperatures in the North Atlantic. Minerals are deposited by rafted ice on the ocean floor. In colder climates the ice drifts farther south before it melts and releases the minerals. In the next illustration, this record is compared for the last nearly 12,000 years with the above-described proxies for the solar activity, the ^{14}C deposition in trees. Clearly, the measurements of temperature and of solar activity run reasonably in parallel, with excursions toward colder climate being particularly well matched by excursions toward a less active Sun.

On a shorter timescale, a direct comparison of temperature records with the (reconstructed) solar irradiance is possible. The next illustration shows two reconstructions of the total irradiance of the Sun combined with measurements for the recent years since about 1980 where satellite data are available, covering approximately the last 150 years (the red curves). They are compared with the temperature on Earth (global average and average over the Northern Hemisphere; blue curves). All curves have been smoothed over 11 years in order to remove the influence of individual solar cycles and the often-large, year-to-year excursions in atmospheric temperatures. Prior to approximately 1980, the curves run roughly in parallel, although from 1910 to 1950 the temperature runs slightly ahead of the solar irradiance change. The Sun may well have contributed to the warming in the first half of the last century, but was clearly not the sole contributor and probably also not the main driver. After 1980, a clear divergence between the two quantities is notable. Whereas Earth has continued to warm at a rapid rate, solar radiative output has slightly declined when averaged over the solar cycle.

This figure supports, but by no means proves, the view that the Sun has had an important, possibly even dominant influence on our climate in the past (at least for the northern Atlantic). The message from the next figure is less clear for the first half of the 20th century. After roughly 1980, however, the Sun cannot have been the dominant source of this latest temperature increase, with manmade greenhouse gases being the likely dominant alternative.

Because solar radiation is the principal source of energy for Earth, it appears natural to expect that any variation in the solar net radiative output will affect the energy balance of Earth's surface and atmosphere. But the processes by which the variable solar input affects climate change are not yet well understood. One promising pathway involves the solar ultraviolet irradiance, which varies by a far larger relative amount (10 to 1,000 times, depending on the wavelength) than the solar total irradiance, and such variations have a pronounced effect on the chemistry of Earth's upper atmosphere, in particular the balance between ozone production and destruction.

The difficulty is that the solar signal is not just a fluctuation entering a passive system. The complex interrelated system of Earth's atmosphere, land and oceans can transfer, smooth off, amplify or depress this signal. Solar energy is deposited and redistributed from the thermosphere down to the troposphere and Earth's surface, and a number of different mechanisms are involved in the process: direct absorption of solar radiation, generation and modification of chemically active substances and planetary waves. This all makes the solar-climate relationship highly nonlinear, such that the dynamical and physical feedbacks of Earth's system need to be considered, in order to reliably assess the magnitude and mechanisms of solar influence on climate.

The Sun is now recognized to be a (weakly) variable star. Since it is the major source of external energy input, this clearly has implications for the climate on Earth. Correlation analyses suggest that, prior to the recent rapid rise in global temperature, the Sun likely had a discernible influence on climate, but the magnitude of the influence of the Sun's variability is not clearly known. This is partly because the magnitude of solar variability itself is not known.

However, the rapid rise in global temperatures during the past 30 to 40 years is very unlikely to have been driven by solar variability.

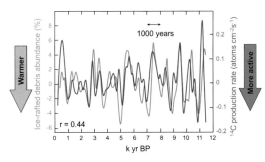

COMPARISON OF ^{14}C RECORDS WITH TIME SERIES OF STACKED MARINE RECORDS ACCORDING TO BOND AT AL. (2001). FIGURE KINDLY PROVIDED BY M. LOCKWOOD.

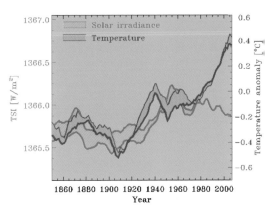

TWO RECONSTRUCTIONS OF TOTAL SOLAR IRRADIANCE COMBINED WITH MEASUREMENTS, WHERE AVAILABLE (ENCLOSING THE RED SHADING) AND TWO CLIMATE RECORDS (GLOBAL AND NORTHERN HEMISPHERE TEMPERATURES, ENCLOSING THE YELLOW SHADING) SPANNING ROUGHLY 150 YEARS. ALL CURVES ARE SMOOTHED BY 1-YEAR RUNNING MEANS. CREDIT: FIGURE BY N.A. KRIVOVA AND S.K. SOLANKI.

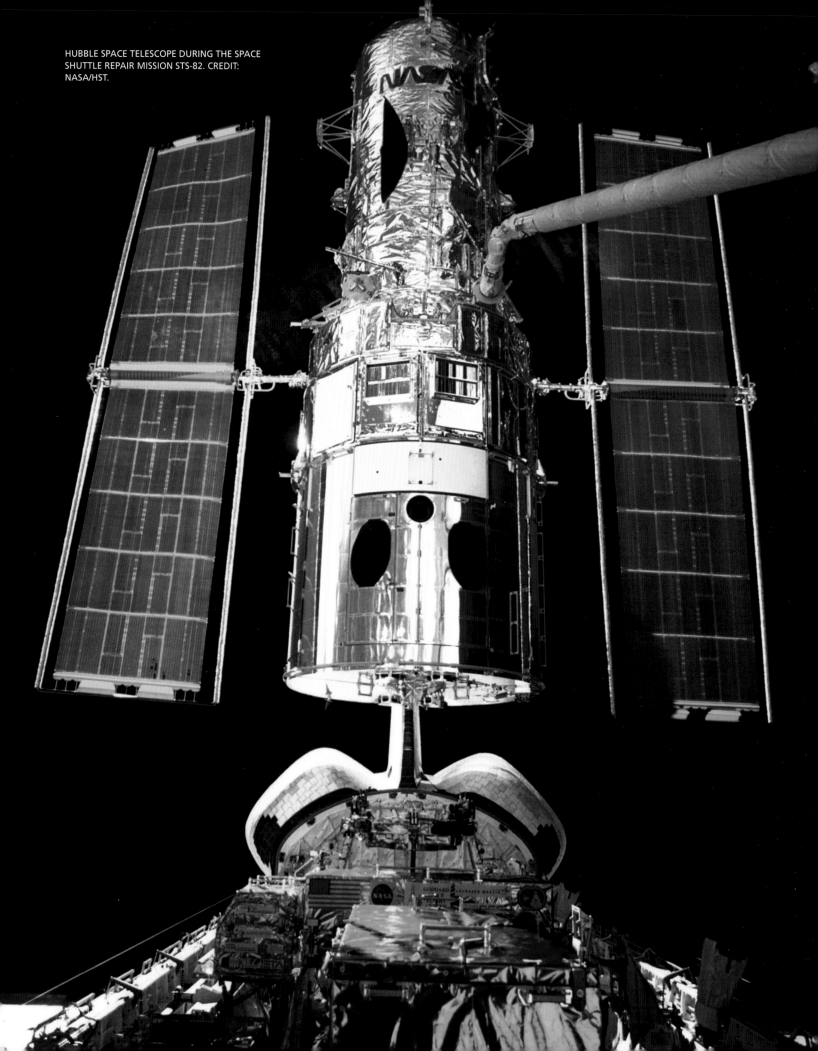

HUBBLE SPACE TELESCOPE DURING THE SPACE SHUTTLE REPAIR MISSION STS-82. CREDIT: NASA/HST.

LESLIE SAGE

How Astronomy has Changed what it Means to be Human

LESLIE SAGE AT STARMUS.

Leslie Sage is senior editor for physical sciences of the journal Nature and is a research associate in astronomy at the University of Maryland in College Park. Sage held postdoctoral fellowships at New Mexico Tech and the Max Planck Institute for Radio Astronomy. He is also a longtime columnist for the Journal of the Royal Astronomical Society of Canada. He grew up in the western suburbs of Toronto, Canada, but now lives with his family in Potomac, Maryland. In his spare time, he studies the gas content and star-forming properties of galaxies, and cooks new recipes found by his wife.

I am going to try to make a case that astronomy has had a profound effect on how we see ourselves, and how we relate to the universe around us. Let us start by imaging what the world looked like to our ancient ancestors. Storms, floods, earthquakes, droughts, and plagues happened with no apparent explanation.

Although these ancestors did not have our knowledge, they were keen and sophisticated observers of nature — in many ways, more so than most modern people. They observed the regular march of the seasons, and that the seasons were associated with particular patterns of stars in the sky. The regularity and predictability of the night sky were in striking contrast to the unpredictability they saw around them in their daily lives.

Somewhere around 585 B.C., Thales, a pre-Socratic Greek philosopher living in the town of Miletus, on the coast of modern Turkey, determined the cycle of lunar and solar eclipses. He successfully predicted the solar eclipse that occurred on May 28, 585 B.C. But beyond that, he made the following statement: that for everything we see around us there is a rational explanation. We may not know what the explanation is, but it is out there waiting to be found. This was the beginning of science.

It is a curiosity of human nature to try to impose order on what we see. For example, stars are distributed in a random way in the sky, with a wide range of brightness. To bring some order to this apparent chaos, constellations were invented. The ancients made up stories about their gods and heroes, and how those gods and heroes came to be immortalized in the sky.

Of the 6,000 or so stars they could see on a clear night, only five — along with the Sun and the Moon — moved in the sky. The Greeks called them planets, which was their word for a "wandering star." The planets, and indeed the Sun and Moon, followed the same basic path through the sky, which led the Greeks to conclude that the constellations along that path were in some way special. In this way, the zodiac and astrology were born.

The ancients were keen observers of nature, and one of the strangest things they saw was that the planets did not move uniformly relative to the stars. Mars, Jupiter and Saturn all did little "dances" where they would slow down, move backwards in the sky for a while, then resume their forward motion. Venus and Mercury did not do this, which was very puzzling. They had in mind that the planets were attached to crystalline spheres — that is what kept them up in the air. (Everything not so

A SEQUENCE OF IMAGES OF A TOTAL SOLAR ECLIPSE, AS THE MOON MOVES IN FRONT OF THE SUN FROM OUR PERSPECTIVE ON EARTH. CREDIT: STARMUS.

2003 Retrograde

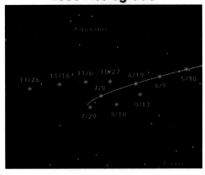

2005 Retrograde

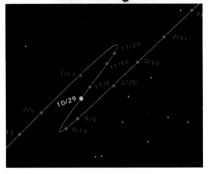

THE RETROGRADE MOTION OF MARS IN THE SKY DURING THE 2003 AND 2005 'OPPOSITIONS'. IMAGE CREDIT: NASA/JPL-CALTECH.

supported would fall to Earth.) But why would a sphere slow down, run backwards for a while, and then move forward again?

Around 100 A.D., an astronomer named Ptolemy proposed the idea of epicycles, where the planet was attached to a separate, smaller circle that was attached to the larger orbital circle. (This would not work with spheres, but in fact the idea of the spheres persisted in a vestigial sense until the time of Galileo, 1,500 years later.) As observations of the planets increased in accuracy over the next 1,400 years, more and more epicycles had to be added in order to explain the data. The Spanish King Alfonso X is supposed to have remarked, upon seeing a model of the system around 1300 A.D., that if the Almighty had consulted with the King, he would have advised a simpler system.

It was around that time that William of Occam, an English philosopher, crafted one of the guiding principles of modern science, known as Occam's razor. When there are competing possible explanations, the one that is the simplest and makes the fewest assumptions is the most plausible until shown to be wrong.

In 1514 the secretary to Pope Gregory XIII wrote to a mathematician, Copernicus, who also happened to be a priest, asking him to investigate reform of the calendar. The Church then, and to this day for events like Easter, uses a calendar based on the motions of the Moon. The seasons of course follow the motions of the Sun, and by the early 16th century the two calendars had drifted so far apart that it was becoming impossible to determine saints' days, which then was of great importance to the Catholic Church.

Copernicus wrote back that it would be impossible to sort out the calendars until the relationship between the motions of the Sun and Moon were determined. On the first of May 1514, he circulated a manuscript titled "A Little Commentary" in which he proposed that Earth and the other planets orbited the Sun. The fully developed model was not published until just after he died, which suggests that Copernicus was aware of the revolution he was proposing. He was not the first person, though, to suggest the "heliocentric model," or Sun-centered solar system.

That honor, at least as recorded in the history books, lies with the Greek philosopher Aristarchus of Samos, somewhere around 270 BC. It was simple, elegant and appeared to fit most of the observations. It did fail one crucial test, however, and was abandoned until the time of Copernicus. The crucial test was as Earth went around the Sun, the relative positions of the stars in the sky should shift — this is known as parallax.

A simple demonstration of parallax is holding your finger up with one eye closed and noting the position of the finger relative to background objects. Then close that eye and open the other one. The finger appears to have shifted position relative to the background objects. The problem with Aristarchus' model was that no parallax was observed. The critical element that was missed at the time was that people assumed that the stars were much closer to Earth than they actually are. We can now measure parallaxes, but they are far below what the naked eye can see.

Copernicus' model was straightforward and elegant — thereby satisfying Occam's razor — but it did not match the observations, because he assumed that planetary orbits were circular, while they actually are elliptical. While his model was widely discussed at the time, and found a great deal of support among educated people of the day, there was that stubborn problem that the best epicyclic model was a better match for the data.

Two things then happened relatively close together. Kepler found out that the planets actually move in elliptical orbits — that was the best fit to the careful observations made by his mentor, Tycho Brahe.

And Galileo turned his telescope onto the night sky. With his telescope he found mountains and craters on the Moon, many faint stars that were not visible to the naked eye, spots on the surface of the Sun, and that Jupiter had four moons orbiting it.

But the conclusive observations for Galileo, in terms of supporting Copernicus' model, were the phases of Venus. When Venus was close to the full phase — what astronomers call "gibbous" — it was smaller than when it was in the crescent phase. The only explanation for this was that Venus was farther away from Earth when it was in the gibbous phase, which it would be if it were on the far side of the Sun from Earth. The larger crescent phases happened when Earth and Venus were on the same side of the Sun. This conclusively demonstrated that Venus shone by reflected light and orbited the Sun.

Sir Isaac Newton built upon the work of Kepler and Galileo, and ultimately formulated the laws of motion and universal gravitation. Many people have heard the story that Newton got the idea for gravity when sitting in the garden. It turns out to be mostly true, as documented in a manuscript released from the Royal Society's archives in 2010. He saw an apple fall, and it made him wonder why everything fell perpendicular to the ground. A simple question, but with a very profound answer. He made the conceptual — and correct — leap that the Moon is continually falling toward Earth, and Earth is continually falling toward the Sun. The reason the Moon does not hit Earth, or Earth hit the Sun, is the momentum the bodies have — as the Moon falls toward Earth, it moves an identical distance sideways.

Asking simple questions about nature often leads to profound answers. Einstein asked himself what the world would look like to a person riding on a beam of light. The profound answer to that was Special relativity.

Newton's gravity was wildly successful. Using it, Edmond Halley discovered that comets are periodic, with the first identified periodic comet named after him. The observed deviations of Jupiter and Saturn from uniform orbits led to the discoveries of Uranus and Neptune.

Astronomers were therefore disturbed to find that by the beginning of the 20th century the change in the position of Mercury's perihelion (the point at which the planet is closest to the Sun) deviated substantially from that predicted by Newton's gravity. This is a critical element in science — when you see deviations from what you expect, there is often something important going on. The best scientists follow those deviations and try to understand why they happen.

Einstein solved the problem of Mercury's perihelion with his General relativity. The common representation of Einstein's gravity in this illustration captures some of the key elements. Einstein proposed that space is curved by mass, with the amount of curvature dependent on the mass (and density). Objects appear to follow orbits but are really just moving in a straight line in a curved space. Because of this curvature of space, light should be bent as it passes by a massive body. This key prediction was confirmed in 1919, during a total eclipse of the Sun, by Sir Arthur Eddington and his collaborators.

But Einstein's General relativity, as originally formulated, predicted an expanding universe. Einstein inserted a parameter — the cosmological constant — that countered that expansion. He later called it his biggest mistake.

Edwin Hubble and (separately) Georges Lemaître demonstrated that the "spiral nebulae," whose nature had been debated for 50 years (filling many pages of the journal Nature), were almost all moving away from us, and moving faster as they got fainter. This was the discovery of the expansion of the universe, and it shifted us from living inside a relatively small universe, to living in a galaxy that was simply one of many in a much larger universe. It became apparent that Einstein's cosmological constant was not necessary — his original equations accurately described the universe, but he ignored what those equations were telling him. Even the best scientists can be blinded by their own prejudices about what the answer ought to be.

Hubble and Lemaître completed what has come to be called the Copernican revolution. To the ancients, Earth was at the center of the universe. Then it was displaced to being one of a number of planets, but it was not clear whether we were near the center of the universe — seeing roughly the same numbers of stars in all directions carried the implication that we might be. As a result of Hubble and Lemaître, our true place in the universe was revealed as living on a tiny planet around an average star, itself located in the outer suburbs of an entirely ordinary

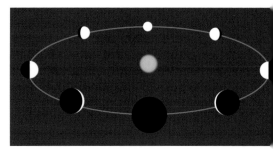

THE PHASES OF VENUS AS SEEN FROM EARTH.
CREDIT: NASA.

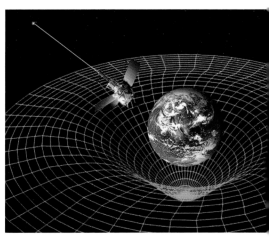

SPACETIME IS WARPED BY THE PRESENCE OF MASS. THE MORE MASSIVE, THE MORE WARPING. IMAGE CREDIT: NASA.

THE DISCOVERY OF A PLANET IN PEGASUS.
IMAGE CREDIT: NATURE.

galaxy.

Of course, if the universe is expanding, the implication is that it either is infinite, or it had a beginning. More or less contemporaneous with this was a debate about the age of the universe. Some astronomers favored the "long" timescale — with the universe being about 10^{13} years old — while some favored the "short" scale where the universe was about 10^{10} years old. Students of the history of science might be interested to know that Victor Ambartsumian made a correct and prescient argument in favor of the short scale in Nature. One of his arguments was opaque, and the second based upon false assumptions, but the third was correct.

Sir Fred Hoyle was a leading proponent of the infinite view, and even coined the term "Big Bang" to ridicule the other view. (The name stuck, however, much to his annoyance.) In the mid 1960s, two radio engineer/astronomers at Bell Labs were trying to develop very sensitive radio receivers, but found that there was a level of noise that they could not track down or eliminate. It turned out that the radio noise they were hearing — what is now called the cosmic microwave background — was left over from the Big Bang. Almost overnight, support for Fred Hoyle's infinite universe collapsed — this was the definitive proof that the Big Bang had actually happened. (Although Hoyle spent the rest of his career railing against the Big Bang, it was to no avail. The data are overwhelming.)

When the universe was very young, it was a soup of matter and light. Literally a soup — a fluid that was sloshing. When the temperature dropped below about 3000 K, the electrons combined with protons to form hydrogen atoms and the radiation began to stream freely. The cosmic microwave background is the remnant of that streaming. Tiny differences in the temperature of the microwave background reflect the ripples in the universe from that time, and the relationships between the features can tell us how much matter is in the universe, how rapidly it is expanding and even how much hydrogen there is relative to helium.

It turns out that the matter that makes up our planet, our star, even our bodies, is just 4 percent of the total matter and energy in the universe. Not only do we live on a tiny planet in an average galaxy, but all that we are and all that we see are essentially inconsequential in the bigger picture.

The next revolution took place in our own backyard. Everyone born before roughly 2000 A.D. learned in school that there are nine planets in the solar system. Now we know there are eight. What happened?

Pluto's orbit was known to be very unlike those of the other planets. It is very eccentric — sometimes it is closer to us than Neptune — and highly inclined, while the others orbit in an essentially flat plane. The change started with the discovery in the early 1990s of Kuiper Belt objects. These are large-ish and very cold bodies beyond Neptune that have some of the properties of asteroids, and some of comets. But it was their orbits that got astronomers interested — they were quite eccentric, and often highly inclined. As more were found, it became increasingly clear that Pluto was really just another Kuiper Belt object, and not a planet at all. Pluto's demotion was well deserved.

For many years, starting with the early 1970s, it had been clear to astronomers that planet formation was an inevitable part of the star formation process, so people started looking for planets around other stars. There were quite a few embarrassingly wrong claims until Michel Mayor and Didier Queloz found the first extrasolar planet orbiting the star 51 Pegasi in 1995.

But this planet was completely unlike anything anyone had expected. It was a Jupiter-sized planet orbiting not far from the surface of the star! Such planets are now known as hot Jupiters.

Now that we know that planets exist around other stars, the question inevitably arises about whether there is life on those planets. Let us break the life question into three categories: 1) simple life, such as existed on Earth for about 3 billion years before the Cambrian explosion of life about 560 million years ago, 2) multicellular life, with intelligence and tool making ability, and 3) a civilization capable of communicating with us. In 1960 Frank Drake, then a young astronomer working at a Green Bank, West Virginia radio telescope, came up with a way of characterizing our ignorance about what was possible, in the form of the Drake equation.

$$N = R^* \times f_p \times n_e \times f_l \times f_i \times f_c \times L$$

- N is the number of civilizations able to communicate with us right now
- R is the rate of star formation in the Milky Way
- f_p is the fraction of those stars with planets
- n_e is the number of planets per star capable of supporting life
- f_l is the fraction with life
- f_i is the fraction of those with intelligent life
- f_c the fraction of those with a civilization capable of communicating with us
- L is the length of time such a civilization lives.

Curiously, the last two terms — and especially the last — are now the most uncertain. Based on the many careless things we are doing to our planet — polluting it and causing it to warm, perhaps catastrophically — the evidence suggests that L may be short.

At a recent workshop on the search for extraterrestrial intelligence, I was surprised to discover that young people are just not as engaged in the search for extraterrestrial intelligence as older people like me. But even more surprising is the reason: it is not that they do not want to know, but rather they have already accepted that such civilizations exist and are just awaiting the proof.

Will we ever travel to the stars? If Einstein's Theory of Special Relativity always holds true, then the answer likely is no. But time and again the universe has surprised us, so I am not willing to make any bets on this.

The examples of pivotal points where astronomy has changed how we see ourselves and our place in the universe are both instructive and sobering. Thales laid out the foundation upon which all of science is built — that there are explanations for everything we see. Aristarchus and Copernicus looked for simplicity and moved Earth away from the center of the universe. Galileo demonstrated that their explanation was the correct one. Einstein's brilliant insight into the structure of the universe was led astray by the preconception that it must be static and only 10 years later did he realize it was his biggest mistake. Hoyle convinced himself that the universe had to be infinite, despite all the evidence to the contrary. I often wonder what mistakes we are making right now, and which preconceptions we hold, that are holding back our deeper understanding in fundamental ways.

In closing, I'd like to reflect on how astronomy is affecting our lives right now. The Kepler mission is expected to find an earthlike planet in an earthlike orbit around a Sun-like star sometime in the next few years. When that happens — and it will happen — I hope that it will help humans to see that there is far more we have in common across the globe than we have in differences, and that we will start thinking and acting as a single race, for the benefit of the planet.

CLAUDE NICOLLIER

YURI BATURIN

SERGEI ZHUKHOV

202

SECTION 7

THE NEW SPACEFARERS

What is the future of space exploration? With some programs stopped, in the process of winding down, and other efforts in their infancy, where will the exploration of space go? Will humans discover and widely support the funding and completion of new worlds of discovery?

Space historian, enthusiast, executive, and qualified cosmonaut Sergei Zhukov examines the Russian space program, its past, present, and future, in a detailed presentation that looks to a new era.

Swiss astronaut Claude Nicollier, a veteran of space shuttle flights that included two repair missions for the Hubble Space Telescope, describes his adventures in orbit. Because of these missions, Hubble was able to capture countless images of the universe like never before and to solve important riddles of astrophysics.

Russian cosmonaut, professor, and former politician Yuri Baturin describes how spaceflight changes people, giving them a vastly widened and new perspective on planet Earth, on their fellow human beings, and on the future of our world.

VALERI POLYAKOV WATCHING DISCOVERY'S RENDEZVOUS WITH MIR. POLYAKOV SPENT A RECORD 240 DAYS IN SPACE. CREDIT: NASA.

SERGEI ZHUKOV

RUSSIAN COSMONAUTICS: TRENDS FOR FUTURE DEVELOPMENT

Sergei Zhukov is Executive Director of the Space Technologies & Telecommunications Cluster of the Skolkovo Foundation and a Member of the Russian Academy of Cosmonautics. Zhukov is from Dzhezkazgan, in Kazakhstan (now the landing site for Soyuz landing modules). He graduated from Bauman Moscow State Technical University and conducted post-graduate work on gas core nuclear installations for space applications.

Since 1990, Zhukov has been President of the Moscow Space Club, a non-profit NGO aiming to support national and international space activities. He was instrumental in founding the Russian Space Agency (established in 1992) and has been an active member of the Russian Cosmonaut Corps since 2003. He has graduated courses at the Gagarin Space Training Center and is qualified as a test cosmonaut. He has published two collections of poems and written several scientific articles.

SERGEI ZHUKOV AT STARMUS.

National space projects are an integral part of the Russian scientific, industrial and spiritual heritage. For more than half a century, our country has remained one of the leaders of outer space development and use. Until recently, Russian cosmonautics has also been a sphere of national profitability, placing the country among the leading developed powers.

The development of space projects fortifies Russia's defense, accelerates economic modernization, and pushes forward progress in science, engineering and social spheres. Therefore, it is a key factor of socioeconomic progress of the country, improvement of well being, and national security.

The utilization of space can also solve problems of communication, TV and radio broadcasting, remote probing of Earth from outer space, monitoring of objects and resources, navigation and mapping. This creates a reliable foundation of the territorial and systematic integrity of the country, the information and spiritual unity of its multinational people. Cosmonautics and Russian space achievements inspire pride in the home country.

The achievements of cosmonautics also grow scientific knowledge and expand horizons to make space accessible to all humanity. What Russia has achieved in outer space helps to govern our place as fully-fledged active participants in world affairs.

Currently, however, Russian cosmonautics programs face complex scientific, technological, economic, and institutional problems. Some of them are a logical outgrowth of the country's general economic situation — in particular, the collapse in the 1990s. Also, the economic situation has changed; industrial areas resisted transformation and carried on in some ways with an inertia inherited from the era of the Soviet Union.

As a result, the world's leading countries broke away, while Russia lagged behind in space technologies, adequate quality assurance systems, profitability of national industries, and so on. Discipline and responsibility have become intolerably poor. Sadly, one of the world's best systems of scientific and research education was dramatically harmed, and the natural change of generations involved in the enterprise has almost failed.

Russian cosmonautics have certainly contributed to mighty achievements. Russian rockets maintain the International Space Station, its crew replacement and cargo delivery. A Russian enterprise supplies engines for American rockets. Recently, the first Soyuz rocket was launched at the Guiana Space Center near Kourou. We launch more than 40 percent of the rockets into space and lead the world market. But if we weigh the total world space market (including the services to end users of

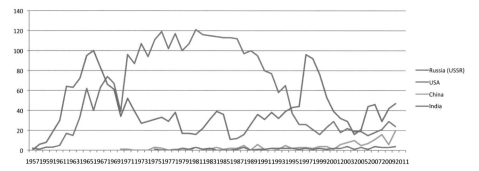

NUMBER OF SATELLITES INJECTED INTO ORBIT BETWEEN 1957 AND 2010.

satellite communications, Earth monitoring from space and other application trends) with the value, which exceeded $200 billion in 2010, the share of Russian enterprises amounts to a mere 3 percent. This situation should be solved.

It is now impossible for Russian cosmonautics to develop further unless the space branch is reformed significantly. Space projects should become a true instrument of innovation and progress, and capabilities should be expanded over all regions, including state and private users.

More than 50 years ago, in 1957, the Soviet Union launched the first satellite, Sputnik. Since then, more than 6,800 satellites, manned vehicles, long-term habitable and automatic interplanetary missions have been launched successfully.

Space projects of the United States, China, India, and Russia (the U.S.S.R.) are summarized in the illustration.

It shows the peak of space projects in Russia occurred between 1970 and 1991. The Soviet Union used to launch about a hundred space vehicles every year. Later, that number dropped abruptly so that Russia launched only 214 missiles successfully during the first decade of the 21st century, or slightly more than 21 missiles in an average year.

Up until 2010, Russia launched 3,479 space vehicles, and 3,250 were successfully injected into orbit. Thus, Russia achieved a success rate of 93.4 percent. After the first launches, the average active life of Russian space vehicles kept increasing and reached a historic maximum in the 1990s. Yet, at present, the average life of satellites is diminishing, causing a reduction of Russian satellites in orbit during the last decade.

The illustration shows that, in the 1960s, the United States launched on average about 70 satellites per year. During this time, American scientists and engineers perfected the technology of satellite manufacture, extending the average satellite life from 10 to 15 years; as a result, the United States reduced the launches to 30 per year. The United States has been able to maintain this average annual number during the last 30 years. In the late 1990s, a peak of satellite launches resulted from the development of low-orbit satellite communication systems such as Iridium, Globalstar, and Orbcomm.

From 1958 through 2010, the United States launched 2,402 satellites, with 2,147 of them reaching orbit successfully, equaling an 89.4 percent success rate. One should note that U.S. manufacturers created more than 300 satellites for other countries.

What tendencies characterize the modern progress of global space projects? The experts of the Space and Telecom Cluster, Skolkovo Foundation, identify a number of trends. First, the competition of space technologies in the mass market with alternative land surface solutions. Second, the growing value of international cooperation while implementing space projects, especially with large-scale projects. Third, introduction of purely private initiatives into all segments of space technologies. And fourth, a reduction of common thought about humanity expanding into outer space.

These tendencies have affected different nations with different intensities. Let us evaluate specific aspects governing the problems of cosmonautics in Russia.

State-of-the-art Russian space projects are characterized by competitive advantages of launches, fulfilling the country's needs with stationary space communications and broadcasting, completion of deployment of the GLONASS system, and fulfillment of Russia's international obligations with the International Space Station. Other areas, such as hydrometeorological observations and remote Earth sensing, orbital means of fundamental space exploration, personal satellite communications, and relaying and rescue of objects in distress, lag behind.

The challenge of creating and maintaining a modern telecommunication infrastructure in the Russian Federation can be solved by broad application of satellite communications. Satellites are particularly effective when they solve the problem of communications in outlying regions and areas with severe climatic conditions, like the Caucuses, Siberia, and the Far East.

There are now five fewer civil communications satellites than there were in 2000. With its unique space technologies, Russia has become almost unable to develop radio engineering satellite components, due to the grave crisis of the last two decades. This means that some communications satellites of the last decade have poor quality components and insufficient power, aside from the Gonets space vehicle, which is manufactured abroad.

At the same time, Russian stationary communications and broadcasting satellites are developing more or less stably, with the encouragement of the space communications state enterprise, the situation with two other trends of space communications, such as personal communications and relaying satellites, is far more complicated.

Remote Earth sensing techniques have been stably and dynamically developing during the last decade. The space information has become the important source for solving the practical tasks of governmental and local rule. The data from these satellites serve to explore natural resources; monitor and eliminate the aftermath of natural disasters; man-made emergencies; meteorology; climatology; urban, forest and rural economies; mapping; geology, geophysics, and geochemistry; oceanography; and other Earth sciences. The data have changed everyday human life on the planet.

Increased quality of equipment, of satellites and technologies, along with space data processing, have led to a rapid growth of remote Earth sensing satellites in orbit, along with the development of national and regional remote Earth sensing programs. In Russia and in the world at large, this is an emerging technology and is growing at a rate of about 15 to 25 percent per year. The Russian market amounts to about 10 to 15 percent of the world market. At present, locally made satellites Resurs-DK1, Meteor-M 1, and Elektro-L are in operation.

Resurs-DK1 has been operating since 2006. An improved Resurs-P 1 satellite is being developed in Russia which is projected to be launched in the second quarter of 2012. The Resurs-P system will comprise two similar satellites. In addition, the Kanopus-V space system is being developed with two satellites to monitor artificial and natural emergencies based on the broad use of the engineering solutions of the British SSTL Company (which has merged with EADS Astrium).

Interestingly, the single Russian Resurs-DK1 satellite was developed beginning in 1996 and launched only in 2006, 10 years later. This satellite transmits data in real time via a radio channel. Nevertheless, the satellite functions with severe limitations due to the failure of a number of onboard systems. With just three, Russia lags behind other countries in remote Earth-sensing satellites: the United States has 21, China 15, Germany 12, India 11, and several operated by France, Canada, Japan, the U.K., Italy, Israel, and several other countries.

Radar satellite development and deployment has traditionally been dominated by the United States, Japan, China, Germany, France, Canada, Italy, India, Israel, and Korea. In terms of radar space stations, Russia lags behind the international community and has lost the experience of Soviet scientists in this area.

Because of the current situation, Russia has virtually no remote Earth sensing system. Satellites scheduled to be launched in 2010 to monitor emergencies, like Kanopus-V and REP Resurs-P, were postponed until 2011.

To exploit the remote Earth sensing trend, an independent market model for remote Earth sensing satellites seems expedient. One should also note that the redundant classification of data processing results have led to the full loss of market position by Russia which existed in the early part of this century when foreigners came to us for data collected by the Kometa satellites. The present situation compels one to believe that Russian industries will manage to overcome the lag in the development of these systems only by borrowing the relevant technologies and training from European and American companies. One possible alternative is to directly import these satellites; it will, in turn, dictate final loss of expertise in that area.

Something Russia has implemented is the GLONASS system, short for Global Navigation Satellite System. It has comparable characteristics in accuracy, accessibility, and functionality with foreign counterparts (GPS) at the present time. The main problems with satellite navigation stem from needs to integrate the space-based system originally developed for national defense into a public system. The American GPS system is already well-established. In the future, this system will have to be integrated into the European Galileo system as well as Chinese and Indian systems.

Due to apparent budgetary reasons, the development of space research using Russian rockets has remained a low priority. Between 2001 and 2010, 12 satellites were launched to serve research. Several smaller satellites and university satellites failed to reach orbit and were not actuated due to rocket accidents. The Foton-M 11 satellite was lost while injecting into orbit. Only three satellites — Koronas-F, Foton-M 2 and 3 — operated throughout their lives.

The Koronas-Foton satellite was launched in 2009 to monitor the Sun from terrestrial orbit. During the mission, a considerable amount of scientific data was gathered. Still, the satellite failed in less than one year after launch due to a faulty power supply. Thus, the development of modern long-lasting satellites for space research is a grave challenge for the Russian space industry. The launching of the research observatory mission Spektr-R was a formidable success in July 2011. But four years later, the Lavochkin designers' interplanetary Fobos-Grunt mission, bound for the martian moon Phobos, failed to start from the bearing terrestrial orbit, having put an end to the revival of the Russian interplanetary research program after a 20-year-long pause. Thus, the development of complex, unique, non-standard multitask interplanetary missions is becoming an apparent problem for the Russian industry. The present-day approaches to the planning of programs of fundamental space research should be revised radically.

At the same time, one should note that use of relatively cheap Foton-M spacecraft based on a single-use retrievable capsule made it possible to obtain a range of results in the field of microgravity research. These included the discovery of new effects in fluid physics; phase transitions and condensed matter physics; new biophysical and biochemical phenomena in subjects; and measurements of physico-chemical parameters of the processes occurring in liquid phase. We have received reference samples of materials for electronics, alloys and composites, strains of microorganisms for tackling environmental challenges and producing animal feed, as well as 3D tissue and chondral structures for applications in clinical medical practice. Applied projects in the field of microgravity offer promising areas for the commercialization of space research.

While Russia lacked any possibility to launch an interplanetary mission, the scientists of the Russian Academy of Sciences and Russian universities take part in international research projects. They have produced experiments installed onboard foreign space vehicles. Thus, Mars Express, a European Space Agency mission operating in martian orbit since 2003, is equipped with Russian instruments

ARTIST RENDERING OF THE KORONAS-FOTON SATELLITE. CREDIT: ROSKOSMOS.

SPICAM-M, OMEGA-M AND PFS-M. Venus Express, the European Space Agency mission operating in orbit from 2005, conducts experiments using Russian-made instruments SPICAM-V, OMEGA-M, and PFS-M. Mars Odyssey, a NASA mission, has operated at Mars since 2001 and contains experiments created with the Russian-made HAND equipment. NASA's Lunar Reconnaissance Orbiter conducts experiments using LEND, a Russian-made Lunar exploration neutron detector. Mars Science Laboratory/Curiosity, launched on November 26, 2011, contains DAN, a detector provided by the Russian Space Agency.

New players in space exploration — China, India, Japan, and the European Union — have caused an essential revival of activity during the last decade. Their projects and current science research load are amazing in scale. The scope of permanent research covers the near-Earth space environment, the solar system, the planets, and astrophysical processes. Lunar flights became the focus of space research of the last and coming decades. The Mars program is also essential to space operations. We hope that Russian interplanetary missions and observatories will find their unique way into international research cooperation.

Today's manned Russian space program is connected with the extension and operation of the International Space Station (ISS) and with a complex of research and applied activities conducted at the station. The ISS has been operating in low-Earth orbit since November 1998. The station has been manned since October 2000. Today, the ISS comprises 14 main modules, including five Russian modules.

According to the Russian development program, in 2013 a multifunctional laboratory module will be added, and in 2014 a node module will be included that will make it possible to dock up to four additional modules to the Russian ISS segment. Later on, two scientific and research modules are expected to be docked, in 2015–2016.

Since May 29, 2009, a crew of six members, including three Russians, has been working at the station. Transportation and technical support is provided by the Russian spacecraft Soyuz TMA and Progress M, European transport spacecraft ATV, and Japanese transport spacecraft HTV. Long-term ISS operation has demonstrated a high level of reliability and flexibility of the architectural and technical approaches, as well as the existence of certain organizational and technical problems. Delays in construction of the ISS (in particular, of its Russian segment) considerably reduced the duration and field of its target use. Although the station is automated to the greatest extent possible, a nearly permanent crew presence is still necessary, which is a disadvantage. The station is not comfortable enough for its crew: although it has large sealed compartments, most of them are used for placement of service systems and equipment. A safe manner of performing certain important experiments at the ISS is problematic or even impossible.

Nevertheless, some important results have been obtained in the Russian ISS Segment. By the end of 2010, 38 experiments were completed, while 55 experiments were at the stage of flight implementation and 79 more experiments were at the stage of ground preparation. The results of these experiments gave birth to such developments as an axial loading suit for non-pharmaceutical treatment of neurological patients; a Cardiosleep-3 complex, which is used for evaluation of the functional state of the body during nighttime sleep; and a cardiovascular heart screening computer system. A new medication was also developed. Practical results have been obtained during the development of oil biodegradation agents and also the isolation of clones for an investigational batch of hepatitis B vaccine.

A crystallization experiment aimed at studying the structure of insulin crystals, grown in the Russian ISS segment, provided results that made it possible to launch Russian manufacture of a genetically engineered insulin product to be used for the treatment of severe diabetes.

The studies conducted within a plasma crystal experiment revealed a number of totally new effects in plasma with strongly charged microparticles.

Educational and popular science projects are among the most important objec-

THE LAUNCH OF THE ZVEZDA SERVICE
MODULE OF THE INTERNATIONAL SPACE
STATION ON A PROTON ROCKET. CREDIT:
NASA.

tives of activities at the International Space Station. Such projects as Ten'-Mayak (Shadow-Beacon), MAI-75, MATI-75, and others made it possible to engage school-children and students from Russia and all over the world in space experiments.

Notwithstanding all the diversity of research and experiments conducted in the Russian ISS segment, the station's efficiency in terms of important scientific and applied results is not high enough. This fact connects with the problems of creation of new Russian modules, limited resources, and unsuitability of the ISS for certain scientific and applied studies (in the field of microgravity, energy, radiation, etc.). Implementing a program of commercial applied research at the ISS could become an important area of innovative activity.

Despite preserving competitiveness in the market, most Russian rockets are outdated. Almost all currently used launch vehicles and cosmodromes were put into operation 20 or more years ago. Rockets are constructed with outdated components, and ground-based complexes have undergone numerous overhauls. In addition, light and heavy rockets still use toxic fuel components.

A construct of the government, the Federal Space Program 2015 provides for the development of a system of launch vehicles based on such carrier rockets as Proton-M, Rus, and Ankara. The top priority area of activity is completing the development and test performance of the Soyuz-2 rocket with Fregat upper-stage rocket at the Plesetsk Cosmodrome. Starting in 2013, Ankara rockets will be required for launching prospective spacecraft from this cosmodrome.

Design activities have begun to create a unified transport module that will use a solar electric propulsion unit and a nuclear power propulsion unit. Flight tests are expected to start after 2015. Technical proposals have been elaborated to develop a reusable first-stage space rocket system called MRKS-1. It is expected that the results of the contest of design concepts will be announced in 2012.

Today, Baikonur Cosmodrome remains Russia's main facility used for manned launches and placing spacecraft in a geostationary orbit. Work on a new Russian cosmodrome commenced in April 2007 at a meeting under the supervision of the president of the Russian Federation. The decision was made to create a new facility in the Svobodny District, Amur Region. As a result, on November 6, 2007, the president signed the Order on the Vostochny Cosmodrome.

The top-priority task within the construction of the new cosmodrome is to create an industrial base, without which it will be difficult to build the required ground-based space infrastructure in due time. Commercialization of a range of services provided at the cosmodrome and development of a public-private partnership during construction and operation are among the promising directions for mid-term development.

The new cosmodrome will enable Russia to implement its space policy, launching manned spacecraft and space vehicles operating at a geostationary orbit from its own territory. The president approved several projects on November 19, 2009. They include: first, development of a GLONASS service market. Second, creation of animate objects monitoring and control systems. Third, creation of intelligent systems of monitoring and control of the condition of technically complicated devices. Fourth, creation of a full technological cycle of new generation solar battery manufacturing. Fifth, creation of a transporting and energetic module on the ground for atomic energomotional installation of a megawatt class.

Four participants also visited the ISS as space tourists, all from the United States and Canada, and one of them twice.

Accumulated experience of creation and long-term operation of manned space complexes allows starting joint projects beyond low-Earth orbit, and perhaps to the Moon and Mars. Since November 2008, an experiment called Mars 500 has produced a simulated flight to the Red Planet, using three representatives from Russia and one each from France, Italy, and China. This project became the first step in preparation of an actual manned expedition to Mars, implementation of which would be possible only with strong international cooperation.

Analysis of the funding of space exploration reveals that civilian space programs in Russia in 2010 pushed past the 100 billion ruble mark for the first time. During the first decade of the 21st century, funding of civilian activity exceeded $13 billion.

According to the investigation of the Ministry of Economic Development of Russia, labor productivity in the Russian space industry is far behind the leading countries of the world. According to the data, the country's rocket and space industry produces $14,800 per employee annually, whereas European workers produce $126,800 and the United States $493,500 per employee. This situation, as a whole, is characterized by the lag of quantitative and qualitative levels of the used and developed Russian space vehicles.

The manufacturing, scientific and technical potential of the space industry, which was created in the Soviet Union for large scale manufacturing of spacecraft of various designations, needs serious reconstruction, aimed at overcoming the growing technological and scientific lag of Russia behind other countries.

Along with the obvious problems of the creation and operation of spacecraft, institutional problems add to the present state of Russian cosmonautics. They include program and target planning; institutional development and public support of design documentation; a lack of a harmonized system of state targeting of strategic issues of development of space activity; information closure of political, program and planning basics of space activity; immaturity of mechanisms of public discussion and independent examination; preserving uncertainty of distribution of roles between customers and contractors; a lack of strategic vision of the space agency; and a lack of large and medium businesses in the operation of spacecraft.

In the field of ground space infrastructure, there is no national net of ground stations corresponding to international rates and connection standards. In the field of organization of application of results of space activity in the economy, there is a lack of good operators of space services who could provide services for consumers in corresponding markets such as remote Earth sensing.

In the field of functional space technologies, we need long term production of separate satellite-borne systems and spacecraft as a whole. We need more advance development of prospective spacecraft, a better transition to new unified space platforms, and an improved condition of developing electronic components.

In the field of legal safety, we need more investments in entrepreneurship in the field of space activity.

In the field of the rocket-and-space industry and production technologies, there is continuing uncertainty in industrial competition and reservation of production powers and project schools. There is a lag behind other countries with technological powers, a low level of capital productivity and labor productivity, an absence of good industrial systems, an insufficient number of qualified specialists, a high average age of employees, and an undeveloped system of staff training at all levels.

Staffing problems of the industry should be considered more thoroughly. Like the other high-tech industries of the national economy, the space industry was damaged during the change of state authorities in 1991. In the 1990s, funding of the space program decreased by more than a factor of 12. Thus, from 1992 to 1999, the industry added few people from 20 to 40 years old, which caused an overall negative effect.

Now the primary problem is how to replace the generation of Soviet scientists (average age up to 60 years), engineers and qualified employees (average age over 50) that form the industry's current personnel. Unfortunately, this problem became a very Russian one and relates not only to space industry, but others with technical, engineering and scientific staff. This is the reason why qualified specialists of the rocket-and-space industry are nowhere to be found.

The analysis shows that if, during the next five to seven years, Russia cannot close the gap in the space industry from the obvious leaders (the United States and Europe), or at least with the second tier up-and-comers, China and India, then it will never be able to do so.

The current situation with Russian cosmonautics does offer some positives, however. They include a unique geographical location and a good distribution of power and resources within the country; competitive production in rocket-building, special materials, systems and components of manned spacecraft and long-term orbiting stations; and economic decisions that will help to build a new working system of space services. There is also much accumulated experience in interaction with western high-tech partners. There are also significant reserves of "goodwill"— a positive image in the social consciousness in Russia and abroad.

The government has also created a vision document for a future strategy, which can be viewed here: http://www.federalspace.ru/354/.

The Skolkovo Foundation and its Space & Telecom Cluster also has an important role to play. In response to the Soviet Union launching Sputnik in 1957, the United States created the Defense Advanced Research Projects Agency (DARPA), intended to oversee development of high-level technologies for space exploration. Large-scale reforms of education, directed at training youth for a new reality and new

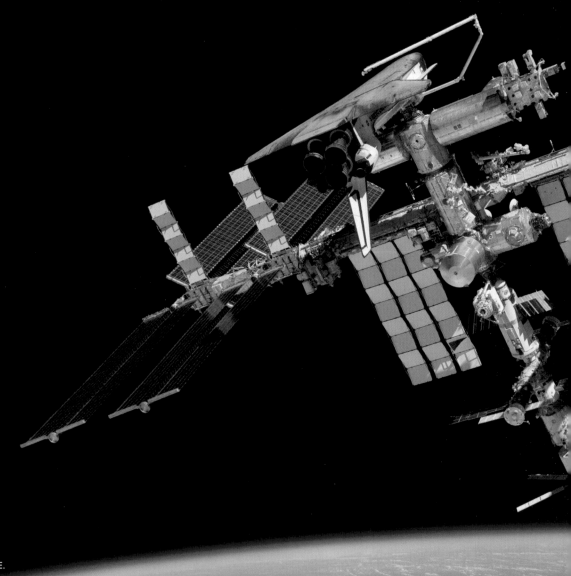

THE INTERNATIONAL SPACE STATION WITH
EUROPE'S AUTOMATIC TRANSFER VEHICLE
(ATV2) AND THE ENDEAVOR SPACE SHUTTLE.
CREDIT: ESA.

technological life, commenced. In my view, we should now act as a Russian DARPA in systematizing and consolidating breakthrough technologies. We should also create a "school of the future," wherein achievements and the possibilities of cosmonautics shall form a basis for education in the natural sciences, from the secondary school to post-graduate programs. That will give us the basis for a bright future.

Note: The Expert Group of the Skolkovo Foundation's Space & Telecom Cluster took part in the preparation of this paper. They include S. A. Zhukov, D. B. Payson, G. G. Malinetsky, V. R. Anpilogov, K. S. Elkin, A. G. Ionin, O. N. Kapelko, A. M. Krylov, M. V. Serov, A. Y. Baurov, Y. L. Leshkov, A. V. Potapov, and V. A. Rubanov.

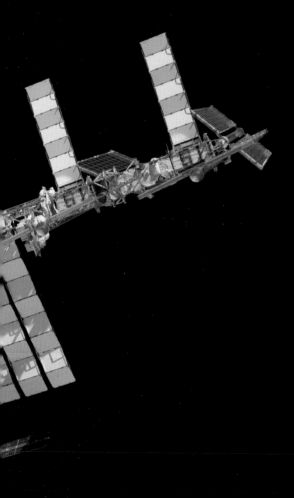

CLAUDE NICOLLIER

Revisiting Hubble

Claude Nicollier was born September 2, 1944, in Vevey, Switzerland. He is the first Swiss astronaut and has flown on four space shuttle missions, the first in 1992 (STS-46) and the last in 1999. He participated in two servicing missions of the Hubble Space Telescope.

Nicollier studied physics at the University of Lausanne and graduated in 1970 before moving to Geneva for graduate work at the Geneva Observatory and the University's Institute for Astronomy. He obtained his Master's Degree in astrophysics in 1975. Also a pilot, he holds a commission as captain in the Swiss Air Force and has logged 5,600 hours of flying time.

Nicollier has spent more than 1,000 hours in space, including one space walk lasting 8 hours and 10 minutes. He has received many honors and medals, including the IAF Yuri Gagarin Gold Medal. Nicollier installed the famous Wide Field and Planetary Camera 2 (WFPC2) on the Hubble Space Telescope. This camera was used to image the Hubble Deep Field in 1995, the Hourglass Nebula and the Egg Nebula in 1996, the Hubble Deep Field South in 1998, and many other important objects.

CLAUDE NICOLLIER AT STARMUS.

I'm an astronaut, but I did not go to the Moon like many of my colleagues here. My engagement was during the space shuttle program, as an ESA astronaut based at NASA's Johnson Space Center in Houston. I had the privilege to take part in two missions to the Hubble Space Telescope (Servicing Missions 1 and 3A) in order to perform repairs and improve the orbiting observatory's scientific capability. At that time, we always had seven crewmembers on board the space shuttle so that I shared this activity with my fellow mates, with a lot of additional support from the ground team in Mission Control Center in Houston!

Unlike my colleagues in the Apollo program, we did not stray too far from Earth's surface, but working on a complex and delicate scientific instrument in the environment of space was challenging. Also, operating a winged spacecraft in low-Earth orbit brought with it complexity and hazard. Still, what a superb technological and engineering achievement the space shuttle was! It also made both Hubble and the International Space Station programs possible.

Low-Earth orbit (LEO) was a magnificent place to be, as seen in this illustration. We didn't go as far as Neil and Buzz and all the Apollo astronauts, some 400,000 kilometers away to the Moon. We reached LEO, and we simply worked in this near-Earth environment. The sky is black there, and a bright star shows up in the sky at a rate of one hour per orbit: the Sun! I've always been amazed by the fact that the Sun looks like a star when you are in space — simply a very nearby star! If you hide the Sun with your thumb, then you see the bright planets and some bright stars around it. It is really stunning.

The Hubble Space Telescope's optical system is pretty much like the equivalent of a ground-based reflecting telescope, with a 2.4-meter primary mirror and a Ritchey-Chrétien configuration (two hyperboloids). It is, however, heavily baffled to minimize stray light. The scientific instruments, cameras and spectrometers, are arranged as a cluster of so-called axial instruments behind the primary mirror. We also have three radially mounted instruments, one being the wide-field camera, and the other three fine guidance sensors. During manufacture of the telescope, the primary mirror was very precisely shaped but unfortunately with a slightly biased optical reference and it suffered from a quite significant spherical aberration undetected until the telescope was already in orbit.

The Hubble Space Telescope was launched with the space shuttle on mission

THE LOW EARTH ORBIT (LEO) ENVIRONMENT.
CREDIT: NASA.

STS-31 in April 1990. The pilot of that mission was Charlie Bolden, a classmate of mine from Group 9 of NASA astronauts — we had started our astronaut training together in 1980. Charlie later became and currently is the NASA Administrator. The telescope was installed on a 600-kilometer altitude, 28.5°-inclination orbit (the latitude of the launch site at the Kennedy Space Center, Florida).

The plan was to perform a servicing mission of the telescope every three to four years, in order to perform repairs or maintenance as needed, or to replace focal scientific instruments with the aim of keeping Hubble as a modern and productive astronomical research facility over the planned 20 years of its lifetime. Five such missions were performed. After the telescope was launched and NASA discovered the optical problem, the obvious primary goal of the first visit to Hubble became the installation of an optical corrector for all axial scientific instruments, and to exchange the radially installed Wide-Field Camera. In addition, it was necessary to replace the solar sails, install a coprocessor to increase the memory capacity of the telescope's main computer, exchange the solar array drive electronics, and perform a few more maintenance tasks.

The first servicing mission occurred in December 1993, the second in 1997, the third in 1999, the fourth in 2002, and finally, the last in 2009. The last mission took place after a long hesitation in order to weigh the benefits of such a mission versus the risks (to the shuttle and its crew) following the loss of Columbia and its crew in February 2003. Lots happened during this fourth and last visit to Hubble, with the hope of giving the telescope another 10 years of trouble-free operation until well beyond its successor, the James Webb Space Telescope, would be installed and operated from the L2 Lagrangian point of the Sun-Earth system.

I had the privilege to be a crewmember on both the first (SM1) and the third (SM3A) Hubble servicing missions. The pressure on the crew to be successful was high on the first mission. The crew consisted of Commander Dick Covey, Pilot Ken Bowersox, and Mission Specialists Story Musgrave, Jeff Hoffman, Tom Akers, Katy Thornton, and me. The following illustration was taken shortly after we had designed the patch for the mission but we had not started the training yet. The training took about a year from the end of 1992 to the end of 1993, with the launch occurring on December 2, 1993.

Training was very intense for the first servicing mission. We had never visited a complex scientific instrument in space with the intention to do repair work on it, using a combination of robotics and spacewalking, so it was really going to be a first. We used virtual reality to try to figure out how we were going to access the different worksites and with which body orientation, to be able to do the required work at each of them. At a later stage, we trained on a full-size mockup of the telescope immersed in a large water tank at the Marshall Space Flight Center in Huntsville, Alabama.

In addition, we trained intensely with shuttle-related tasks such as ascent, on-orbit reconfigurations, life on board, re-entry, and final approach and landing. These training sessions consumed a significant amount of time, at least for some of the crewmembers, typically the commander, pilot, and the flight engineer, which was my position on this flight. We trained for a little more than a year, and then rushed to the Kennedy Space Center (KSC) in a formation of four T-38 jets three days before launch. We spent the last nights at the KSC crew quarters, and we were ready to go. At 2 a.m. on December 2, a small van took us from crew quarters to the launch pad. The view of Endeavour, brightly illuminated by floodlights, was really impressive! We boarded, performed the usual checkout of systems and equipment during the last 2.5 hours of the countdown, and roared at 4:26 a.m., heading for Hubble. The rendezvous was planned to take place in 48 hours, coming from below and behind the target, and slowly increasing the energy (altitude) of our orbit, stepwise, to finally match the telescope's state vector (position and velocity vectors).

The rendezvous was flawless, the final approach skillfully executed by Dick Covey. We got in the proper relative position and attitude to the telescope, in close forma-

THE CREW OF HUBBLE SPACE TELESCOPE'S SERVICING MISSION 1. CREDIT: NASA.

tion flying at 28,000 kilometers per hour. Hubble looked really impressive with its huge size — about the size of the shuttle payload bay — and with its slightly warped, fully deployed solar sails. I captured Hubble with the robot arm, and carefully installed it on a small platform in the back of the payload bay, according to plan, and as we had trained multiple times in the simulator. We were now ready for the repair work, to be executed on five spacewalks, one per day — a day is 24 hours on the flight plan — following the telescope capture and installation.

Most of the time, during the servicing mission, we had the payload bay aimed down toward Earth, to take advantage of the infrared radiation from our planet slightly warming up our worksites. Each spacewalk was performed by two astronauts, one on a small platform at the end of the robot arm, brought to the desired worksite by the robot arm operator (me), the other spacewalker being the "free floater" responsible for all of his displacements, normally using yellow-painted handrails in the payload bay and on the surface of the telescope. This is the way we had trained and it worked well in reality, providing the necessary safety margin and efficiency in each spacewalk. We used special tools to do work on the telescope. These tools had been developed, built, and gradually improved to a high level of excellence by tool experts and technicians, and always with our participation during the more than 12 months of training.

We had a few snags during these five busy spacewalks, but we were used to facing problems or equipment failures from our training. Sometimes we had a little help from the experts at Mission Control. We finally performed 100 percent of the planned repairs and equipment exchanges on the telescope, including the restoration of its optical capability, and the exchange of the solar wings. In this illustration you see the payload bay, the telescope and two spacewalkers — Story Musgrave on the robot arm, managing tools, and Jeff Hoffman as "free floater" in the payload bay — during our fifth spacewalk. The solar sails have been replaced, but not yet unfolded. This picture was taken as we were passing over Australia. You can see the peninsula of Adelaide between the telescope and the vertical portion of the robot arm.

Servicing Mission 1 was undoubtedly a huge success, and the strategy put in place by the team, plus a lot of training and a disciplined execution, plus some luck, paid off with big rewards. From that time on, the telescope had full scientific data gathering capability, and outstanding results started to flow down to the telescope's control room at the Goddard Space Flight Center in Greenbelt, Maryland, and to the Space Telescope Science Institute in Baltimore.

At the end of 1998, I was happily back in training, this time as one of four spacewalkers, for the third visit to Hubble. This mission had been planned originally for the year 2000 and was later split in two, with the first part, Servicing Mission 3A, to be performed "as soon as possible" because of multiple failures in the rate sensor units. A fine guidance sensor, or pointing camera, also had to be replaced, in addition to the telescope's main computer. This time we had a neutral buoyancy facility available in Houston for training the spacewalks, with an immersed high fidelity model of the telescope. We also used a high fidelity mechanical simulator of Hubble in a clean room at the Goddard Space Flight Center. This proved to be very valuable in handling connectors in crowded spaces, and for practicing using special tools with gloved hands.

After a series of delays, we finally lifted off on December 19, 1999, with the promise to be back on the ground before the New Year. NASA was not confident about having a shuttle in space during the transition to the next millennium. Again, we had about 48 hours for the rendezvous with Hubble (which had lost attitude control capability a few weeks before), capture, and installation in the back of the payload bay. And then we were ready for spacewalking again. I was on the second spacewalk of three with Mike Foale, taking care of the telescope's main computer exchange and the replacement of pointing camera number 2, as shown in this illustration as shown in the image on page 214.

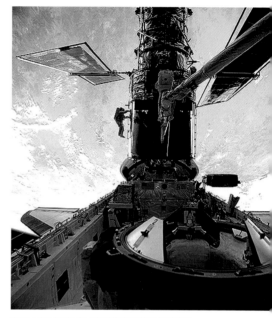

REPLACEMENT OF FINE GUIDANCE SENSOR NUMBER 2 DURING SERVICING MISSION 3A. CREDIT: NASA.

STAR V838 MONOCEROTIS WITH A LIGHT "ECHO" EFFECT IN A DUSTY CLOUD STRUCTURE SURROUNDING THE STAR. CREDIT: NASA, HUBBLE AND ACS.

This second spacewalk lasted a long time, more than eight hours, because of a severe problem in the insertion of the fine guidance sensor. We couldn't get it in because of too much friction along the guiderails. We "scratched our heads," came back pretty rapidly with an alternative technique with help from the support team at Mission Control, and it finally worked, but put us more than one hour behind the timeline.

After the third spacewalk, we had met all the objectives. We then spent a few orbits with the solar sails oriented toward the Sun in order to charge the telescope's batteries, and then performed the release on Christmas Day, 1999. What a sight and a wonderful Christmas gift for us! Again, we had a fully functional telescope on completion of this servicing mission. What a relief, giving us deep satisfaction.

Two more Hubble servicing missions followed. In 2002, a brand new camera was installed in the axial scientific instruments cluster, the Advanced Camera for Surveys (ACS), which has since then provided a high fraction of the stunning Hubble pictures, one of which is shown in this illustration. On the same mission, new solar sails were also installed, smaller ones than the originals that were rigid and more efficient.

The last visit to Hubble took place in May 2009. The crew installed a new scientific instrument, the Cosmic Origin Spectrograph (COS), and the malfunctioning ACS was repaired. Batteries and rate sensor units were replaced, with the idea to give the telescope about 10 extra years of useful, productive lifetime. In addition to their telescope and instrument repairs and improvements, the crew installed a docking port on the base of the telescope, as shown in this illustration. This device would allow docking of a robotic spacecraft (not yet designed and built) to perform a controlled deorbit of the telescope after the end of its useful life. There is plenty of time to do this. With its high orbit at 600 kilometers above Earth's surface, the erosion of Hubble's orbit is very slow, and it will remain up there for several decades.

In 2016 or 2017, the successor to Hubble, the James Webb Space Telescope (JWST), an infrared telescope with a 6.5-meter reflecting primary mirror, will be deployed on the L2 Lagrangian point of the Sun-Earth system. The primary objective of this new facility will be to look farther away and further back in time compared to Hubble. The JWST, fruit of collaboration between NASA, ESA and the Canadian Space Agency, will be launched with an Ariane 5 rocket from the Kourou spaceport in French Guyana. We expect that numerous discoveries will be made in the future with this very powerful instrument!

In the meantime, Hubble will continue its wonderful journey of exploration, well into this decade. For me, I feel very privileged to have been able to contribute serving the scientific community by participating in two of the telescope's repair missions. This very capable "discovery machine" also serves the general public because it provides all of us with extraordinary pictures of celestial objects of the highest aesthetic and educational value.

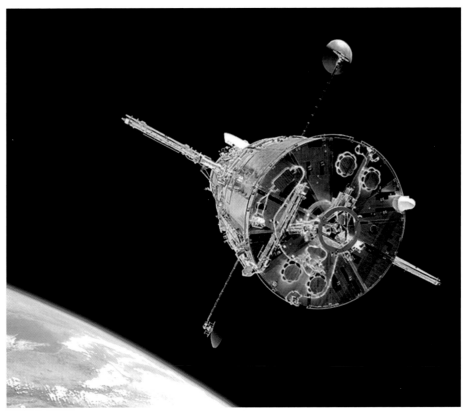

LAST RELEASE OF HUBBLE AT THE END OF THE FIFTH SERVICING MISSION – THE DOCKING PORT INSTALLED ON THIS MISSION IS VISIBLE IN THE BOTTOM PART OF THE TELESCOPE. CREDIT: NASA.

SOYUZ TMA-2 SPACECRAFT ATTACHED TO THE ISS. CREDIT: NASA.

YURI BATURIN

THE ASTRONAUT'S EARTHLY MISSION

Yuri Mikhailovich Baturin was born June 12, 1949, in Moscow. Selected as a cosmonaut in 1997, he flew as a research cosmonaut on Soyuz TM-28/Soyuz TM-27 (this ISS mission was notable for carrying the first paying space tourist, Dennis Tito) and in 2001 on Soyuz TM-32/Soyuz TM-31 as flight engineer. Among his many academic distinctions, Baturin graduated from the Moscow Institute of Physics and Technology in 1973 and from the Law Institute of Moscow State University, where he also obtained a Doctorate of Law, in 1980. A former politician, he has been Head of National Security and has served on the National Defense Council. Baturin is a professor at Moscow State University and a corresponding member of the Russian Academy of Sciences. He is a director of the S. I. Vavilov Institute of the History of Science and Technology.

YURI BATURIN AT STARMUS.

Originally, the habitation of space on Earth was a piecemeal affair; it was a world of distributed locations. Navigation made it more connected. The degree of geospace connectivity significantly increased with the appearance of aviation. Communication systems added the final touch — geospace became closed; holistic.

The stages of development in geospace can only be roughly identified with an accuracy of centuries. The qualitative transformation of space, however, occurred instantly — right before our eyes — and we even know the exact date of this event. On the 12th of April 1961, space opened for man. Space not only opened for humans but became infinite.

On that day, Yuri Gagarin performed the first outer space flight in history. "He invited us all into space," American astronaut Neil Armstrong said of Gagarin. In the Outer Space Treaty of 1967, astronauts are regarded as the envoys of mankind. This formula appeared to ensure legal protection for the astronauts who, as a result of inaccurate landings, might find themselves in another state's territory. Precise formulas, however, always hide new meanings, too.

After space missions are accomplished and astronauts return to Earth, their mission as envoys of mankind continues. What is this mission?

Setting up a space station means creating a small Earth with its own atmosphere, comfortable climate, and its own population — albeit very small. In fact, this is a "task for the gods." And humans have solved this task very successfully. And they send their envoys to this small model of Earth. They live and work in the outer space environment in almost terrestrial conditions, protected by manmade systems and using sophisticated equipment.

With the mind-boggling size of the International Space Station, the physical borders of the new world — the space outpost — are very small. And this world's population is very sparse, with everybody not only knowing everyone else but also communicating with them every day.

And if a crewmate fails to properly fix a tiny screw, it may migrate into another crewmate's respiratory system, which is very dangerous. If on waking up you fail to say "good morning" to your mate, it can disrupt the peaceful atmosphere and will inevitably affect the work. The egocentric worldview where everything revolves around you, which is so common on Earth, is replaced by a multipolar one — even if you are the commander.

The astronaut very clearly understands that, if he falls ill, it would be the same as the crew being reduced by one third or one sixth, and his work would have to be performed by his or her mates. Which means that one has to take good care of one's health.

The astronaut sometimes discovers that he should not have given less time to

YURI BATURIN IN SPACESUIT. CREDIT: YURI BATURIN PERSONAL ARCHIVE.

studying some technical device than to important life support systems — when it turns out that the failure of this device threatens to disrupt normal conditions for his on-board existence. And only now he begins to realize that the station's every system is, in a sense, a life support system too.

In this small world, any of his (and his mates') small actions can lead to big consequences. To a degree, he, himself, becomes a threat to his own world, as much a threat as possible meteoroids.

A dramatic narrowing of the world's borders leads to the human, spiritual, and sensual relationships being included in the system of technological relationships he has learned on Earth. For instance, if an experienced astronaut patronizes a first-timer instead of mentoring him, the latter will inevitably respond negatively, which will adversely affect the crew's teamwork. The compromise ought to be reached in the tackling of certain professional tasks and the issues of everyday life. During the space flight, which is no longer a training exercise, no longer a "game" but, rather, a really dangerous enterprise, astronauts feel the whole complicity, interrelatedness, and integrity of the world in which they work outside Earth. It may be said that the space flight triggers the development of the person's humane side.

Sometimes we don't need space flights to feel the integrity of the world. We can feel it on Earth, but we need a tragedy for that. For instance, Fukushima 1. The tsunami (nature) destroyed the machines (reactor), which had an immediate catastrophic impact on people's lives.

When an astronaut returns to Earth, he or she is different from who they were before the flight. Their experience makes them a better fit for living on Earth. This is what people sense (but do not realize) when communicating with those who worked in space. This is what makes astronauts interesting to other people. They unconsciously sense in the astronauts something that they need here, on Earth. Astronauts are the people who have lived in a "simple" universe whose interrelationships and rules are fully cognizable, and therefore they know something about the basic rules of life that will make it safe and interesting. This is what the astronauts' mission on Earth is about.

The world is holistic: man, environment, and machines created by man are all interrelated. Human, spiritual, and sensual relationships are built into the system of technological relationships. Both depend on the natural environment.

The value of life is unconditional. In the holistic world, one should seek harmony. Accept the world as it is — don't nurture illusions and don't deceive yourself. Work conscientiously on every task. If you do your work well, you will survive. Don't be egocentric. Respect your partner. Restrain yourself. Seek a compromise. Look after yourself. See the beauty of the world. And so on.

These are the simple truths. But only an astronaut who has traveled a very narrow path full of dangers begins to truly understand that everything in the world depends on everything else, and treat the life of any living thing with respect. You see a beetle crawling on the ground and, you slow down your motion, shifting your foot aside to avoid stepping on the beetle. Because it was not you who gave it life! And it's not for you to take it away!

Outer space changes everybody who has been there. It changes personality — what the person has from his or her ancestors and from nurturing, including the state of one's soul. Many people, of course, deny the existence of the soul. But I don't know anyone who would say, "I have no soul."

In my opinion, an astronaut has three personalities: before space flight, during space flight, and after space flight. When all these personalities exist in harmony with each other, after the space flight, the astronaut may be considered accomplished. And then the envoy of mankind is ready to continue his or her earthly mission.

The first astronauts felt their mission, have pursued and still pursue it. Later on, the complexity of technical preparation for space flights relegated this mission to the background. And not every astronaut ponders it today. A good example was set by the astronauts of the European Astronaut Corps, who adopted a charter in which they formulated their mission as follows: "We share space with the people of Europe by communicating our vision, goals, experiences, and the results of our missions."

There are many situations such as natural disasters involving mass casualties, after which the United Nations sends football players or actors or singers to the affected countries as goodwill envoys to attract attention to the victims' needs, collect funds, etc. It would also be quite helpful to enlist astronauts to perform these functions. The total number of astronauts and cosmonauts who have flown to space from the 12th of April 1961 to this day is a little over 500. Sadly, many of them are gone. Several hundred people in the entirety of mankind is too few. Not all of them are willing to perform particular international functions — but all of them saw our Earth from "outside" and agree that Earth ought to be protected both from wars and environmental disasters. All of them, due to their unique experiences, think in planetary terms and are respected worldwide.

Many international organizations use the services of various agents. The definition of such agents was first suggested by the International Court in its Advisory Opinion of April 11, 1949, titled "Reparation for Injuries Suffered in the Service of the United Nations." This document states, "The Court understands the word 'agent' in the most liberal sense, that is to say, any person who, whether a paid official or not, and whether permanently employed or not, has been charged by an organ of the Organization with carrying out, or helping to carry out, one of its functions — in short, any person through whom it acts."

This wide definition includes not only the international functionaries, but also the diplomatic intermediaries, consultants, and experts, including those involved in performing temporary tasks. The cosmonauts and astronauts from across the world can act as such consultants, experts, and intermediaries. It would be expedient to assign them the respective privileges and immunities and issue the respective U.N. documents enabling visa-free travel across borders. Astronauts have freely flown over the states' borders and it would only be fair to grant them such right in the interests of peace and humanity.

Yuri Gagarin once said, "Having flown around Earth in the satellite spaceship, I saw how beautiful our planet is. People, let's preserve and increase this beauty, not destroy it!"

Gagarin was the first envoy of mankind in outer space. He was also the first to perform this mission, and he did it perfectly.

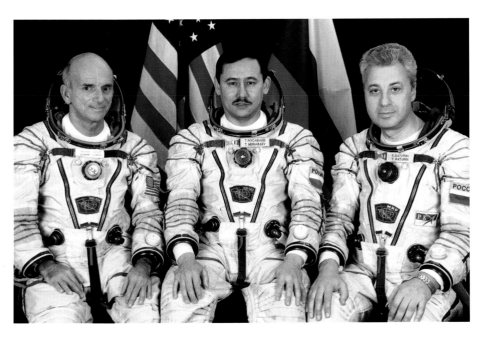

CREW OF SOYUZ TM-32 (LEFT TO RIGHT): DENNIS TITO – SPACE TOURIST, TALGAT MUSABAYEV – COMMANDER, YURI BATURIN – FLIGHT ENGINEER. CREDIT: NASA.

Epilogue by Garik Israelian

The idea of publishing this book emerged during the Starmus Festival in 2011. I was sitting next to Neil Armstrong in the bus going up to the observatory on the island of La Palma for the round table discussion "108 minutes'. I asked Neil if he thought we should publish a book containing the lectures presented during the festival, and he immediately responded "Of course! It will be a unique book dedicated to the 50th anniversary of Yuri Gagarin's flight. You have to do it!" Later, as usual the very epitome of a modest and responsible person, Mr. Armstrong was the first author to e-mail me the manuscript of his presentation. On February 20th 2012, Neil e-mailed me the following

> **Hello Garik,**
> **Here is my essay for the book.**
> **If you have any problems with anything in this draft, let me know and we will make corrections.**
> **Good luck!**
> **Neil A.**

I was proud to find the word "Starmus" in the title of his lecture – ensuring that the name of the festival will never disappear. In the last of many further e-mail exchanges, he congratulated me on my new research article highlighted in *Science Daily*. I didn't know that it was to be his last message to me...

The First Man on the Moon passed away few months later. I was deeply saddened, since we have lost one of the wisest and most honest persons on this planet. I had heard many legends about Neil's professional skills and his strong character. But my personal feelings and impressions will stay with me forever. Brian May and I were privileged to have dinner and share the table with Neil Armstrong, Alexei Leonov and Jim Lovell at the Observatory on La Palma, enjoying the best local white wine. Neil never talked about Apollo 11 during the festival. But suddenly, in this relaxed atmosphere, he began describing his first step on the Moon, and what he was feeling: then Leonov was speaking about his first space walk knowing his chance of survival was less than 1%. Then Jim Lovell was calmly telling us about Apollo 13 's "Houston, we have a problem...".
Brian and I had the same thought ... "This is unreal!"

I e-mailed Neil why he did not write about the Apollo 11 flight in his lecture, and he responded:

> **"I did not talk about my flights and experiences. I tried to take the larger view. I think that was important and I do not want to use Starmus or the Starmus book as a vehicle for autobiographical material."**

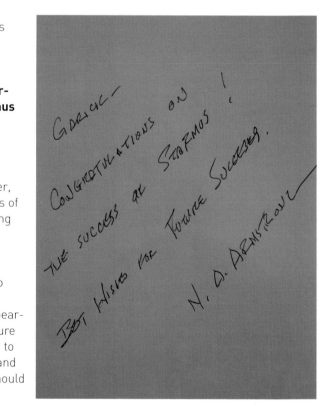

This was him. The Man who always thought and stressed that the credits of his First Step should be equally shared by the hundreds of thousands of people who participated in the Apollo program. Moreover, he told me that the credits have to be shared by the many generations of scientists who created our knowledge in physics, maths etc., beginning with Aristotle. This was his point of view.

After the sad loss of Neil Armstrong in 2012, Brian and I had the strong feeling that, in addition to the original dedication of Starmus to Gagarin, we should specially honor Armstrong. Starmus would never have grown into what it has now become without the Great Man's appearance and unconditional support in all the activities, including his lecture and the round table discussion. He epitomized and very much related to the idea of this festival – the message of Starmus, its unique format and spirit. All our contributors have subsequently agreed that the book should now be dedicated not only to Yuri Gagarin but also to Neil Armstrong.